ENVIRONMENTAL BIOGEOCHEMISTRY AND GEOMICROBIOLOGY

Volume 1: The Aquatic Environment

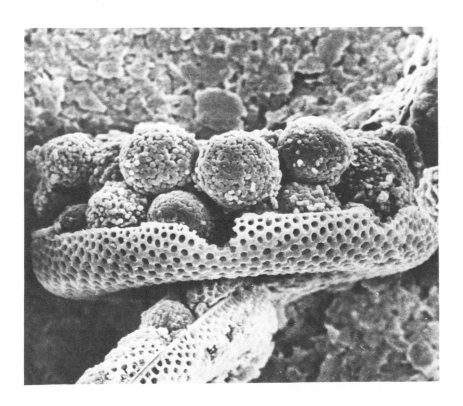

ENVIRONMENTAL BIOGEOCHEMISTRY AND GEOMICROBIOLOGY

Volume 1: The Aquatic Environment

edited by

WOLFGANG E. KRUMBEIN
University of Oldenburg
Environmental Laboratory
Oldenburg, Germany

Proceedings of the Third International Symposium on Environmental Biogeochemistry organized by W. E. Krumbein, University of Oldenburg, and sponsored by the Minister of Science and Arts of Niedersachsen, Deutsche Forschungsgemeinschaft, and the International Association of Geochemistry and Cosmochemistry. The symposium was supported ideally and scientifically by Deutsche Gesellschaft für Hygiene und Mikrobiologie, Gesellschaft für Ökologie, Deutsche Bodenkundliche Gesellschaft, German Local Branch of the American Society for Microbiology. The meeting was held at the Herzog August Bibliothek, Wolfenbüttel.

ANN ARBOR SCIENCE
PUBLISHERS INC
P.O. BOX 1425 • ANN ARBOR, MICH. 48106

Copyright © 1978 by Ann Arbor Science Publishers, Inc.
230 Collingwood, P.O. Box 1425, Ann Arbor, Michigan 48106

Library of Congress Catalog Card No. 77-84416
ISBN 0-250-40218-1

Manufactured in the United States of America
All Rights Reserved

Life on earth has produced earth's present atmosphere, the uppermost parts of the lithosphere, soil structure, water quality and man—to adore it, study it and possibly destroy it. Life has managed to survive long periods of dangerous fluctuations of equilibrium and, according to the "Gäa hypothesis," life may survive even man. Energy and entropy may be more important to our present-day situation but without a doubt, life and its far-reaching consequences are the most prominent factors to be considered in studying the environment and environmental cycles.

Certainly life and its processes may be regarded as mere chemical reactions under certain physical conditions. But though the driving forces are primary and secondary energy sources and flows, and though chemical balances and budgets are possibly more basic, and though the cycle of substances in space and time can always be expressed in chemical terms and reactions, it must be stressed that as long as this earth can sustain life, man will look at it and its development in terms of a living entity. Therefore, biogeochemistry, geomicrobiology, ecology and exogenic dynamics are always regarded as events controlled and modified, speeded up or slowed down, by life and life processes.

The production cycle for reduced carbon compounds, their growing degree of organization, their pathway through the food or energy chain in nature, the apparent death and final annihilation by mineralization and oxidation to simple compounds—all this can take place in a small lake or in soil within a single day. In other circumstances, it may require billions of years to complete a cycle. Many examples may be given for the hypothesis that any atom that has reached or established itself in the outer few kilometers of the earth's crust will have passed a living organism at least once since life emerged or, at least, will have been influenced or modified in its energy level, spatial position, or physical-chemical condition by organisms. It therefore seems that biogeochemistry, though relatively far from man—at least farther than medicine, sociology or music—will increasingly attract the attention of society. Geomicrobiology and biogeochemistry will probably increase in importance with man's growing influence on the exogenic cycle, with man's accelerating sections of the huge "mill wheel" of masses passing up and down in the earth's crust and along the energy levels.

Regarding our consternation about the carbon dioxide cycle, the importance of nitrogen compounds in the atmosphere, enormous amounts of stored energy, and reduced carbon compounds, we see the need to increase our biogeochemical activities. If we consider the acceleration of metal cycles, if we look at the enormous number of organic chemical compounds, if we take note of the changes and manipulations man produces on genetic matrices and the stress we exert on the entire ecosystem, we see that the established parameters have been drastically altered in an incredibly short time.

The aim of biogeochemistry and geomicrobiology is to find scales and balances before we so totally change our environment that no traces of the entirely "natural" remain to study, analyze and compare.

The time of holistic approaches, which science lost only 100 years ago, has returned. One major aim of this symposium series on environmental biogeochemistry is to bring together students of the various disciplines concerned with dynamic processes on the earth's surface. The main concerns are not only understanding the importance of the major mineral cycles and their budgeting and balancing, but also analyzing systems and making prognoses on these cycles that control and are controlled by life. Additional factors and study areas will include the biogeochemistry of manmade compounds and their alteration products, and the need to build up new geochemical cycles, since the natural materials used through the centuries are no longer sufficient for humanity's still-growing needs. This means that man will need to study ways to accelerate natural mineral cycles by biological or technical methods.

Isotope fractionation, mobilization and immobilization, oxidation and reduction, mineralization and storage in biological material, transfer, volatilization, catalysis and equilibration of systems—all these are ruled mainly by biological processes in the microscale and most frequently by microorganisms. Therefore, microbiologists, isotope chemists, geochemists and ecologists, and a few botanists, zoologists and physicists were asked and responded to the call for papers for this meeting.

These volumes are based primarily on the papers given at the Third International Symposium on Environmental Biogeochemistry. It was our original intent to emphasize a more specific area, but the problems and the wealth of information were so broad it became necessary to expand the scope of the conference. Hence, one part of the proceedings is dedicated to defined environments, such as shallow water photosynthetic environments with dominance of blue-green algae, deep sea environments with dominance of manganese nodules, specific soil environments, or the microenvironment of one soil or rock particle, while other major segments of the proceedings are dedicated to the general cycles of elements and compounds and their alteration by man.

The study of biogeochemistry and geomicrobiology is only beginning. We wish to keep the field open and look forward to a time of organization, synthesis and perfection. The growing interdisciplinary field between biology, physical and chemical science, and geoscience cannot reasonably limit itself before the subject is more fully understood.

W. E. Krumbein

ACKNOWLEDGMENTS

The Third International Symposium on Environmental Bio-geochemistry was sponsored by Deutsche Forschungsgemeinschaft, Ministry for Science and Arts of Niedersachsen, IAGC, Balzers, Cambridge Instruments, Jürgens und Co., E. Merck, Arbeitsgemein-schaft für meerestechnisch gewinnbare Rohstoffe, Ortec, Carl Zeiss. Their help is gratefully acknowledged.

The following persons were extremely helpful in planning and encouraging the development of the meeting: E. T. Degens, K. H. Domsch, W. Flaig, P. Hirsch, M. Kürsten, G. Müller, W. Schwartz, K. Wagener and D. H. Welte of the national com-mittee; M. Alexander, G. Eglinton, H. Ehrlich, P. H. Given, R. O. Hallberg, G. W. Hodgson, I. R. Kaplan, K. A. Kvenvolden, A. D. McLaren, P. A. Meyers, J. O. Nriagu, E. A. Paul, M. Schnitzer, J. Skujinš and G. Stotzky of the international committee, and namely J. Skujinš, chairman of the IC, K. Kvenvolden and E. Ingerson of IAGC, J. W. M. la Rivière of SCOPE, and A. Meyl of DFG.

It is my pleasure to acknowledge the support of P. Raabe of the Herzog August Bibliothek, Wolfenbüttel, and his staff. Without their aid and acceptance, and especially the calm and efficient stability of D. E. Petersen, the meeting would not have been possible. I also wish to extend my thanks to W. Schwartz who was so kind to cooperate and coordinate the "Roundtable Conference on Leaching" with this symposium.

Christine Lange, Peter Rongen, Elisabeth Holtkamp, Joachim Leibacher, Cornelia Wilcken, Monika Michaelsen, Ulrike Kant and G. Koch have made a major contribution to the success of the practical arrangements and to the well-being of the participants.

Finally I wish to express my gratitude to all partici-pants for attending and submitting their contributions on schedule.

W. E. Krumbein, Associate Professor at West Germany's University of Oldenburg, is the chairman and coordinator of the Third International Symposium on Environmental Biogeochemistry. An expert on microbiological rock weathering, his work has concentrated on geomicrobiology, environmental biogeochemistry, productivity and element cycles in natural environments.

Dr. Krumbein received his Vordiplom (BSc) in geoscience from the University of München, and his MSc and PhD (both magna cum laude) from the University of Würzburg. He studied soil microbiology and microbial ecology at the Institut Pasteur and the Sorbonne in Paris and the Landgebouwhoogeschool Wageningen in the Netherlands, and was the recipient of a research grant for postgraduate study at Jerusalem's Hebrew University. He then spent six years as a research scientist at the Biologische Anstalt Helgoland, a government laboratory for marine research.

The editor has taught on the faculties of the Universities of Würzburg, Freiburg and Hamburg. He was a guest scientist at the Scripps Oceanographic Institute in La Jolla, California, and was recently a Visiting Professor at Hebrew University.

Dr. Krumbein has been a speaker at many international scientific conferences, was active as Convener of the International Congresses of Sedimentology and Ecology, and has completed three lecture tours in the U.S. For his active promotion of the fields of geomicrobiology and biogeochemistry, Dr. Krumbein has received awards from the Deutsche Geol. Ges. (German Geological Society) and the Institut Pasteur. He is a member of the Advisory Board of the MBL, Elat, ISEB's International Committee, the National Building Research Council and ICES/ECOMOS. He is also Associate Editor of *Geomicrobiology Journal*.

At present, Dr. Krumbein and his colleagues are planning to establish an institute for salt water biology in Germany. In recent papers he has dealt with hypersaline environments and calcification in prokaryotic organisms as well as with nitrogen and phosphorus budgets of intertidal cyanobacterial communities of the Gulf of Aqaba and the North Sea coast.

TABLE OF CONTENTS

SECTION III
SHALLOW PHOTIC WATERS AND SEDIMENTS WITH SPECIAL REFERENCE
TO STROMATOLITIC ENVIRONMENTS

SECTION IV
DIAGENESIS

VOLUME 2

SECTION I
GEOMICROBIOLOGY, BIOGEOCHEMISTRY AND ENERGY FLOW

SECTION II
PADDY SOILS, PEAT AND COAL

SECTION V
DESTRUCTION, MINERALYSIS, WEATHERING

VOLUME 3

SECTION I
METHODS TO ASSESS BIOGEOCHEMISTRY AND GEOMICROBIOLOGY
OF THE ENVIRONMENT

SECTION I

MICROBIOLOGY, CHEMISTRY AND GLOBAL CYCLES
IN THE AQUATIC ENVIRONMENT

CHAPTER 1

CYCLES OF SOME ELEMENTS THROUGH RECENTLY DEPOSITED SEDIMENTS

EDWARD D. GOLDBERG

Scripps Institution of Oceanography
La Jolla, California   92093   USA

INTRODUCTION

The concept that recently deposited sediments are sinks for chemical species in the major sedimentary cycle has numerous exceptions. Over the past decade or so, many clear-cut examples of elements returning from the deposits to the overlying waters through diffusional processes in the pore solutions have been presented. Herein we will review these reactions and propose other substances that might be mobilized. The movement of solid phases through physical or biological mechanisms will not be considered. Only the diffusion of dissolved materials that takes place through interstitial waters will demand our attention.

The remobilization of an element may take place as a consequence of radioactive decay, the combustion of organic matter, the formation or dissolution of minerals or the displacement of pore waters. The detection of movements of chemicals in the sedimentary column rests upon the identification of concentration gradients within the sedimentary column or upon differences in pore water composition from that of the waters overlying the sediment. In the former case, the elegant demonstration rests upon the assay of the concerned substances in the pore waters. Both the squeezing of the recovered sediment to express the liquid phases and the more advanced *in situ* samples have been used to establish the existence of concentration gradients.

RADIOACTIVE DECAY

Koczy (1958) pointed out that radium-226 in deep-sea sediments, produced through the radioactive decay of thorium-230 in the uranium–238 series, can diffuse through the interstitial waters into the overlying ocean. His argument was based in part upon the rather high values of this nuclide in the top layers of the sediment and in part upon its maximum sea water concentration at depths near the bottom (Figure 1). The immediate parent thorium–230 comes to the deposit essentially unsupported by previous members of the uranium–238 series. It is highly reactive in solution and readily associates with solid phases that fall to the sea floor. On the other hand, radium–226 is relatively more soluble and can enter easily into the aqueous phase. Koczy recognized the importance of this nuclide with a half–life of 1600 years in the study of water movements and mixing processes.

A verification of this concept was provided by Goldberg and Koide (1963), who noted that thorium–230 and lead–210, a daughter nuclide arising from the decay of radium–226, were not in radioactive equilibrium at depths from the surface to 10 and 15 cm in pelagic sediments of the Indian Ocean (Table I). The lead–210 was presumed to proxy for radium–226. The former nuclide was readily measurable; the latter, much more difficult, if not impossible, with the available amounts of sediment. Using a simple Fickian model, the investigators concluded that molecular diffusion does not explain the migration of radium from the sediments to the sea water but that subsequent sorption reactions of radium on the surfaces of the solids influenced the movement of this element. More sophisticated diffusional models were needed to describe the behavior of radium. Nonetheless, the production through radioactive decay of a soluble chemical was shown to result in its transfer to the overlying waters.

Another isotope of radium, radium–228, has been implicated in a sedimentary diffusional process (Moore, 1969). In the thorium–232 series, the parent isotope is not in radioactive equilibrium with its daughter thorium–228 in sea water. Radium–228 is an intermediate decay product between the two thorium isotopes. A model in which the radium diffuses out of the sediments into the overlying waters has been proposed to account for this radioactive disequilibrium.

Other diffusional processes most likely operating involve radionuclides generated in the sediments from the natural radioactive series or from the artificial nuclides produced in weapons tests or in the nuclear fuel cycles. Because the levels of some highly toxic radioelements, such as plutonium, are increasing in the sediments adjacent to nuclear reprocessing plants, it is becoming urgent to ascertain if the deposits are a sink or a reservoir for such species. In the latter case, the residence time in the sediments may be of great importance in determining allowable discharges to a given area.

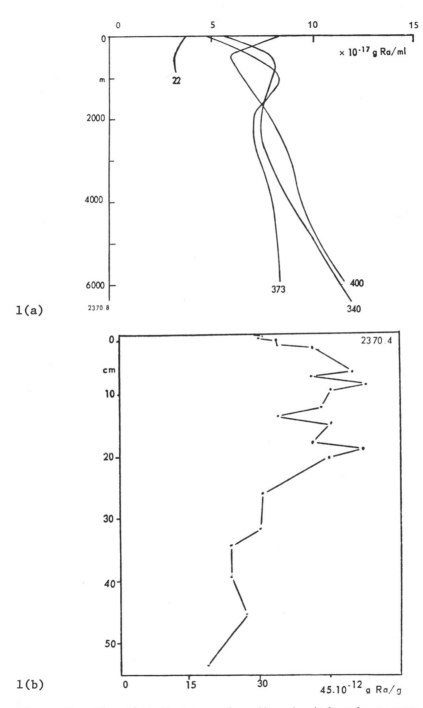

Figure 1. The distribution of radium in Atlantic waters (a) and in a sediment from the equatorial Pacific (b). From Koczy (1958).

Table I

The Th-230 and Pb-210 Activities in Arbitrary Units
in Indian Ocean Core Monsoon 57G[a]

Depth (cm)	Th-230	Pb-210
0 – 3	137	72
3 – 6	213	162
6 – 9	219	173
9 – 12	181	167
12 – 15	144	
15 – 18	134	127
18 – 21	92	98
30 – 33	44	44
40 – 43	46	44
50 – 53	26	28
60 – 63	34	
70 – 73	23	28
73 – 77		
80 – 83	17	
90 – 93	13	
100 – 103	9.0	8.7
110 – 113		
120 – 123		
130 – 133	3.9	

[a]From Goldberg and Koide, 1963.

THE COMBUSTION OF ORGANIC MATTER

The cycling of manganese is perhaps the textbook case of
the diagnetic mobilization of a metal and is a consequence of
the combustion of organic matter. First described in Lynn and
Bonatti (1965), it has been observed by many subsequent investigators. The initial identification of manganese movements
was made upon several deep-sea cores from the Pacific in which
there were relatively high concentrations in the top strata.
The sediments beneath the manganese-rich layers contained evidences of reducing conditions--the presence of pyrite and other
iron sulfide phases, as well as redox potentials ranging between -150 and -250 mV. The model to account for this observation involved the precipitation of manganese in an oxidized
form, probably the tetravalent state. Upon burial in the
sediment, the organic matter degraded, leading eventually to
anoxic conditions and the reduction of manganese to the soluble
divalent form. The dissolved manganese diffuses into the
oxidized zone and subsequently into the overlying waters.
A more recent example derives from our studies upon the
metal pollution recorded in the sediments of the Palace Moat

in Tokyo, Japan (Goldberg *et al.*, 1976). Some metals--zinc, copper, chromium, silver, lead, cadmium, cobalt and nickel-- are identified as pollutants on the basis of higher contents in the recently deposited or uppermost strata (Figure 2). On the other hand, the elements that are primary components of weathered rocks, such as iron and aluminum, are essentially uniform in concentration throughout the sedimentary column. Only manganese displayed an increasing concentration with depth in the sediment. Apparently, it diffuses to the overlying waters following reduction of higher valence state solids to the soluble divalent state in these highly anoxic deposits.

But what of the other metals associated with the manganese phases that are solubilized? Can they also be put into solution as a consequence of the dissolution of manganese? Studies on the compositions of interstitial waters of such sediments might reveal whether other diffusional processes are set up in cores where reducing strata underlie an oxidized zone.

The coastal zone sediments are sites for the degradation of organic matter, mediated by bacteria. Following the exhaustion of oxygen in such processes, there is a series of anoxic processes that takes the following order: nitrate reduction, sulfate reduction and bicarbonate reduction. Also, fermentation reactions can take place, in which high molecular weight organic materials are broken down to smaller units. The products of these reactions, if soluble, can diffuse to the overlying waters. On the other hand, the reactants, such as nitrate or sulfate, which undergo depletion in the interstitial waters, can be diffused into the deposit from the overlying waters. Illustrations of the cycling of carbon and nitrogen as a consequence of such reactions will be taken from recent work carried out in my laboratory.

The methane produced in deep strata of the Santa Barbara Basin diffuses upward in the sedimentary column to the zone of sulfate reduction, where apparently it is consumed by the bacterial population (Figure 3; Barnes and Goldberg, 1976). However, methane can enter the water column where the zone of sulfate reduction is relatively shallow and where there is an intense production of the gas.

A somewhat more involved series of reactions takes place in the reduction of nitrate. Barnes *et al*. (1975) studied the consequential production of molecular nitrogen in the sediments of the Santa Barbara Basin. These reactions appear to govern relatively large fluxes of nitrate, nitrite and ammonia into and out of the sediment. The amounts of nitrogen found in the interstitial waters, above that associated with dissolved air, is attributed to denitrification reactions. However, this increase is greater than that expected from the direct reduction of sea water nitrate in the pore waters. A model has been proposed in which the ammonia, derived from the degradation of organic matter, diffuses to zones of low oxygen tension, where it is oxidized to nitrite. The nitrite can be subsequently reduced

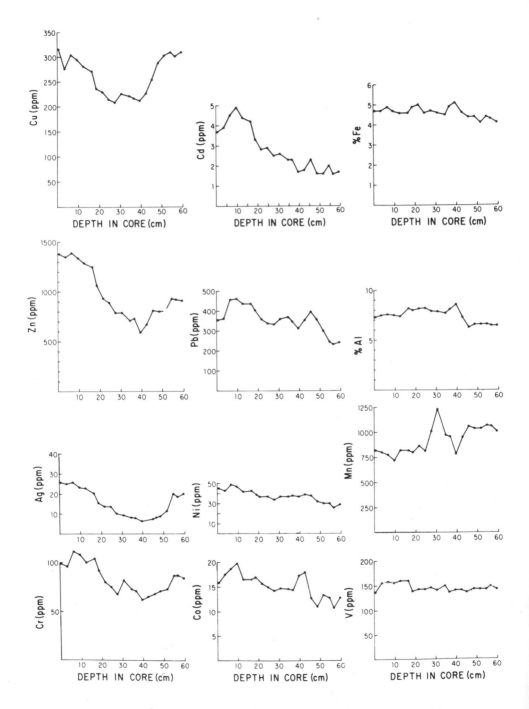

Figure 2.   Heavy metal profiles in the Palace Moat sediments
(Goldberg *et al.*, 1976).

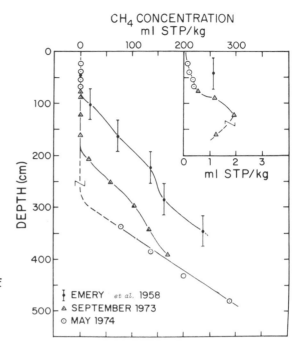

Figure 3. Methane profiles in sediments from the Santa Barbara Basin, off the coast of southern California (Barnes and Goldberg, 1976).

to nitrogen gas, whereas there is as yet no evidence that ammonia can be directly oxidized to the elemental state, even though it is the stable thermodynamic species. The consequences of these reactions are illustrated in Figure 4.

With the depletion of nitrate in the interstitial waters, a diffusion of this ion from the overlying waters is expected and is found (Figure 4). Likewise, there is a diffusion of nitrogen gas from the interstitial waters to those immediately above the sediment.

DIAGENESIS IN DEEP PARTS OF THE RECENT SEDIMENT COLUMN

The cores recovered from the Deep Sea Drilling Project have provided stimulation for extensive studies of diagenesis. The work of Sayles and Manheim (1975) pioneered the methods to be followed later. Through studies of the changes in the make-up of pore waters, relative to normal sea waters, they were able to propose the types of diagenetic reactions taking place. For example, the depletion of sulfate and the enrichment of bicarbonate and ammonia in the interstitial solutions were related to the decomposition of organic matter. Calcium losses from the water were attributed to the precipitation of calcium carbonate. In some sediments, the pore waters were depleted in calcium but enriched in magnesium, usually on a mole for mole basis. Such changes, Sayles and Manheim argued, came about by the recrystallization of biogenic calcite, high in magnesium (perhaps a dolomitic phase) and the substitution of divalent magnesium for divalent calcium. Subsequent work has

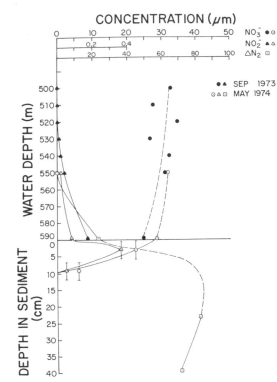

Figure 4. Vertical distribution of nitrate, nitrite and relative nitrogen concentrations in pore waters of the Santa Barbara Basin sediments (Barnes *et al.*, 1975).

modified this latter hypothesis, but the patterns for understanding the reactions evolved.

A more extensive investigation of the chemistries occurring within a deep-sea sediment was made by Perry *et al.* (1976) on a Caribbean core whose interstitial water chemistries as well as the sediment chemistries and mineralogies were ascertained. Four hundred meters of sediment were analyzed. With increasing depth the pore waters exhibited a marked depletion in magnesium and a corresponding enrichment in calcium (Figure 5). Silicic acid was essentially uniform in the upper 100 m of interstitial solution but was dramatically enriched between 100 and 400 m. Both the dissolved potassium and the 0-18/0-16 ratios of the power waters decreased with depth.

Three mineralogical regimes appear to exist in the sediment column: an upper 100 m portion of detrital clays, an intermediate section with calc-alkalic volcanics that have been weathered to smectites, and a lower phase of biogenic silica with authigenic smectites. Perry *et al.* (1976) argued that these observed curves can be explained by the submarine weathering of volcanics, primarily to smectites. The degradation of the volcanic rocks introduces calcium and magnesium to the interstitial waters with consequential increases in alkalinity. The formation of the smectites utilizes the magnesium and thus decreases the alkalinity. Also, the weathering allows the build-up in the pore waters of silicic acid.

The decrease in the 0-18/0-16 ratio is explained by the alteration of volcanic debris to smectite. It cannot be

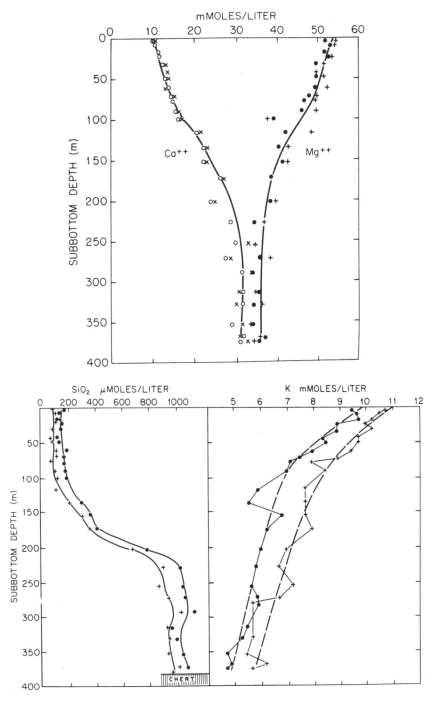

Figure 5. Vertical concentration profiles of calcium, magnesium, silica and potassium in the sediment pore waters of a Caribbean core (Perry *et al.*, 1976).

resolved by reactions involving the transformation of biogenic
calcium carbonates to limestones or of biogenic silica to
cherts. The depletion of potassium at the top of the core is
attributed to its irreversible fixation upon the clay mineral
illite, a reaction invoked many times in the past.

Clearly, calcium or silicon may diffuse into the overlying waters, or potassium or magnesium may diffuse into the
sediments from the overlying water, within the experimental
errors of the results. Undoubtedly, movement of these species
occurs within the sediment column, most probably by molecular
diffusion. Other species must be moving within the sedimentary
column through the pore waters as a consequence of these chemistries. Studies on heavy metals, enriched in the parent volcanic material, may be very rewarding. With our present abil-
ities to analyze nanogram or smaller amounts of heavy metals
and with the availability of substantial amounts of core material, such investigations are possible. It is possible that
waters near the bottom may have their heavy metal concentrations
influenced by such sedimentary reactions.

In a like manner, diffusional gradients have been observed for sulfate ions into the sediments and sulfides out of
the sediments. Perhaps of greater interest is the movement of
the organic products of reduction reactions. With the development of very sensitive gas chromatographic techniques, their
assays are clearly possible today. Also, the mobilization of
elements out of the sediments through methylation reactions
should be thoroughly investigated. It is conceivable that
such substances as methyl iodide, dimethyl mercury, methyl
arsenides, and dimethyl sulfide are entering sea waters from
anoxic deposits.

DISPLACEMENT PROCESSES

Recent investigations on interstitial water chemistries
of estuarine sediments have introduced the concept of rapid
changes in such parameters as salinity. Sometimes, these alterations can be accounted for by molecular diffusion. On the
other hand there appear to be both physical and biological dis-
placements of some pore waters that govern their chemical compositions.

One of the first studies on the pore water composition
as a function of time was carried out on Chesapeake Bay deposits (Matisoff *et al.*, 1975). In one core, the upper 20 cm
displayed changes in the salinity of the interstitial waters
over very short time periods (Figure 6). For example, Core 11,
taken five days after a tropical storm was markedly depleted
in chloride. A month later (Core 12), chloride is essentially
absent. Two months later the sediment had responded to an
increase in chloride as a consequence of the entry of high salinity waters to that part of the estuary from which samples
were taken. Molecular diffusion with a constant $D = 5 \times 10^{-6}$

cm^2/sec could explain these curves (Holdren *et al.*, 1975).
    On the other hand, another core (Figure 7) showed no
time variance in the chloride contents of the interstitial

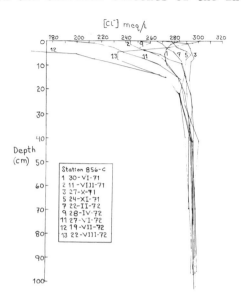

Figure 6.   Variation with time of chlorinity in a Chesapeake
  Bay core.   Dates are given as day-month-year (month in
  Roman numerals).

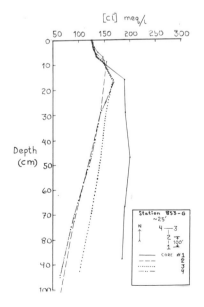

Figure 7.   Chloride ion
  profiles in four adja-
  cent Chesapeake Bay
  sediments where there
  is a decrease in
  chlorinity with depth
  (Matisoff *et al.*,
  1975).

waters, but there was a lower chlorinity at depth (Matisoff *et al.*, *op. cit.*) which is attributed to the intrusion of freshwater aquifer in the Bay environment, diluting and displacing the more saline waters. Such a process may have a effects on the exchange of chemical species between the water and the sedimentary solid phases.

Elder (1977) argues that storm events can flush sediments at rates about 100 times faster than that predicted by molecular diffusion. Reeburgh (1977) suggests that such processes may be density driven.

The bioturbative activities of marine organisms can bring about marked changes in the composition of sediments by overturning both the sediments and the water (irrigation) (Day, 1977). Marine microfauna can bring down oxygenated surface waters to zones which are being depleted in this dissolved gas. The polychaete *Arenicola loveni* makes U-shaped burrows which can extend down almost a meter into sulfide-rich sediments and pumps oxygenated waters to such depths Burrowing bivalves, according to Day, act in a similar fashion in bringing oxygenated waters through their inhalent syphons and discharging the waters through their exhalent syphons, altering both the chemistry of the water and disturbing the sediments. The chemical reactions brought about by such activities are yet to be described in detail, but they may seriously affect the compositions of the sediments.

CONCLUSION

For some chemical species, the marine sedimentary column is a sink; for others, it is a reservoir.

REFERENCES

Barnes, R.O., and E.D. Goldberg. "Methane Production and Consumption in Anoxic Marine Sediments," *Geology* 4:297-300 (1976).

Barnes, R.O., K.K. Bertine and E.D. Goldberg. "N_2: Ar, Nitrification and Denitrification in Southern California Border Land Basin Sediments," *Limnol. Oceanog.* 6:962-970 (1976).

Day, J.H. "The Effect of Plants and Animals on the Chemistry of Estuarine Sediments," in *Biogeochemistry of Estuarine Sediments*, E.D. Goldberg, Ed. UNESCO Press (1977).

Elderfield, H. "Chemical Variability in Estuaries," in *Biogeochemistry of Estuarine Sediments*, E.D. Goldberg, Ed. UNESCO Press (1977).

Goldberg, E.D., and M. Koide. "Rates of Sediment Accumulation in the Indian Ocean," in *Earth Science and Meteoritics*, J. Geiss and E.D. Goldberg, Eds. (Amsterdam: North Holland Publishing Co., 1963), pp. 90-102.

Goldberg, E.D., Vern Hodge, Minoru Koide and John J. Griffin. "Metal Pollution in Tokyo as Recorded in the Sediments of the Palace Moat," *Geochim J.* 10:165-174 (1976).

Holdren, G.R., O.P. Bricker and G. Matisoff. "A Model for the Control of Dissolved Manganese in Interstitial Waters of Chesapeake Bay," in *Marine Chemistry in the Coastal Environment,* T.M. Church, Ed. (ACS Symposium Series 18, 1975), pp. 364-381.

Koczy, F.F. "Natural Radium as a Tracer in the Ocean," *Proc. 2nd U.N. Internat. Conf. Peaceful Uses Atomic Energy* 18: 351-357 (1958).

Lynn, D.C., and E. Bonatti. "Mobility of Manganese in Diagenesis of Deep-Sea Sediments," *Marine Geol.* 3:457-474 (1965).

Matisoff, G., O.W. Bricker, G.R. Holdren and P. Kacrk. "Spatial and Temporal Variations in the Interstitial Water Chemistry of Chesapeake Bay Sediments," in *Marine Chemistry in the Coastal Environment,* T.M. Church, Ed. (ACS Symposium Series 18, 1975), pp. 343-363.

Moore, W.S. "Measurements of Ra-228 and Th-228 in Sea Water," *J. Geophys. Res.* 74:694-704 (1969).

Perry, E.A., J.M. Gieskes and J.R. Lawrence. "Mg, Ca and 0-18/0-16 Exchange in the Sediment Pore Water System, Hole 149, DSDP," *Geochim. Cosmochim. Acta* 40:413-423 (1976).

Reeburgh, W.S. "Convective Mixing in Sediments," in *Biogeochemistry of Estuarine Sediments,* E.D. Goldberg, Ed. (UNESCO Press, 1977).

Sayles, F.L., and F.T. Manheim. "Interstitial Solutions and Diagenesis in Deeply Buried Marine Sediments: Results from the Deep Sea Drilling Project," *Geochim. Cosmochim. Acta* 34:103-127 (1975).

CHAPTER 2

MICROORGANISMS AND THEIR AQUATIC ENVIRONMENT

HOLGER W. JANNASCH

Woods Hole Oceanographic Institution
Woods Hole, Massachusetts 02543 USA

An introductory chapter with a discussion on separating the aquatic from the terrestrial should, indeed, go back as far as the genesis. However, even the attempt of reviewing only the most recent and major contributions to aquatic biogeochemistry would exceed the given space limit. This chapter, therefore, will be restricted to a few general remarks followed by two or three examples of relevant experimental work.

In the biochemical context, the environment of a microbe can be visualized as consisting of three phases mixed in widely varying proportions: solid (inorganic and organic particulate matter), liquid (mainly aqueous), and gaseous. This general scheme covers soils, sediments, natural waters and, to a degree, the atmosphere. The range of microbial environments extends from extremely arid soils with little and solidly bound pore water to offshore oceanic waters, low in dissolved nutrients and having no suspended particulate matter.

This concept eliminates any sharp dividing line between aquatic and terrestrial microbiology. Indeed, the establishment of the two academic disciplines has remained on the institutional level where terrestrial research was done in agricultural laboratories and aquatic research in limnological and oceanographic labs. More recently, textbooks as well as publications of professional societies deemphasize this distinction under the label of ecological, environmental or--as the present international symposium demonstrates--biogeochemical microbiology.

The above concept is important with respect to the scale at which the microbial environment must be viewed. The vegetative microbial cell with its relatively large reactive surface responds quickly to the changing physicochemical conditions of its immediate surrounding. Consequently, the effective

environment of the microbial cell is the *micro*environment,
i.e., its immediate surrounding in a compatible scale of space
and time with relation to its radius of metabolic action and
interaction.   Much confusion has been created by linking the
occurrence of specific microorganisms with *macro*environmental
characteristics.   In the early days when microbiological studies often had to be taken on by trained botanists and zoologists, isolates of specific bacterial species were related to
locations on the geographical scale.   A classical case is
Nathanson's abortive attempt, originally and ingenuously con-
trived by Anton Dohrn in the late 1890s, to collect the data
for a monograph of the bacteria of the Gulf of Naples.   However,
his accomplishment was appreciated only much later, namely the
discovery of the chemosynthetic hydrogen sulfide and sulfur-
oxidizing bacteria of the thiobacillus group (Nathanson, 1902).
As an example, these bacteria occur in water as well as in
soils.   Their actual ubiquity, due to their ability to survive
in the absence of their source of energy, is of much less importance than their actual activity in environments where the
occurrence of reduced sulfur compounds leads to a microbial
acidification of water or soil followed by the well-known
leaching and environmental deterioration processes.

This is not to say that there are no microorganisms
specifically adapted to live primarily in aquatic habitats.
If we focus our attention on the metabolically active and inactive existence of microorganisms (primarily prokaryotes) in
aquatic environments, the two groups can be distinguished:
(a) the incidental inhabitants, carried in by air or soil runoff, physiologically making the best of it, and (b) the typically aquatic microorganisms that are largely absent from terrestrial or other environments.   A well-known example of the
former is *Escherichia coli*, frequently occurring and surviving
in polluted waters.   As an example of the latter, the requirement for high motility in the chemotactic behavior of *Thiovulum*
sp., which seeks a sulfide oxygen interface, characterizes this
organism as typically aquatic.   There are a number of other
physiological and morphological traits, especially among the
prosthecae- and stalk-forming bacteria, that enable these organisms to live in aquatic environments.   They owe their widespread occurrence and quick appearance in newly formed suitable
environments to their ability to produce easily distributable
stages.

The basic feature of the aqueous phase, in contrast to
the solid and gaseous phases, is the physicochemical property
of water, especially its ability to carry those organic and
inorganic chemical species, which are essential and readily
available for microbial metabolism in dissolved and ionic form.
The easy motility of nutrients by diffusion, advection and currents provides for the characteristic constancy of environmental
conditions upon which many of the typical aquatic microorganisms
depend.

Chemical and physical interfaces represent highly selective environments for specific organisms, environments that take advantage of their potential in catalyzing certain reactions (Marshall, 1976). Similar to the aerobic sulfide-oxidizing organism mentioned above, photosynthetic bacteria carry out the same function but anaerobically in the presence of light. To be able to move chemo- and phototactically into optimal chemical or light gradients, they depend on cellular motility or the regulation of buoyancy. The uppermost surface layers of natural water, the neuston, is characterized largely by physical forces, and little is known of a truly typical microflora, especially for bacteria. Physical interfaces exist between strongly stratified layers of water and, of course, on the sediment surface where microbial populations usually are extremely high and active, largely due to the sedimentation of solid nutrients or to the diffusion of metabolic intermediates produced, often anaerobically, in the deeper sediments.

On the microscale, the aqueous-solid interface appears to be an important factor in the activity of microorganisms associated with submerged solid surface or particles freely suspended in water. Some species, especially the prosthecate forms, appear to be equipped specifically for the attachment to submersed solid surface, while others seem to profit fortuitously from this association. The advantages of attachment of microbial cells to the various kinds of suspended particles are readily conceivable and have been discussed at length (Jannasch and Pritchard, 1972). They deal primarily with effects of microbial "Aufwuchs" in relation to the typical shortage of dissolved substrates, mainly organic carbon and energy sources, in the aquatic environment.

Although this prefatory chapter cannot deal with any particular question in much detail, it may be of sufficient biogeochemical interest to elaborate briefly on microbial life in the absence and presence of suspended particles. Selected examples will be discussed. It is important to distinguish between inert particulate materials and detrital plant and animal remains. The latter represent particulate organic substrates that serve as food sources to be utilized ectoenzymatically. The inert particulate matter or submersed solid surface, although not attacked by microorganisms *per se*, may exert a distinct effect on the metabolic activity of suspended microorganisms.

Figure 1 shows the results of an experiment measuring the bacterial oxygen uptake in the presence and absence of chitin particles that cannot be utilized as a food source by the particular organism used. There was a distinct increase of the respiratory activity of the bacterial population in the presence of chitin particles, but only when relatively low concentrations of the complex energy and nutrient source (peptone) were provided. Microscopic observations showed a pronounced clumping of cells around particles, again, however, only at

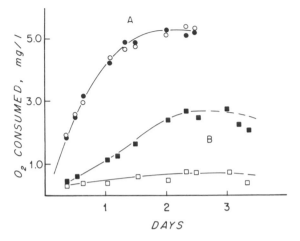

Figure 1. Respiratory activity of *Achromobacter* sp. in the presence of 5.0 mg (A) and 0.5 mg (B) peptone/1 and in the presence (dots and filled squares) and absence (circles and empty squares) of chitin particles (5–20 μ diam., *ca.* 10^4/ml). (From Jannasch and Pritchard, 1972.)

the relatively low concentration of peptone. The variability of this clumping of microbial cells and its dependence upon the nutrient concentration is often overlooked in the interpretation of plate counts of bacteria in water samples.

A more precise study on the dehomogenization of microbial cell suspensions by particulate matter and its effect on microbial metabolism has been done with a denitrifying bacterium (Jannasch, 1960). As a "pure" denitrifier, *Pseudomonas stutzeri* uses oxygen as an electron acceptor but switches to nitrate respiration, producing nitrogen gas almost quantitatively (van Niel and Allen, 1952), when the concentration of dissolved oxygen reaches a certain low level. Cultures of this organism were aerated with a finite amount of air in a closed system (Figure 2). Various kinds of inert particulate materials were added in three quantities (Figure 3). Increases or decreases of gas were measured with a volumetric burette and qualitative changes by mass spectrometry. The results demonstrated that inert particulate matter strongly affects the rate of oxygen uptake by the bacterial cell suspension. There was no evidence that adsorption, and thereby a local enrichment, of the dissolved organic medium (0.04% Difco yeast extract) had taken place during the 47-hour period. Nevertheless, microscopic observation showed that growth occurred largely around the particles. The ability of *Pseudomonas stutzeri* to reduce nitrate to nitrogen gas under near anoxic conditions was used as an indicator that microbial growth on particles can lead to the formation of anaerobic microenvironments. An oxygen electrode with the common size of a cathode surface will not detect such a dispersed anaerobiosis, while the production of nitrogen gas represents a valid and highly sensitive biological test.

Seemingly inert mineral particles may also affect microbial activity in a quantitative and qualitative fashion. In a chemostat experiment (Jannasch and Pritchard, 1972), the microbial breakdown of valeric acid, as an intermediate product

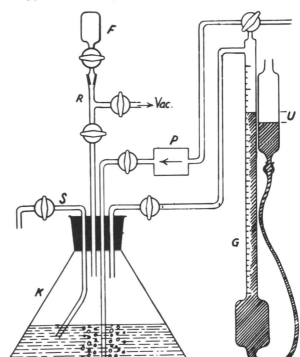

Figure 2. Apparatus for measuring denitrification in the presence of various concentrations of suspended particulate matter. K, 1.5-liter Fernbach flask containing the culture; S, port for taking liquid samples for mass spectrometric analysis; P, gas burette for volumetric measurements. (From Jannasch, 1960.)

of hydrocarbon decomposition, was tested in the presence and absence of suspended kaolinite particles. The study was performed with two different bacterial isolates (Figure 4). One of them (A) was found to attach to the articles more readily than the other (B). Propionic and acetic acids occur as intermediates. Their concentration in the outflow of the chemostat indicates the efficiency of their conversion, the absolute quantity depending on the particular dilution rate of the system. Most of the valeric acid is completely oxidized. The bacterial strain exhibiting the tendency to attach to kaolin particles is clearly more efficient in the breakdown of valeric acid in the presence than in the absence of suspended kaolinite particles. This effect is even more pronounced in the conversion of propionate but not at all perceivable in the production and further oxidation of acetate. Metabolism of strain (B) appears to be affected negatively by kaolinite particles.

In the absence of any particulate matter, the complete utilization of dissolved carbon sources, usually limiting growth of heterotrophic bacteria, is hampered by low dilutions, another trait of the aquatic environment. It is of competitive advantage for freely suspended cells to take up these limiting concentrations of organic substrates with high efficiency. From theoretical considerations and from chemostat experiments (Jannasch and Mateles, 1974) it is known, however, that bacterial populations are unable to strip the water completely of a dissolved nutrient or carbon source. The substrate affinity

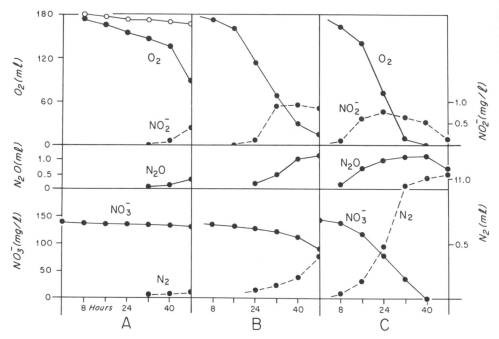

Figure 3. Oxygen uptake and denitrification in the absence
(circles) and in the presence (dots) of 1.0 (A), 10 (B) and
100 (C) g/l of fine quartz sand, cellulose fibers, diatomic
earth and chitin particles in weight portions of 20:5:1:1.
The growth medium of the denitrifying bacterium (*Pseudomonas
stutzeri*) was: 0.68 liter tap water, 400 mg Difco yeast extract, 100 mg KNO_3, 20 ml citric acid—phosphate buffer, pH
7.0. (Data from Jannasch, 1960.)

coefficient, either for growth or for uptake and principally
similar to the Michaelis—Menten constant in enzymatic reactions,
indicates an asymptotic approach to the complete removal of a
dissolved substrate from an aqueous medium. The degree of this
removal does largely depend on specific environmental factors.
Threshold concentrations of a particular substrate for microbial metabolism can be considered identical with "left-over"
concentrations not available to further microbial consumption.
Change of environmental conditions as well as increase of the
concentration of the particular substrate may result in renewed
microbial activity.

An example of such an interaction was demonstrated
(Jannasch, 1970) with aquatic spirilla grown on minimum levels
of lactate in a highly oxygenated medium. Like many aerobic
bacteria, these spirilla prefer slightly reduced conditions
and provide themselves the "reducing power" for their specific
optimum rH when sufficient growth occurs. If growth is highly
diminished at low levels of lactate, the rH rises and growth
ceases altogether. Lowering the rH by adding ascorbic acid or
increasing the concentration of lactate will both result in the

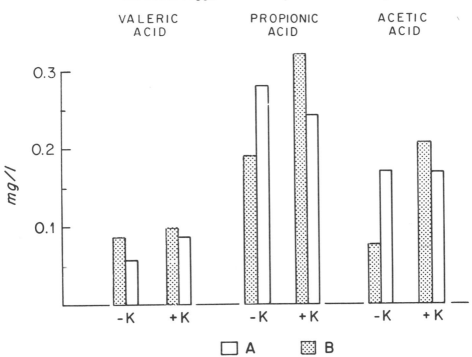

Figure 4. The oxidation of valeric acid and the intermediate
products propionic and acetic acids by two different bacterial isolates (A and B) in a chemostat run with artificial
sea water medium containing 10 mg valeric acid/l with (+K)
and without (-K) suspended kaolinite particles during steady
state at a dilution rate of 0.25/hr. (Data from Jannasch
and Pritchard, 1972.)

resumption of growth. It is probable, but has not been demonstrated, that an addition of inert particles would result in
a similar effect, provided clumping of cells around the particles and the formation of reduced microenvironments does occur.
        As demonstrated by these examples, aquatic microbiology
offers a definite experimental advantage over terrestrial microbiology for certain investigations of ecological nature:
the organisms can be studied legitimately in more or less ho-
mogeneous aqueous suspension so that the immediate environmental conditions of the individual cell, *i.e.*, the microenvironment, are largely known.
        For a concluding thought, however, a point must be made
in relation to the ultimate macroscale of the environment:
although 99.9% of the biosphere is sea water, the biogeochemical activity of the relatively thin animated terrestrial cover
of the continents and their surface waters is still greater.
The same is true of our knowledge of agricultural processes as
compared to that of microbial transformations under conditions
of high substrate dilution in the ultimate biogeochemical sink,

the ocean. Rates of the most important biogeochemical transformation are often extremely slow, too slow for a straight-
forward experimental assessment. This is a foremost area of
research where microbiologists and geochemists need close
cooperation.

REFERENCES

Jannasch, H. W. "Versuche über Denitrifikation und die Verfüg-
barkeit des Sauerstoffes in Wasser und Schlamm," *Arch. Hydrobiol.* 56:355-369 (1960).

Jannasch, H. W. "Threshold Concentrations of Carbon Sources
Limiting Bacterial Growth in Sea Water," in *Organic Matter
in Natural Waters*, D. W. Hood, Ed. (U. of Alaska, Inst. Mar.
Sci., 1970), pp. 321-328.

Jannasch, H. W., and R. I. Mateles. "Experimental Bacterial
Ecology Studied in Continuous Culture," *Adv. Microb. Physiol.*
11:165-212 (1974).

Jannasch, H. W., and P. H. Pritchard. "The Role of Inert Particulate Matter in the Activity of Aquatic Microorganisms,"
Mem. 1st. ital. idrobiol., suppl. 29:289-308 (1972).

Marshall, K. C. *Interfaces in Microbial Ecology.* (Cambridge,
Mass.: Harvard University Press, 1976).

Nathanson, A. "Über eine neue Gruppe von Schwefelbakterian und
ihren Stoffwechsel," *Mitteil. Zool. Stat. Neapel* 15:655-680
(1902).

van Niel, C. B., and M. B. Allen. "A Note on *Pseudomonas
stutzeri*," *J. Bact.* 64:413-414 (1952).

CHAPTER 3

ORGANIC MATTER IN AQUATIC SEDIMENTS

G. EGLINTON
P. J. BARNES

Organic Geochemistry Unit
University of Bristol
Bristol BS8 1TS, UK

INTRODUCTION: THE BIOGEOCHEMICAL CYCLE

The carbon cycle involves processes by which parent compounds or ions are broken down into small molecules that are either incorporated into other larger molecules or lost to the atmosphere. Phytoplankton, the primary producers of the aquatic environment, recycle carbon dioxide by photosynthesis and provide a source of organic carbon for the growth of animals and bacteria. Some carbon, in the form of dissolved organic matter (DOM) and particulate organic matter (POM) escapes from the immediate cycle by deposition and burial in the bottom sediments of lakes, rivers and oceans. The organic matter preserved in these aquatic sediments is a useful indicator of the original environment of deposition (Philp *et al.*, 1976; Cranwell, 1976). It can yield information as diverse as the increase in concentration of pollutants in the twentieth century and the detection of cycloalkanes in sediments > 10^9 years old. The molecular structures of organic compounds isolated from aquatic sediments serve as biological markers, indicating the type of organisms living in the water column at the time of deposition. A comparison can be made between the organic chemical composition and the content of microfossils in the sediment. In practice, the selection of samples must be carried out in conjunction with organic geochemists, who perform the analyses in order to obtain the maximum amount of useful information. As an example, the Deep Sea Drilling Project, when choosing drilling sites, draws upon the experience of a wide range of scientists including paleontologists, mineralogists, oceanographers and organic geochemists.

To understand the origin of the organic matter, the organic geochemist must study the nature, distribution, source and fate of organic matter in the contemporary water column.

The allochthonous organic matter is that which enters the body of water by river or glacier transport or as wind-blown dust and is derived mainly from terrestrial biosynthesis and man's industrial activities. It will have been subjected to considerable microbial degradation and could be enriched in the more resistant molecules. Allochthonous organic matter may only be a small proportion of the total in a lake or sea but could thus represent a much greater proportion of that material buried in the sediment.

The autochthonous organic matter is composed of the organisms of the aquatic flora and fauna, both living and dead, and the products of their secretion, excretion, autolysis and digestion. A convenient division can be made into the dissolved organic matter, which is thought to consist of the more soluble excretory and decomposition products of the biota, and the particulate organic matter, which includes microorganisms and other living and nonliving organic particles (Morris and Eglinton, 1976; Menzel, 1974; Mel'nikov, 1974).

Little is known of the transport of carbon compounds through the water column. It is likely that soluble organic compounds interact with the particulates to become insoluble and also that the particulates lose organic compounds to the solution phase. Thus, the process of exchange would involve the input and removal of compounds, but the fluxes are not known and in any case must be highly dependent on the water column. Both solubles and particulates will be transported by currents, upwellings and the biota. Soluble compounds will, in addition, proceed by diffusion, though this will not be a fast process. The rates of sedimentation of particulates are not known.

The fate of the organic matter in the water column will depend on many factors, including the molecular environment, the number and nature of reactive groups, accessibility of the reaction site to reagents and the nature and concentration of the reagents (both biological and chemical). In addition to the transformation, degradation, aggregation or polymerization that occurs in the water column, the organic matter that reaches the surface of the bottom sediment is again subjected to chemical and biological activity (Eadie and Jeffrey, 1973). The nature of the organic matter and the processes occurring in the water and sediment are highly dependent on the physico-chemical properties such as salinity, oxygen concentration, temperature, light intensity and pressure (ZoBell, 1973).

One might define the fate of an organic molecule from a particular source as the average history of that molecule until (a) no portion of the original structure is identifiable, or (b) its carbon atoms have been incorporated into other molecules, or (c) it is interred in the sediment beyond immediate recycling. However, this definition suffers from several problems. Individual molecules of a pure substance from a single source may have different fates, several sources may contribute the same compound and selective degradation corresponds to effective fractionation of the original material.

Organic matter and individual organic compounds can be classified according to their ease of degradation in the aquatic environment; they may be "hard" (refractory) or "soft" (readily degraded). This concept is particularly important to the organic geochemist because the "hard" compounds are those most likely to be found in a sediment and give some indication of the original source of organic matter. The "soft" compounds in the sediment will be derived from living organisms in the immediate vicinity rather than in a distant part of the water column. However, the "hard/soft" properties of a compound depend upon several parameters, particularly those that influence microbial activity. High molecular weight hydrocarbons are more resistant to microbial oxidation at lower temperatures (Cundell and Traxler, 1973) and lower oxygen concentrations (Hayaishi, 1974), while some compounds are resistant unless another specific compound is present that allows cometabolism to occur (Gibson, 1975).

A significant portion of the organic matter of aquatic sediments is in the form of small colloidal particles made up of heteropolycondensates—complex organic matter consisting of extensively cross-linked polymeric material with strong resistance to biological and chemical degradation in the environment. This insoluble material can only be analyzed in the laboratory after treatment with powerful chemical reagents to release smaller molecules that can be studied by the normal techniques. If more were known about the nature of the cross-links in heteropolycondensates, it might be possible to achieve selective degradation, but the types of bond available lead to great complexity of linkages (Table I). The possible variation is particularly evident when one considers that a cubic polymer particle of edge 0.5 μm could contain the equivalent of approximately 10^{10} molecules of C_{20} size, packed as units 5 x 10 x 50 Å.

ANALYSIS OF THE ORGANIC MATTER IN SEDIMENTS

The organic matter consists of living and dead phytoplankton, zooplankton, meiofauna, fungi and bacteria, together with fecal pellets, pollen grains, cuticle fragments from higher plants, polymeric debris and mineral particles with adsorbed organic compounds. The sediments also contain interstitial water with its own DOM, together with volatile compounds and gases such as CO_2, CH_4, H_2S and N_2. Thus, the individual compounds will have very different molecular environments, depending on the phase or particle in which they are found (ZoBell, 1973; Conge, 1974; Meadows and Anderson, 1966).

A wide range of organic compounds is found in aquatic sediments (Table II) but the water-soluble molecules are of only limited interest to the geochemist because they diffuse,

Table I
Possible Cross-Linkages in Heteropolycondensates

Bonds Available	Weak Cross-Linkage	Strong Cross-Linkage
— OH	— OH - - - - — O$^\ominus$ M$^\oplus$	$\begin{array}{c}O\\\parallel\\-O-C-R\end{array}$
$\diagdown$ C $=$ O $\diagup$	$\begin{array}{c}\diagdownOH\\C\\\diagupOR\end{array}$ $\begin{array}{c}\diagdownO-R\\C\\\diagupO-R\end{array}$ $\diagup$ C $=$ O - - - - $\diagup$	$\begin{array}{c}\diagdownOH\\C\\\diagup\diagdown\end{array}$
$\begin{array}{c}O\\\parallel\\-C-OH\end{array}$	— COO$^\ominus$ M$^\oplus$	$\begin{array}{c}O\\\parallel\\-C-O-R\end{array}$ $\begin{array}{c}O\\\parallel\\-C-NH-\end{array}$
— O —	— O —	——
$\begin{array}{c}-N-\\\|\end{array}$	$\begin{array}{c}-N-\\\|\end{array}$ $\begin{array}{c}\|\\-N-X^\ominus\\\oplus\\\|\end{array}$	$\begin{array}{c}O\\\parallel\\-N-C-\\\|\end{array}$
$\begin{array}{c}\diagdown\diagup\\C=C\\\diagup\diagdown\end{array}$	$\begin{array}{c}\diagdown\diagup\\C=C\\\diagup\diagdown\end{array}$	$\begin{array}{c}O\\\diagdown\|\diagup\\C-C\\\diagup\|\diagdown\\OH\end{array}$
— SH	— SH - - -	— S — S —— S —
— CH CH — CH$_2$ —	— CH $=$ CH — CH$_2$ —	$\begin{array}{c}\|\\-CH=CH-CH-\end{array}$

Table II
Compound Classes That May Be Present
in Recent or Ancient Sediments

Class	Examples
Hydrocarbons	Alkanes, including steranes and sterenes, triterpanes, aromatics, carotenoids
Alcohols	Normal and branched-chain aliphatics, sterols
Carboxylic acids	Normal, branched and cyclic acids, unsaturated fatty acids, dicarboxylic acids, hydroxy acids
Heterocycles	Porphyrins, indole, flavones
Esters	Triglycerides, phospholipids, sterol esters, waxes, cutin
Amino acids	α-Amino acids, diamino-, dicarboxylic-, aromatic, thio-, heterocyclic acids
Sugars	Pentoses, hexoses, glycosides
Polymers	Polysaccharides, oligosaccharides, proteins, peptides, DNA, cutin, kerogens, heteropolycondensates, polyphenols
Others	Pesticides, detergents, DDT, PCB and phthalate esters

are rapidly metabolized by microorganisms and show little specificity with regard to source (Swain, 1970; Fleischer, 1972; Cowey and Corner, 1963; Raymont *et al.*, 1975). Proteins and polysaccharides are hydrolyzed by microbial extracellular enzymes (Corpe and Winters, 1972) and the products further utilized in cellular metabolism. The heteropolycondensates described above and the kerogen of ancient sediments are refractory and provide useful information for the geochemist (Simoneit and Burlingame, 1973; Philp and Calvin, 1976), but they are difficult to analyze. Several types of kerogen can be distinguished according to hydrogen/oxygen ratios (Saxby, 1976) and can be used to estimate the maturity of a sediment with respect to oil exploration.

The most useful compounds for organic geochemical studies are the lipids. Generally, the more complex the lipid,

the greater its "information content." The distribution of
fatty acid or alkane chain lengths and predominance of odd or
even carbon numbers can give some indication of whether the
major input to a sediment was higher plant material or phytoplankton (Brooks *et al.*, 1976;   Simoneit, 1976);   the presence
of *iso-* or *anteiso-*C_{15} branched-chain fatty acid would be a
strong indication of bacterial activity.   Certain hydroxy-
fatty acids are characteristic of the protective cuticles (cutin and suberin) that cover higher plant surfaces (Eglinton
and Hamilton, 1967;   Cardoso, 1976a;   Cranwell, 1975). Carotenoids and porphyrins reflect the presence of pigments in living
organisms (Watts, 1975;   Gorham, 1974;   Watts and Maxwell,
1977), and aromatic hydrocarbons may be disseminated during
the burning of fossil fuels (Blumer, 1976).   Steroidal and ter-
penoidal lipids are widely distributed in living organisms
(Goodwin, 1973;   Thomas, 1969) and exhibit specificity that allows detailed reconstruction of the environment in which a sediment was deposited.   In addition to the natural organic materials, the concentration of xenobiotics such as DDT and PCBs
must be monitored and their behavior in the carbon cycle eluci-
dated (Albone *et al.*, 1972).

The major analytical methods of the organic geochemistry
of lipids involve extraction, separation, identification and
quantitation of individual compounds.   Ultraviolet and infra-
red spectroscopy, nuclear magnetic resonance spectrometry (NMR)
and mass spectrometry (MS) are commonly used, together with
thin-layer (TLC) and gas-liquid chromatography (GLC).   High
pressure liquid chromatography is finding greater application,
particularly in the analysis of labile compounds such as the
carotenoids (Watts *et al.*, 1977).

The analysis of lipids in a sediment may be accomplished
as follows (Eglinton *et al.*, 1975) (Table III).   The lipids
are extracted from the sediment by ultrasonic vibration in the
presence of solvent and the resulting solution is fractionated
by TLC or HPLC to yield separate compound classes.   The individual components of each fraction may then be resolved and
quantitated by GLC;   identification of the components is facil-
itated by coupling the GLC to a mass spectrometer (GC-MS) and
observing the fragmentation patterns of the molecules under
chemical- or electron-induced ionization.   The most efficient
resolution is achieved by capillary column GLC, but the benefits can only be realized when such a GLC is coupled to a MS
capable of extremely rapid scan rates.   To cope with the vast
volumes of data generated, a dedicated computer is required,
and combined systems (C-GC-MS) are now recognized as essential
for detailed organic geochemistry.   From the acquired data,
normalized mass spectra or mass fragmentograms can be plotted
on paper or programs are available by which the computer can
assign each component to a compound class or identify individual compounds by comparison with spectra of known standards
(Gray *et al.*, 1975;   Gronneberg *et al.*, 1975).

Table III
Outline of Analytical Method for Lipid Content
of Aquatic Sediments

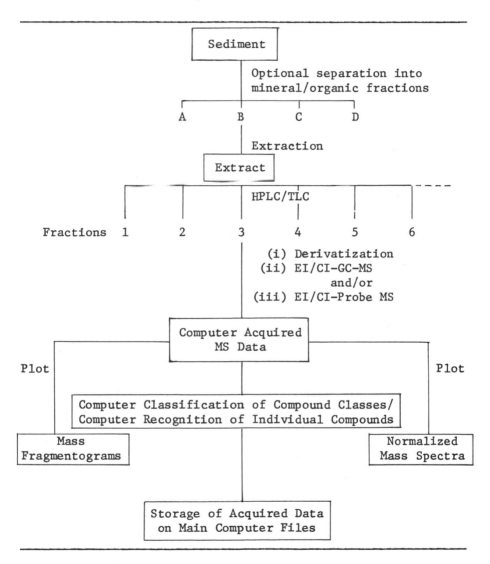

The extremely low concentrations of lipids in ancient sediments sampled by the Deep Sea Drilling Project (Simoneit and Burlingame, 1971; Simoneit, 1976; Cardoso *et al.*, 1977) has led to the installation at Bristol of a quadrupole MS capable of routinely analyzing nanogram quantities of lipid. To prevent contamination, the initial extraction and separation procedures are performed in a clean-room facility formerly used for samples from the Apollo Lunar Project.

Increasing emphasis is being placed on full structural elucidation of compounds, including relative and absolute stereochemistry. The (24R)- and (24S)-isomers of steranes from crude oil and Green River shale have been distinguished by the application of optical rotatory dispersion and high resolution NMR (Mulheirn and Ryback, 1975), but in many cases the amount of pure component available for analysis is limiting. Elucidation of the stereochemistry of di- and tri-hydroxyacids aids in identification of the input to sediments (Cardoso *et al.*, 1976b).

EXAMPLES FROM VARIOUS ENVIRONMENTS

As an example of the resolution achieved using capillary GLC, the chromatograms of alkene fractions from two levels of sediment (Rostherne Mere, England) are shown in Figure 1. Cholest-2-ene (peak 3) and the stereoisomer of hop-22(29)-ene (peak 4) have not been characterized in Rostherne organisms, and their presence in only the deep sediment layer suggests that they may be products of short-term diagenesis (Cardoso, 1976a). Hop-22(29)-ene is present in both layers and is probably derived from microorganisms (Gelpi *et al.*, 1970; De Rosa *et al.*, 1971).

A study of an algal mat from Laguna Mormona (Baja California) has demonstrated the presence of sterols and stanols, with the saturated compounds predominating (Cardoso *et al.*, 1976). More recently, an algal mat from the coastline of Abu Dhabi was shown to contain a similar suite of Δ^5 and $\Delta^{5,22}$ sterols, although the relative abundances differ (Figure 2) (Cardoso, 1976). The two mats have a similar cyanophyte flora but L. Mormona is sparsely vegetated with *Salicornia* and *Distichlis*, while black mangroves (*Avicennia marina*) line the drainage channels of the Abu Dhabi algal flats. Stanols may be formed by bacterial reduction of the sterols in sediments (Gaskell and Eglinton, 1975), although cholestanol, ergostanol and stigmastanol have been found in the diatom *Melosira granulata*, and the corresponding sediment from Lake Suwa, Japan (Nishimura and Koyama, 1976).

The importance of stereochemistry applies not only to the complex lipids but also to the identification of simpler compounds such as unsaturated fatty acids. In a study of an estuarine sediment, 92 percent of the monounsaturated fatty acids were found to have the *cis* configuration characteristic of most living organisms, but 8 percent had the *trans* structure (Van Vleet and Quinn, 1976). Separation of the isomers was achieved, after conversion to the methyl esters, by Ag^+-TLC, and it is thought that the *trans*-isomers arise by direct input or microbial modification of *cis*-acids (Table IV).

Currently, organic geochemists are involved in the analysis of cores from ancient sediments provided by the Deep Sea Drilling Project. The organic matter in these core samples

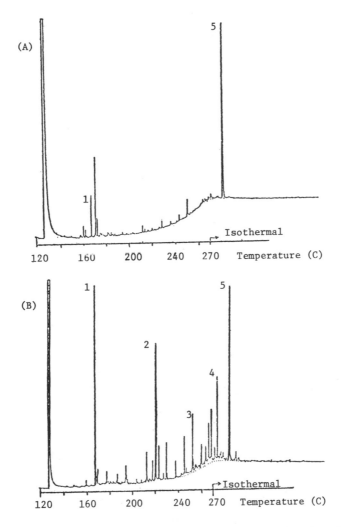

Figure 1. Capillary gas chromatograms of branched/cyclic alkenes isolated from a lacustrine sediment.

Legend. (A) 0-8 cm sediment level. (B) 28-35 cm sediment level.
Identification of components:
Peak 1. Acyclic isoprenoidal alkene
Peak 2. Aromatic hydrocarbon
Peak 3. Cholest-2-ene
Peak 4. C_{30} triterpene
Peak 5. Hop-22(29)-ene

Cores were taken from the deepest part of Rostherne Mere
(England) and the lipids were extracted as previously described
(Brooks *et al.*, 1976; Gaskell and Eglinton, 1976). GLC analysis was performed on a OV-101 glass capillary column (20 m x
0.25 mm i.d.) with temperature programming from 120°-270°C at
5°C/min. Carrier gas was nitrogen flowing at 1 ml/min.
(Cardoso, 1976.)

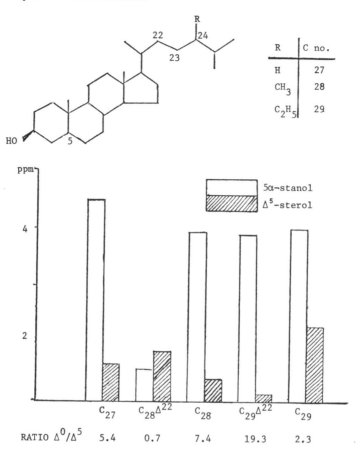

Figure 2. Δ^5-Sterol and 5α-stanol distributions in Abu Dhabi algal mat.

Legend. The core was taken (0-25 cm) from a recent marine algal mat on the coastline of Abu Dhabi and comprised both the living surface mat and underlying sediment. Non-saponifiable extracted lipids were fractionated by TLC and the fractions analyzed by GLC and GC-MS. Assignments were made by comparison of the spectra with those of authentic standards, or by comparison with literature mass spectra and spectral interpretation. (Cardoso, 1976.)

gives some indication of the living organisms and the environment at the time of deposition, which may be as much as 10^8 years ago (Table V). The cores must be handled with great care on board the drill ship and all sources of contamination, such as lubricating oil and grease, hydraulic fluids and corrosion inhibitors, must be scrupulously avoided or controlled. Not only do the sediments permit a study of the paleoenvironment to be made, but an estimation of the petroleum yield potential can be made for commercial oil exploration (Hammond, 1976; Kaneps, 1976; Hood *et al.*, 1976).

Table IV
Monounsaturated Fatty Acid Isomers
in Recent Estuarine Sediment[a]

16 : 1 *cis*	17.1 $\mu g \cdot g^{-1}$
16 : 1 *trans*	1.7 $\mu g \cdot g^{-1}$
18 : 1 *cis*	9.6 $\mu g \cdot g^{-1}$
18 : 1 *trans*	0.8 $\mu g \cdot g^{-1}$

(μg acid per gram dry weight of sediment)

DOUBLE BOND POSITION

Δ^9 *cis* . . . . ∼62% Δ^9 *trans* . . . ∼70%
Δ^{11} *cis* . . . . 19% Δ^{11} *trans* . . . 23%

other positions   other positions
          (*cis*) 19%   (*trans*) 7%

[a]The samples were taken from the upper 8–10 cm of surface sediment in Narragansett Bay, Rhode Island. Fatty acids were extracted after saponification, methylated and the monounsaturated *cis* and *trans* esters isolated by Ag^+-TLC. Quantitation was by GLC, and configurational assignments were verified by IR spectroscopy and GC–MS. Double bond positions were determined by $KMnO_4$ oxidation. (Van Vleet and Quinn, 1976.)

LABORATORY STUDIES OF THE DIAGENESIS OF ORGANIC MATTER

As a result of the biological and chemical transformations that take place in sediments, the extracted lipids often differ in detailed structure from those of the organisms in the water column; for example, cholestanol rather than cholesterol may be found in recent sediments (Gaskell and Eglinton, 1975) and cholestane in ancient sediments (Murphy *et al.*, 1975) and cholestane in ancient sediments (Murphy *et al.*, 1967). Some of these diagenetic processes have been simulated in the laboratory using radio-labeled compounds to facilitate detection of the products. When ^{14}C-cholesterol was incubated in anoxic lake sediment in the laboratory at 10°C, small amounts of labeled cholestanol were formed (Table VI) together with lesser amounts of cholestanone and cholest-4-en-3-one (Gaskell and Eglinton, 1975). Once again, the stereochemistry is important, and the ratio of 5α- to 5β-cholestanol was approximately 4, whereas incubation in anaerobic sewage sludge yielded a ratio of 0.5. This difference probably reflects the different microbial flora of the two environments.

Similar direct diagenesis experiments using ratio-labeled

Table V
Abundances of Lipid Classes in Sediment Samples
from DSDP Leg 44, Site 391

Abundances (ppm dry wt of sediment)	Sediment Depth (m)		
	525	691	958
Hydrocarbons			
n–Alkanes	0.07	0.11	1.44
Branched–Cyclic	0.04	0.18	2.87
Carboxylic Acids			
n–Alkanoic	absent	0.02	1.60
n–Alkenoic	absent	0.0007	0.005
B/C Alkanoic	absent	0.002	0.007
Hydroxy	trace	trace	trace
Carotenoid Pigments	0.045	absent	trace

Table VI
Laboratory Studies of Diagenetic Reactions of Hydrogenation
of Cholesterol in Sediment[a]

Total 4-^{14}C-cholesterol injected	14.67 µCi
Total lipid extracted after incubation	69%
^{14}C–Cholesterol extracted	45%
^{14}C–5α–Cholestanol extracted	0.47%
^{14}C–5β–Cholestanol extracted	0.11%

[a]The sediment core (50 cm x 6 cm) was taken from Rostherne Mere (England) and incubated intact at 10°C for 90 days after injection of 4-^{14}C-cholesterol at 4 cm below the surface. The total lipid extract, after incubation, was separated by shaking with KOH (7%), and the neutrals were further separated by silica TLC. Δ^5-Sterols, 5α–stanols and 5β–stanols were resolved by Ag$^+$ TLC and characterized by radio-TLC, radio–GLC and GC-MS. The results are expressed as percentage of radio-label injected, with no allowance for experimental losses. (Gaskell and Eglinton, 1975, 1976).

oleic acid in samples of estuarine sediment produced quite different results (Figure 3). The simple fatty acid was rapidly degraded, with most of the ^{14}C-label appearing as CO_2, thus suggesting that microbial respiration was responsible. However, significant proportions of ^{14}C were found in monohydroxy fatty acids and in C_{12}-C_{18} *n*-alkanoic acids, which exhibited relative proportions similar to those of the *n*-alkanoic acids indigenous to the sediment (Gaskell *et al.*, 1976).

A second type of diagenesis experiment is that in which an unlabeled complex mixture of organic compounds, rather than a single compound, is subjected to decomposition. Using the cyanophyte *Oscillatoria agardhi*, a comparison has been made of the lipids in the freshly collected material and those present in the remaining detritus, after allowing oxic or anoxic decomposition to take place in the laboratory (Cranwell, 1976). The *n*-alkanoic and mono-alkenoic acids were both reduced to lower concentrations after aerobic decomposition, but in the anoxic experiment the *n*-alkanoic acid concentration increased (Figure 4). This result suggests that the alkanoic acids were resistant to breakdown in the absence of oxygen. However, the differences in fatty acid composition of the oxic and anoxic microbial populations might also be a contributing factor. In the same experiments, sterols were observed to accumulate in aerobic incubation but disappeared almost completely in anoxic conditions; exactly the reverse result would be predicted from current knowledge of the microbial degradation of sterols. The pathways of aerobic sterol degradation in bacteria are known in detail (Sih and Whitlock, 1968), but there is no known biochemical pathway to account for the degradation of the sterol ring structure or side-chain without the participation of molecular oxygen.

CONCLUSIONS AND FUTURE PROSPECTS

The organic matter of aquatic sediments can give valuable information about the organisms and environment at the time of deposition. To make the most efficient use of this information, the organic geochemist must study the nature, distribution, source and fate of organic matter in contemporary aquatic environments. It may be present in solution or as particulates, some of which may be identified by visual inspection, *e.g.*, pollen, algal cells. Of the compounds studied, lipids are especially suited to use as biological markers, but very sensitive analytical equipment is required for detection and measurement of concentration, together with computerized handling of data. The analyses permit a detailed comparison of environments to be made and paleoenvironments to be interpreted. In addition, the processes by which biolipids are transformed into geolipids can be studied by incubation in sediment cores in the laboratory.

Future studies in biogeochemistry must include the

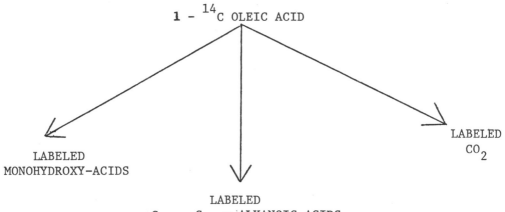

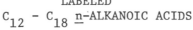

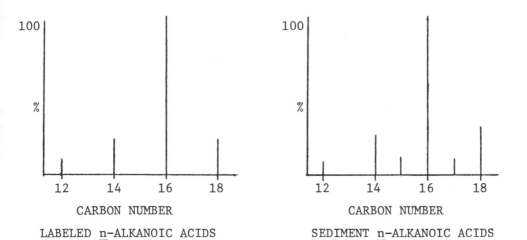

Figure 3. Laboratory studies of diagenetic reactions (2)
Fate of oleic acid in sediment.

Legend. A normalized carbon number distribution of the
labeled *n*-alkanoic acids formed during incubation
of $1-^{14}C$-oleic acid in sediment compared to the distribution
of $C_{12}-C_{18}$ *n*-alkanoic acids in a fresh sample of sediment.
Odd carbon-number acids were not determined in the labeled
sample.
    Labeled sodium oleate in aqueous solution was injected into
an intact sediment core (4 x 20 cm) taken from tidal mud flats
of the Severn Estuary. After incubation for 14 days at the
ambient temperature of the laboratory, the lipids were extracted by acid hydrolysis, purified by TLC and preparative
GLC, then quantified by liquid scintillation counting.
(Gaskell *et al.*, 1976.)

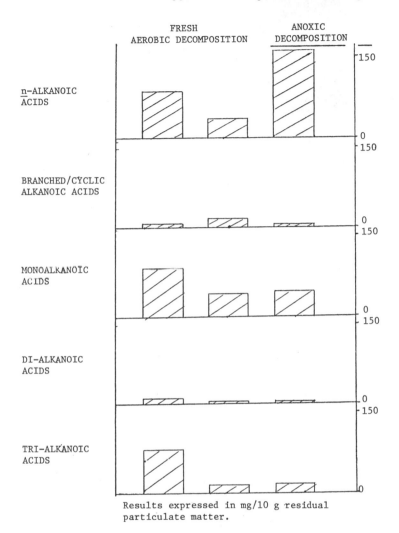

Results expressed in mg/10 g residual
particulate matter.

Figure 4.   Decomposition of the cyanophyte *Oscillatoria
agardhi* var. *isothrix*.

Legend. The concentration of fatty acids in particulate
matter remaining after aerobic or anoxic decomposition of *Oscillatoria agardhi* compared to the composition of
the fresh alga. *Oscillatoria agardhi* var. *isothrix* was collected from Blelham Tarn (England) and concentrated by centrifugation. Aerobic decomposition was achieved by passing air
through an aliquot of the concentrate kept at 8°C for eight
weeks. For anoxic decomposition, a portion of concentrate
was flushed with N_2, then sealed in a container and incubated
at 8°C for 28 weeks. Both concentrates were kept in the dark.
Lipids were extracted into benzene/methanol (3:1) in a soxhlet
apparatus, saponified and methylated, and concentrations determined by GLC. (Cranwell, 1976.)

selection of a limited number of water columns for intensive
investigation, especially the multiple sampling of water,
sediment and biota. The anoxic Black Sea and oxic South
Antarctic Convergence would be suitable examples of marine environments. The study of organic geochemistry is gaining considerable benefit from the Deep Sea Drilling Project, but even
more information could be obtained if the DSDP drilling were
complemented by sampling of the uppermost sediment layer (this
portion is lost in DSDP coring). The organic matter that is
carried into seas and lakes by wind and river transport must
be identified and quantitated, and then compared to the compounds in aquatic sediments.

The "processing" of organic material by the microorganisms and meiofauna of the sediments and water column requires
greater attention. We need to study the transformations of
organic compounds, especially the biological markers such as
steroids, triterpenoids and carotenoids, both *in situ* and in
the laboratory, in aerobic and anaerobic sediments. Rigorous
microbiological techniques must be used to isolate, count,
and identify the dominant sediment microflora. This is particularly important for anaerobic sediments in which preservation of alkanes could occur. Once isolated, these pure cultures of microorganisms must be cultivated under extremely
"clean" conditions on defined media to provide sufficient cell
material for determination of lipid composition. It will then
be possible to give an estimate of the contribution of lipid
to the sediment by each species studied and to detect any complex organic compounds, such as triterpenoids, that are synthesized by the organism. Use of radio-labeled substrates
would confirm *de novo* synthesis of these compounds. Also in
the field of microbiology, there is a growing need to distinguish between living and dead cells in the sediment and to
determine at what depth microbial activity ceases.

The invertebrate fauna of the sediment and sediment/water
interface are also responsible for extensive processing of organic matter and warrant detailed investigation. Not only is
the sediment physically disturbed but, in the case of sediment
feeders, organic matter is removed during passage through the
gut and returned to the environment only by excretion or death
and decomposition of the organism. Filter-feeders and carni-
vores living at the interface represent a direct transport of
organic material from the adjacent water layer to the sediment.
Planktonic invertebrates process material in the water column
and produce fecal pellets that are often sculptured and protected by a chitinous coat. The organic content of the fresh
pellets must be compared to the composition of the animal's
diet to establish whether compounds are dietary or synthesized
in the animal tissue. During the lifetime of the pellet decomposition will occur due to the presence of bacteria, and
the residue that enters the sediment may have a significantly
different composition.

The study of polymeric material is still a problem, and a more detailed knowledge of the cross-linkages is essential, both for a deeper understanding of the origin of this material and to improve methods of analysis. Valuable assistance might be obtained by collaboration with polymer chemists of biological, academic and industrial background. Laboratory experiments must also attempt to simulate the formation of these complex polymer particles. The particulates require a detailed and, to some extent, standardized classification to allow their presence in sediments to be recorded routinely and compared between samples. Considerable variations have been observed in the composition of a lake sediment as a function of particle size (Thompson and Eglinton, 1976), and these changes in composition could condition different degrees of diagenesis of the organic matter in the various fractions.

A combined effort is required from the organic geochemists and the marine and freshwater organic chemists and biologists to promote a better understanding of the processes, mechanisms and interactions affecting organic matter in the aquatic environment. Collaboration could permit the systematic sampling of water column, sediments, biota and atmosphere from several specific sites of known geography, geology, temperature, productivity, oxicity, depth and pollution. Sampling expeditions could be arranged in which experts from the appropriate disciplines would participate, and the material could then be distributed among a number of laboratories for subsequent analysis.

Finally, the organic geochemists, marine chemists and environmental organic chemists must attempt to standardize analytical procedures and data-bases used in the determination of organic compounds in the aquatic environment. By this means the productivity of the scientific community can be maximized and a greater understanding of the global carbon cycle will develop.

ACKNOWLEDGMENTS

The author wishes to thank the Natural Environment Research Council for financial support.

REFERENCES

Albone, E. S., G. Eglinton, N. C. Evans, J. M. Hunter and M. M. Rhead. "The Fate of DDT in Severn Estuary Sediments," *Environ. Sci. Technol.* 6:914-919 (1972).

Blumer, M. "Polycyclic Aromatic Compounds in Nature," *Scientific Am.* 234:35-45 (1976).

Brooks, P. W., G. Eglinton, S. J. Gaskell, D. J. McHugh,
J. R. Maxwell and R. P. Philp. "Lipids of Recent Sediments,
Part I: Straight-Chain Hydrocarbons and Carboxylic Acids
of some Temperate Lacustrine and Subtropical Lagoonal/Tidal
Flat Sediments," *Chem. Geol.* 18:21-38 (1976).

Cardoso, J. N. *Ph.D. Thesis,* University of Bristol (1976).

Cardoso, J. N., P. W. Brooks, G. Eglinton, R. Goodfellow,
J. R. Maxwell and R. P. Philp. "Lipids of Recently-Deposited
Algal Mats at Laguna Mormona, Baja California," in *Environ-
mental Biogeochemistry,* Vol. 1, J. Nriagu, Ed. (Ann Arbor,
Michigan: Ann Arbor Science Publishers, 1976a), pp. 149-174.

Cardoso, J. N., G. Eglinton and P. J. Holloway. "The Use of
Cutin Acids in the Recognition of Higher Plant Contribution
to Recent Sediments," *Advances in Organic Geochemistry*
(Oxford: Pergamon Press, 1976b).

Cardoso, J. N., A. M. K. Wardroper, C. D. Watts, P. J. Barnes,
J. R. Maxwell, D. G. Mound and G. C. Speers. "Preliminary
Organic Geochemical Analyses; Site 391, Leg 44 of the Deep
Sea Drilling Project," in *Initial Reports of the Deep Sea
Drilling Project* (Washington, D.C.: U.S. Government Printing
Office, 1977).

Corpe, W. A. "Periphytic Marine Bacteria and the Formation of
Microbial Films on Solid Surfaces," in *Effect of the Ocean
Environment on Microbial Activities,* R. R. Colwell and R. Y.
Morita, Eds. (University Park Press, 1974), pp. 397-417.

Corpe, W. A., and H. Winters. "Hydrolytic Enzymes of some
Periphytic Marine Bacteria," *Can. J. Microbiol.* 18:1483-1490
(1972).

Cranwell, P. A. "Environmental Organic Chemistry of Rivers and
Lakes, both Water and Sediment," in *Environmental Chemistry,*
Vol. 1 (London: The Chemical Society, 1975), pp. 22-54.

Cranwell, P. A. "Organic Geochemistry of Lake Sediments," in
Environmental Biogeochemistry, Vol. 1, J. Nriagu, Ed.
(Ann Arbor, Michigan: Ann Arbor Science Publishers, 1976),
pp. 75-88.

Cranwell, P. A. "Decomposition of Aquatic Biota and Sediment
Formation: Lipid Components of Two Blue-Green Algal Species
and of Detritus Resulting from Microbial Attack," *Freshwater
Biol.* 6:481-488 (1976).

Cowey, C. B., and E. D. S. Corner. "On the Nutrition and Metabolism of Zooplankton, Part II," *J. Mar. Biol. Assoc., U.K.* 43:495-511 (1963).

Cundell, A. M., and R. W. Traxler. "Microbial Degradation of Petroleum at Low Temperature," *Mar. Poll. Bull.* 4:125-127 (1973).

De Rosa, M., A. Gambacorta, L. Minale and J. D. Bu'Lock. "Bacterial Triterpenes," *J. Chem. Soc., Chem. Commun.* 619-620 (1971).

Eadie, B. J., and L. M. Jeffrey. "δ^{13}C Analyses of Oceanic Particulate Organic Matter," *Mar. Chem.* 1:199-209 (1973).

Eglinton, G., and R. J. Hamilton. "Leaf Epicuticular Waxes," *Science* 156:1322-1334 (1967).

Eglinton, G., B. R. T. Simoneit and J. A. Zoro. "The Recognition of Organic Pollutants in Aquatic Sediments," *Proc. Roy. Soc. London B.* 189:415-442 (1975).

Fleischer, S. "Sugars in the Sediments of Lake Trummen and Reference Lakes," *Arch. Hydrobiol.* 70:392-412 (1972).

Gaskell, S. J., and G. Eglinton. "Rapid Hydrogenation of Sterols in a Contemporary Lacustrine Sediment," *Nature* 254: 209-211 (1975).

Gaskell, S. J., and G. Eglinton. "Sterols of a Contemporary Lacustrine Sediment," *Geochim. Cosmochim. Acta* 40:1221-1228 (1976).

Gaskell, S. J., M. M. Rhead, P. W. Brooks and G. Eglinton. "Diagenesis of Oleic Acid in an Estuarine Sediment," *Chem. Geol.* 17:319-324 (1976).

Gelpi, E., H. Schneider, J. Mann and J. Oro. "Hydrocarbons of Geochemical Significance in Microscopic Algae," *Phytochem.* 9:603-612 (1970).

Gibson, D. T. "Microbial Degradation of Hydrocarbons," in *The Nature of Seawater*, E. D. Goldberg, Ed. (Berlin: Dahlem Konferenzen, 1975), pp. 667-696.

Goodwin, T. W. "Comparative Biochemistry of Sterols in Eukaryotic Microorganisms," in *Lipids and Biomembranes of Eukaryotic Microorganisms*, J. A. Erwin, Ed. (New York: Academic Press, 1973), pp. 1-41.

Gorham, E., J. W. G. Lund, J. E. Sanger and W. E. Dean. "Some Relationships Between Algal Standing Crop, Water Chemistry, and Sediment Chemistry in the English Lakes," *Limnol. Oceanogr.* 19:601–617 (1974).

Gray, N. A. B., J. A. Zoro, T. O. Grønneberg, S. J. Gaskell, J. N. Cardoso and G. Eglinton. "Automatic Classification of Mass Spectra by a Laboratory Computer System," *Anal. Lett.* 8:461–477 (1975).

Grønneberg, T. O., N. A. B. Gray and G. Eglinton. "Computer Based Search and Retrieval System for Rapid Mass Spectral Screening of Samples," *Anal. Chem.* 47:415–419 (1975).

Hajibrahim, S. K., P. Tibbetts, C. D. Watts, J. R. Maxwell, G. Eglinton, H. Colin and G. Guiochon. *Analysis by HPLC of Pigments of Geochemical Interest,* in press.

Hayaishi, O. *Molecular Mechanisms of Oxygen Activation,* 1st ed. (London: Academic Press, 1974).

Hammond, A. L. "Paleoceanography: Sea Floor Clues to Earlier Environments," *Science* 191:168–170, 208 (1976).

Hood, A., J. R. Castano and J. W. Kendrick. "Petroleum-Generating Potential and Thermal History of DSDP Leg 38 Sediments," in *Initial Reports of the Deep Sea Drilling Project,* Vol. 38, M. Talwani and G. Udintser *et al.* (Washington, D.C.: U.S. Government Printing Office, 1976), pp. 801–803.

Kaneps, A. "Deep Sea Drilling Project," *Geotimes* 21:16–17 (1976).

Meadows, P. S., and J. G. Anderson. "Microorganisms Attached to Marine and Freshwater Sand Grains," *Nature* 212:1059–1060 (1966).

Mel'nikov, I. A. "Use of Histochemical Reagents To Determine the Biochemical Composition of Detritus," *Oceanology* 14: 922–926 (1974).

Menzel, D. W. "Primary Productivity, Dissolved and Particulate Organic Matter and the Sites of Oxidation of Organic Matter," in *Marine Chemistry,* E. D. Goldberg, Ed., Vol. 5 of *The Sea* (New York: Wiley-Interscience, 1974), pp. 659–678.

Morris, R. J., and G. Eglinton. "Fate and Recycling of Carbon Compounds," *Proceedings of Symposium on Concepts in Marine Organic Chemistry,* Edinburgh, September 6–10, 1976, in press.

Mulheirn, L. J., and G. Ryback. "Stereochemistry of some Steranes from Geological Sources," *Nature* 256:301-302 (1975).

Murphy, Sister Mary, T. J., A. McCormick and G. Eglinton. "Perhydro-β-carotene in the Green River Shale," *Science* 157: 1040-1042 (1967).

Nishimura, M., and T. Koyama. "Sterols and Stanols in Lake Sediments and Diatoms," *Chem. Geol.* 17:229-239 (1976).

Philp, R. P., J. R. Maxwell and G. Eglinton. "Environmental Organic Geochemistry of Aquatic Sediments," *Sci. Prog. Oxford* 63:521-545 (1976).

Philp, R. P., and M. Calvin. "Possible Origin for Insoluble (Kerogen) Debris in Sediments from Insoluble Cell-Wall Materials of Algae and Bacteria," *Nature* 262:134-136 (1976).

Raymont, J. E. G., R. J. Morris, C. F. Ferguson and J. K. B. Raymont. *J. Exper. Mar. Biol. Ecol.,* in press.

Saxby, J. D., in *Oil Shale,* T. F. Yen and G. V. Chilingarian, Eds. (New York: Elsevier, 1976), p. 103.

Sih, C. J., and H. W. Whitlock. "Biochemistry of Steroids," *Ann. Rev. Biochem.* 37:661-694 (1968).

Simoneit, B. R. T. "Sources of the Solvent-Soluble Organic Matter in the Glacial Sequence of DSDP Samples from the Norwegian-Greenland Sea, Leg 38," in *Initial Reports of the Deep Sea Drilling Project,* Vol. 38, M. Talwani and G. Udintsev *et al.* (Washington, D.C.: U.S. Government Printing Office, 1976), pp. 805-806.

Simoneit, B. R. T., and A. L. Burlingame. "Preliminary Organic Analyses of the DSDP (JOIDES) Cores, Legs V-IX," *Advances in Organic Geochemistry 1971* (Oxford: Pergamon Press, 1972), pp. 189-228.

Simoneit, B. R. T., and A. L. Burlingame. "Kerogens Derived from the Oxidative Degradation of Green River Formation Oil Shale Kerogen," in *Advances in Organic Geochemistry,* B. Tissot and F. Bienner, Eds. (Paris: Eds. Technip, 1974), pp. 191-201.

Swain, F. M. *Nonmarine Organic Geochemistry* (Cambridge: University Press, 1970).

Thomas, B. R. "Kauri Resins—Modern and Fossil," in *Organic Geochemistry—Methods and Results,* G. Eglinton and M. T. J. Murphy, Eds. (Berlin: Springer-Verlag, 1969), pp. 599-618.

Thompson, S., and G. Eglinton. *Geochim. Cosmochim. Acta,* in press.

Van Vleet, E. S., and J. G. Quinn. "Characterisation of Mono-unsaturated Fatty Acids from an Estuarine Sediment," *Nature* 262:126-128 (1976).

Watts, C. D. *Ph.D. Thesis,* University of Bristol (1975).

Watts, C. D., J. R. Maxwell and H. Kjosen. "The Potential of Carotenoids as Environmental Indicators," in *Advances in Organic Geochemistry 1975,* in press.

ZoBell, C. E. "Microbial and Environmental Transitions in Estuaries," in *Estuarine Microbial Ecology,* L. H. Stevenson and R. R. Colwell, Eds. (Columbia: University of S. Carolina Press, 1973), pp. 9-34.

CHAPTER 4

INFLUENCE OF MICROORGANISMS AND MICROENVIRONMENT ON THE GLOBAL SULFUR CYCLE

M. V. IVANOV

Institute of Biochemistry and
Physiology of Microorganisms
USSR Academy of Sciences
Puschino, USSR

All the variety of microbiological processes of the sulfur cycle can be schematically presented as three main processes: oxidation of sulfide minerals and native sulfur to sulfuric acid, oxidation of dissolved hydrogen sulfide to sulfur and sulfates, and reduction of sulfates to hydrogen sulfide and sulfides.

This chapter deals with the quantitative characteristics of the microbiological sulfate reduction in different ecosystems. Since it became known that selective concentration of sulfur compounds occurs in sedimentary rocks, this process has continued to attract the attention of microbiologists and geochemists. According to Grinenkos' data (1974), the concentration of sulfur in sedimentary rocks is four times its content in the earth's crust. About 40 percent of sedimentary sulfur is presented by sulfide minerals, with the mean $\delta^{34}S$ value equal to -9.2 percent, which is characteristic of sulfides of the biogenic origin (Grinenko and Grinenko, 1974).

In the last few years the problem of the anaerobic microbiological formation of gaseous sulfur compounds, primarily hydrogen sulfide and dimethylsulfides, has acquired great practical importance in connection with the contamination of the atmosphere and the resulting ultraacid atmospheric precipitation. To solve the latter problem it is essential to know the rate of the microbiological reduction of sulfates under natural conditions. However, there has been little research into this problem.

Table I, citing from Goldhaber and Kaplan's work (1975), presents the rates of sulfate reduction in marine sediments obtained by different investigators using various direct and

Table I
Sulfate Reduction Rate in Recent Sediments

Area	Rate (moles liter^{-1} yr^{-1})	Technique	Source
Santa Barbara Basin	5.9×10^{-4}	Modeling	Berner (1972)
Somes Sound, Maine	3.7×10^{-2}	Modeling	Berner (1972)
Long Island Sound	7.1×10^{-5}	Modeling	Berner (1972)
Carmen Basin Gulf of California	3.1×10^{-4}	Modeling	Goldhaber (1974)
Pescadero Basin Gulf of California	8.4×10^{-5}	Modeling	Goldhaber (1974)
JOIDES Site 147, Cariaco Trench	3.7×10^{-5}	Modeling	Tsou *et al.* (1973)
JOIDES Site 148	7.3×10^{-8}	Modeling	Tsou *et al.* (1973)
Black Sea	5.5×10^{-4}–4.3×10^{-2}	S^{35}	Sorokin (1962)
Littoral of Krasnovodsk Bay	7.4×10^{-2}–1.6×10^{-1}	S^{35}	Ivanov (1968)
Littoral of Barents Sea	1.7×10^{-1}–4.5×10^{-1}	S^{35}	Ivanov (1968)
Lab Study	2.0×10^{-1}–3.1×10^{-1}	Measured SO_4^{2-} Decrease	Gunkel/ Oppenheimer (1963)
Lab Study	2.8×10^{-1}	Measured SO_4^{2-} Decrease	Martens/ Berner (1974)
Lab Study	4.0×10^{-2}	Measured SO_4^{-2} Decrease	Nakai/ Jensen (1964)

calculation methods. Additional material was obtained during the last five years by collaborators from the Institute of Biochemistry and Physiology of Microorganisms, USSR Academy of Sciences.

When working on hydrogen sulfide lakes and reduced sediments of the Pacific and Indian oceans, we applied the method of the direct determination of the rate of sulfate reduction in water and sediments based on the use of labeled sulfate (Ivanov, 1956; 1968). To carry out these investigations we sampled water and mud, added sulfur-labeled sulfate, and incubated samples with sulfate under natural conditions at the same horizons of muds and water thickness from which samples investigated had been taken. Simultaneously, the chemical composition of water and mud samples, isotopic composition of sulfur compounds, and distribution of sulfate reducers in them were investigated by inoculating on the agar Postgate medium $_{mm}$ with yeast autolyzate (Postgate, 1966). Having determined the label distribution in reduced sulfur compounds at the end of the experiment and knowing the initial content of sulfate sulfur in the sample, we calculated the rate of sulfate reduction during the experiment in a definite volume of water or sediment.

The summary data characterizing the rate and productivity of sulfate reduction in water and upper horizons of silty sediments of some brackish and freshwater meromictic lakes of the Soviet Union are presented in Table II. The most intensive processes of sulfate reduction were detected in the eutrophic lakes Repnoe and Weisove. The weakest processes were characteristic of the oligotrophic lakes Okha-lyampi and Kononjer. Without exception, the rate of sulfate reduction in silty sediments in all the lakes is well above that in the water thickness. However, in some lakes (Weisovo, Kuznechikha) that have substantial anaerobic zones, considerable quantities of hydrogen sulfide, comparable with its production in silty sediments, are produced daily in the water column. The data obtained do not confirm a widespread opinion that H_2S of meromictic lakes is generated in silty sediments and then diffused into water thickness. Under peculiar hydrodynamic conditions of meromictic lakes, the detected processes of sulfate reduction in the water column provides the accumulation of hydrogen sulfide in water at the expense of sulfate reduction in the water column itself. This is evidenced also by the results of the analysis of H_2S and SO_4^{2-} isotopic compositions in water and silty sediments of lakes.

Table III presents the data of Vinogradov *et al.* (1962) and Nissenbaum and Kaplan (1976) on the Black and Dead seas, respectively. In both cases the hydrogen sulfide of water thickness differs in $\delta^{34}S$ values from that one of the upper horizons of silty sediments. Analogous data were obtained when investigating the isotopic contents of the hydrogen sulfide of water and silts from Mogilnoye Lake situated on Kildin Island in the Barentsovo Sea (Table IV). That same table also presents results of the investigation on sulfate reduction rate on the section of the water column and silty sediments. In all brackish water basins, the hydrogen sulfide of the water column has a lighter isotopic composition than do the silts. In our opinion such difference is explained by the more active fractionation of sulfur isotopes in the slow process of sulfate

Table II
Rate of Sulfate Reduction and H$_2$S Productivity in Different Lakes

Lake and Location:	Depth (m)	Thickness of H$_2$S Zone	Rate of H$_2$S Production mg x l^{-1} day^{-1}		Daily Productivity H$_2$S mg m^{-2}		Daily Primary Productivity C$_2$ mg m^{-2}
			Water	Sediments	Water	Sediments	
Salt Lakes							
Repnoe Ukraine SSR	6.5	1.5	0.12	15.6	180	1560	1970
Weijsowo Ukraine SSR	16.5	14.5	0.08	19.2	1160	1920	976
Mogilnoye Kildin Is.	16.3	7.0	0.03	10.8	210	1080	335
Fresh Lakes							
B. Kichiyer Middle Volga	16.5	11.5	0.005	6.2	58	620	416
Ch. Kichiyer Middle Volga	11.0	7.5	0.016	13.3	120	1330	445
Sakovo Vologda	16.0	12.0	0.0016	3.9	19	390	71
Kuznechiha Middle Volga	20.0	15.0	0.020	3.6	300	360	160
Kononjer Middle Volga	22.5	12.5	0.0008	5.2	10	520	64
Ocha-Liampi Karelija	17.0	10.5	0.0008	3.2	8.4	320	52

Table III
The Difference in δ^{34}S Values of Hydrogen Sulfide
and Sulfate in the Water and Sediments (percent)

		Hydrogen Sulfide	Hydrogen Sulfate	Source
Dead Sea	Water	−21.1	+14.2	Nissenbaum and
	Sediments	−16.7	+14.1	Kaplan, 1976
Black Sea	Water	−32.6	+19.3	Vinogradov
	Sediments	−26.0	+22.5	*et al.*, 1962

reduction in the water column. However, it is believed that
such change of the isotope composition results from the fractionation of sulfur isotopes during the slow diffusion of hydrogen sulfide from silty sediments.

The substantial difference in δ^{34}S values of hydrogen
sulfide of water and sediments is observed also in freshwater
meromictic basins. And, as seen from Table V, in the karst
Sakovo Lake both hydrogen sulfide and sulfates of the anaerobic
zone have a heavier isotopic composition than analogous compounds in silty sediments.

The difference in the isotopic composition of sulfur
compounds of the water column and silty sediments is defined
more sharply in the karst freshwater lake Bolshoi Kichier
(Table VI), where the isotopically heavier hydrogen sulfide
and sulfates are also observed in the water column. The examples of differences in the isotopic composition of hydrogen
sulfide of water and sediments in different meromictic water
basins are adequate proof that a marked part of H_2S in such
lakes is formed microbiologically directly in the water column.
The key difference in the character of the distribution of isotopically light and heavy sulfur compounds in marine basins
and karst lakes can be easily understood from the scheme given
in Figure 1.

Sulfate diffuses in seas from the water column into silty sediments where, accompanied by the pronounced change in
the isotopic composition, it is reduced. But in karst lakes
sulfate comes from the underground water. Because of this,
sulfate of silty sediments has a light isotopic composition,
and in the water column its reduction occurs accompanied by a
marked change in the isotopic composition with increase in the
part of the isotope δ^{34}S. Once the total content of sulfate in
the lake water is small, the sufficiently heavy hydrogen sulfide with positive δ^{34}S values can be formed, as observed in
the Bolshoi Kichier Lake (see Table VI).

While investigation of sulfur cycle processes in meromictic water basins is fascinating, the processes of sulfate
reduction in marine sediments on a global sulfur cycle scale

Table IV

The Rate of Sulfate Reduction in Mogilnoye Lake

(H_2S ppm·l^{-1}·day^{-1})

Depth	t°C	Eh,mv	O_2 (ppm)	SO_4^{2-} (ppm)	H_2S (ppm)	Rate of H_2S Production	$\delta^{34}S$,%	
							H_2S	SO_4^{2-}
Water (m)								
2	12.5	+205	6.4	288	0	0	—	+14.0
8	12.3	+175	4.7	1746	0	0	—	+15.6
9	11.8	+150	0.64	1851	0	0	—	—
10	9.5	− 50	0	1902	41.5	0.0231	−11.0	+21.0
12	7.5	− 45	0	1995	55.1	0.0337	−20.4	+22.7
14	7.5	− 45	0	1995	155.4	0.0368	−22.3	+24.4
Sediments (cm)								
0-5	—	− 65	—	1613	740[a]	10.38	−18.0	+27.8
5-10	—	− 95	—	1422	452[a]	1.00	−18.4	+29.0

[a] Acid-soluble sulfides.

Table V

The Rate of Sulfate Reduction in the Sakovo Lake
$(ppm \cdot l^{-1} \cdot day^{-1})$

Depth	t°C	Eh, mv	O_2 (ppm)	SO_4^{2-} (ppm)	H_2S (ppm)	Rate of H_2S Production	$\delta^{34}S$,%	
							H_2S	SO_4^{2-}
Water (m)								
2	20.8	+165	6.7	153.6	0	0	–	+13.1
4	10.0	+ 95	2.4	602.0	0	–	–	+14.2
5	6.8	– 15	0	768.0	7.1	0.0035	–15.0	+15.4
7	6.2	– 35	0	726.0	8.7	0.0016	–10.8	+14.5
15.2	5.2	– 55	0	816.0	11.0	0.0006	–	
Sediments (cm)								
0–6	–	–135	–	748	390[a]	3.94	–29.7	+10.3
6–12	–	–185	–	837	121[a]	2.76	–25.4	+13.1
15–20	–	–190	–	828	180[a]	0.57	–23.8	+13.4

[a] Acid-soluble sulfides.
The number of sulfate reducers 8–22 per 1 ml of water and 10^4–10^5 per 1 g of sediments.

Table VI

The Rate of Sulfate Reduction in the Big Kitchier Lake
$(ppm \cdot 1^{-1} \cdot day^{-1})$

Depth	t°C	Eh, mv	O_2 (ppm)	SO_4^{2-} (ppm)	H_2S (ppm)	Rate of H_2S Production	$\delta^{34}S$, % H_2S	$\delta^{34}S$, % SO_4^{2-}
Water (m)								
2	24.8	+215	9.9	—	0	—	—	—
6	7.4	+100	0.6	30.0	1.9	—	—	—
7	7.1	+ 45	0	46.2	3.6	0.0061	+13.6	+17.5
9	6.1	− 15	0	47.7	7.9	0.0044	+11.5	+17.6
14.5	6.0	− 75	0	53.4	13.2	0.0037	+17.1	+19.6
Sediments (cm)								
0−6	—	−105	—	43.2	155[a]	6.18	− 4.9	+10.5

[a]Acid-soluble sulfides.
The number of reducers 5-10 on 1 ml water and 10 -10 per 1 g sediments.

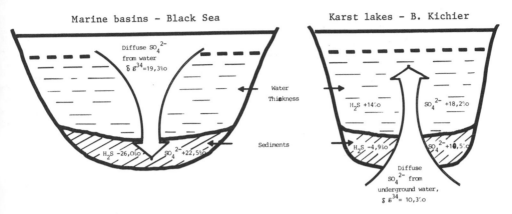

Figure 1. Scheme of fractionation processes of sulfur isotopes in marine basins and karst lakes.

are of particular interest. The rates of this process are practically unknown, a fact evidenced by the interrogative sign that appears in one of the reported schemes of the global sulfur cycle cited in Figure 2.

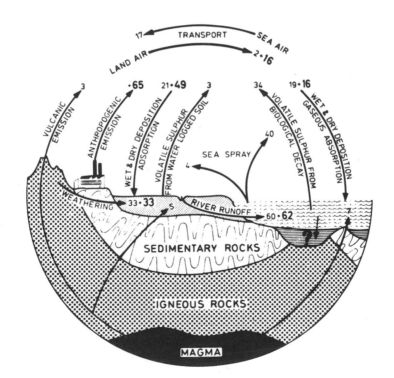

Figure 2. Scheme of global sulfur cycle (Grant, Kodhe and Hallberg, 1976).

During the ninth scientific expedition of the Soviet research ship *Dmitrii Mendeleev*, the distribution of sulfate reducers and rate of sulfate reduction in 13 columns of the Pacific Ocean-reduced silty sediments were analyzed. Five columns were taken from the deep water part of the Gulf of California, two from the Mexico shelf, four from the continental slope near Masatlan and two from the region near the Hawaiian Islands (Chebotarev and Ivanov, 1976). All the experiments on the determination of sulfate reduction rate with labeled sulfate were carried out at 2°C. The radioactivity of all the reduced sulfur forms was determined in the majority of experiments (Ivanov, Lein and Kashparova, 1976).

As seen from the data in Figure 3, the viable cells of sulfate reducers and active process of sulfate reduction were detected in the whole silt thickness up to a depth of 6 m. In silts with the low content of organic matter and high Eh values at the upper horizons of sediments, the process of sulfate reduction began at a given depth from the water/silt interface.

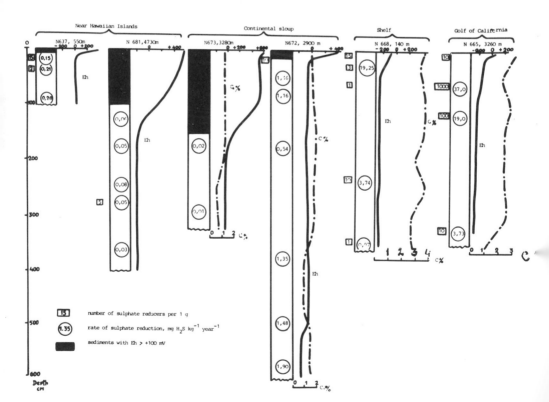

Figure 3. Distribution of sulfate reducers and rate of sulfate reduction in some columns of silt sediments of the Pacific Ocean. Data on Eh and C_{org} from the work of I. I. Volkov, A. G. Rozanov, N. I. Zhabina and L. S. Fomina (1976).

In the substantially reduced sediments of the Gulf of California shelf and continental slope the most intensive processes of sulfate reduction were observed at the upper horizons of sediments down to a depth of 100–150 cm (Table VII). Because of this, only the data on upper horizons of silty sediments were used to make the further calculations of the productivity of sulfate reduction. According to the calculations in Table VIII, the total productivity of the process of sulfate reduction in sediments of the world ocean shelf and continental slope makes up approximately 900×10^6 tons of sulfur per year.

A year ago Dr. S. S. Belyaev and Dr. A. I. Nesterov carried out analogous investigations in the Indian Ocean. The data in Table IX show that sufficiently intensive microbiological sulfate reduction is observed in the reduced sediments of this ocean. However, of particular interest are the results of the work carried out in deep-water basins of the Red Sea. The water in these basins contains an unusually high concentration of mineral salts, and silty sediments are enriched with various sulfides of metals.

It is known that the origin of the hydrogen sulfide of these basins is considered differently, and the attempts to detect living microorganisms in these sediments have failed thus far (Trüpper, 1969). In 1976 my colleagues succeeded in detecting living and active sulfate reducers in bottom sediments of the Suakin Basin at a depth of 2762 m where the bottom water had the temperature of +29°C. Growth on Postgate medium with the addition of 20% NaCl was detected when inoculating samples taken at the depth of 0–10, 65–75 and 330–350 cm from the sediment surface. When labeled sulfate was added to samples of the sediment from this basin and then were incubated at 25°C for two months, we detected the process of sulfate reduction from the transformation of labeled sulfur from sulfate to pyrite one. Therefore, our results on the Red Sea silts correlate well with isotopic investigations carried out by I. Kaplan *et al.* (1969), who showed the availability of the process of biogenic fractionation of sulfur isotopes under the specific conditions of the sediments in deep water basins of this sea.

In summary, hydrogen sulfide formed in silt sediments and the water column of meromictic lakes and seas is removed from the present sulfur cycle in the form of pyrite and organic-bound sulfur of bottom sediments. However, in such shallow water basins as lagoons and coastal salt lakes and in regularly drained littoral sediments the hydrogen sulfide produced has the possibility of entering the atmosphere directly. According to our data, the active process of sulfate reduction taking place in littoral sediments has enough intensity to make up 20–24 mg H_2S per kg per day even at low temperatures (Ivanov, 1968). Therefore, to strike a balance of biogenic sulfur entering the atmosphere, it is necessary to investigate the processes of sulfate reduction in shallow sediments of sea basins with their quantitative characteristics.

Table VII
The Rate of Sulfate Reduction in Sediments
of the Gulf of California and Pacific Ocean

Location	N and Depth (m)	Depth from Sediment's Surface (cm)	Sulfate Reducers per 1 g	Rate of Sulfate Reduction $(mg\ kg^{-1}year^{-1})$
		Gulf of California		
27°09'N	N668	30	5	7.0
111°08'W	1760 m	165	13	1.64
25°31'N	N664	60–70	10	19.40
110°32'W	1170 m	150	2	1.21
25°20'N	N665	40	1000	37.00
109°55'W	3250 m	95	100	18.90
		320	10	3.74
24°53'N	N666	35–40	10	12.03
	120 m	130–140	10	1.84
108°42'W		230–240	–	4.63
23°46'N	N667	10–15	10	19.25
108°40'W	2860 m	35–45	100	9.45
		95	–	8.52
		Pacific Ocean near Masatlan		
23°23'N	N668	15–30	3	20.05
106°45'W	140 m	220	10	3.74
		340	1	0.97
23°13'N	N669	37	3	5.67
107°24'W	1000 m	90	1	2.65
22°35'N	N670	40	10	7.09
108°07'W	1450 m	70	–	6.69
		140	–	7.49
22°02'N	N671	30	–	5.64
108°19'W	2650 m	90	–	2.45
		401	–	3.27

Table VIII
Calculation of Annual Productivity of Sulfate Reduction
in Shelf and Continental Slope Sediments
of the World Ocean[a]

1. Rate of sulfate reduction in shelf sediments (columns of sediments NN 666 and 668)—16.0 $mg \cdot kg^{-1} \cdot year^{-1}$ (by wet weight).

2. Rate of sulfate reduction in continental slope sediments (columns of sediments NN 669, 670, 671)—5.0 $mg \cdot kg^{-1} \cdot year^{-1}$ (by wet weight).

3. Shelf area -27.5×10^6 km^2 (Lisitsyn, 1974).

4. Continental slope area -55×10^6 km^2 (Lisitsyn, 1974).

5. Specific weight of sediments at humidity 50% -1.3.

   Productivity of sulfate reduction in shelf sediments -572×10^6 tons S $year^{-1}$.

   Productivity of sulfate reduction in continental slope sediments -375.5×10^6 tons S $year^{-1}$.

[a]For horizon of sediments 0–100 cm.

Table IX
The Rate of Sulfate Reduction in Sediments
of the Indian Ocean

Location	N and Depth (m)	Depth from Sediment's Surface (cm)	Sulfate Reducers per 1 g	Rate of Sulfate Reduction ($mg \cdot kg^{-1} \cdot year^{-1}$)
04°12'S	N1919	10–30	250	41.0
39°55'0	590 m	0–10	6000	67.7
23°25'N	N1960	190–200	25	25.5
67°15'0	520 m	0–5	600	48.9
23°05'N	N1961	40–60	250	59.7
		150–160	25	27.0
66°59'0	1040 m			
22°37'N	N1963	1–5	60	6.5
66°14'0	1820 m			
Near El-	N1965			
		0–5	60	43.9
Kuveit	43 m			

REFERENCES

Berner, R. A. "Sulfate Reduction, Pyrite Formation and the Oceanic Sulfur Budget," *Nobel Symposium,* D. Dyrssen and D. Jagner, Eds. Stockholm 20:347-361 (1972).

Chebotarev, E. N., and M. V. Ivanov. "The Distribution and Activity of Sulfate Reducers in Sediments of Pacific Ocean and Gulf of California," *Biogeochemistry of Diagenes of Ocean Sediments,* M. Nauka (1976), pp. 68-74.

Goldhaber, M. B. "Equilibrium and Dynamic Aspects of the Marine Geochemistry of Sulfur." Ph.D. Thesis, University of California, Los Angeles (1974).

Goldhaber, M. B., and I. R. Kaplan. "Controls and Consequences of Sulfate Reduction Rates in Recent Marine Sediments," *Soil Sci.* 119(1):42-55 (1975).

Granat, L., H. Rodhe and R. O. Hallberg. "The Global Sulfur Cycle," *Nitrogen, Phosphorus and Sulphur-Global Cycles, SCOPE Reports, Ecol. Bull.* N 22:90-134 (1976).

Grinenko, V. A., and L. N. Grinenko. *Geochemistry of Stable Sulphur Isotopes,* M. Nauka (1974).

Gunkel, W., and Ch. H. Oppenheimer. "Experiments Regarding the Sulfide Formation in Sediments of the Texas Gulf Coast," *Symposium on Marine Microbiology,* C. H. Oppenheimer, Ed. (1963), 674-683.

Ivanov, M. V. "The Use of Radioactive Isotopes for Investigation of Rate of Sulphate Reduction in Lake Belovod," *Microbiologija,* 25(3)305-309 (1956).

Ivanov, M. V. *Microbial Processes in the Formation of Sulphur Deposits* (Jerusalem, Israel: Program of Scientific Trans., 1968), 298 pp.

Ivanov, M. V., A. Yu. Lein and E. V. Kashparova. "The Intensity of Formation and Diagenetic Turning of Reduced Sulphur Compounds in Pacific Sediments," *Biogeochemistry of Diagenes of Ocean Sediments,* M. Nauka (1976), pp. 171-178.

Kaplan, I. K., R. E. Sweeney and A. Nissenbaum. "Sulphur Isotope Studies on Red Sea Geothermal Brines and Sediments," *Hot Brines and Recent Heavy Metal Deposits in the Red Sea,* E. T. Degens and D. A. Ross, Eds. (New York: Springer-Verlag, Inc., 1969), 474-498.

Lisizin, A. P. *The Sedimentation in Oceans,* M. Nauka (1974).

Martens, C. S., and R. A. Berner. "Methane Production in the Interstitial Waters of Sulfate Depleted Marine Sediments," *Science* 185:1167–1169 (1974).

Nakai, N., and M. L. Jensen. "The Kinetic Isotope Effect in the Bacterial Reduction and Oxidation of Sulfur," *Geochim. Cosmochim. Acta* 28:1893–1912 (1964).

Nissenbaum, A., and I. R. Kaplan. "Sulphur and Carbon Isotopic Evidence for Biogeochemical Processes in the Dead Sea Ecosystem," *Environ. Biogeochem.* 1:309–325 (1976).

Postgate, I. R. "Media for Sulfur Bacteria," *Laboratory Practice* 15(11):1239–1249 (1966).

Sorokin, Yu. I. "Experimental Investigation of Bacterial Sulphate Reduction in the Black Sea Using S^{35}," *Mikrobiologija* 31:402–410 (1962).

Trüper, H. G. "Bacterial Sulphate Reduction in the Red Sea Hot Brines," *Hot Brines and Recent Heavy Metal Deposits in the Red Sea*, E. T. Degens and D. A. Ross, Eds. (New York: Springer-Verlag, Inc., 1969), 263–271.

Tson, J. L., D. Hammond and K. Horowitz. "Interstitial Water Studies, Leg. 15. Study of CO_2 Released from Storied Deep Sea Sediments," in B. C. Heezen, I. G. MacGreger *et al. Initial Reports of the Deep Sea Drilling Project*, Vol. XX (Washington, D.C.: US Government Printing Office, 1973).

Vinogradov, A. P., V. A. Grinenko and V. I. Ustinov. "The Isotopic Composition of Sulphur Compounds from Black Sea," *Geochemia* 10:351–371 (1962).

Volkov, I. I., A. G. Rosanov, N. N. Zhabina and L. S. Fomina. "The Sulphur Compounds in Sediments of Gulf of California and Close Part of Pacific Ocean," *Biogeochemistry of Diagenesis of Ocean Sediments*, M. Nauka (1976), pp. 136–170.

SECTION II

ELEMENT CYCLES, BUDGETS AND TRANSFER RATES
IN LAKES AND RIVERS AND THEIR ALTERATION
BY MAN

CHAPTER 5

PASSAGE OF PHOSPHORUS THROUGH A CATCHMENT

F. H. RIGLER

Department of Biology
McGill University
Toronto, Ontario, Canada

INTRODUCTION

Phosphorus is always among those elements in the short-
est supply relative to the needs of living organisms, and, more
often than not, it is the element limiting growth of plants.
Therefore, phosphorus is of interest, not because it is quantitatively significant compared with other elements, but because slight changes in the amount of phosphorus moving through
the biosphere have profound effects on the production and biomass of living organisms. In many lakes it is possible to predict algal abundance with little more than a knowledge of phosphorus loading and flushing time (Dillon and Rigler, 1975).
However, the purpose of this chapter is not to discuss production, but merely to follow the phosphorus that enters a watershed from the atmosphere as it passes through the soil, flows
downstream to a lake and finally leaves the water of the lake
by being incorporated in the sediments or lost through the outflow. Emphasis will be placed on the aquatic components of the
system, and the scope will be restricted primarily to forested
and grazed watersheds in temperate regions. In fact, the subject matter is almost identical to that reviewed by Keup (1968),
although processes that Keup did not discuss thoroughly will be
emphasized and some quantitative generalizations that have
emerged in the last decade will be presented.

INPUT OF PHOSPHORUS FROM THE ATMOSPHERE

The sources of the phosphorus that supplies and is exported by the terrestrial component of a catchment are weathering of parent rock and soil, and atmospheric input (here called
aeolian loading), which includes wet fallout with rain and snow
and dry fallout. It would be interesting to know the total

supply but unfortunately neither source has been adequately quantified, presumably because most of the efforts of geochemists have been directed toward the major cations.

Aeolian loading values, summarized by Likens and Bormann (1975) fall between 10 and 60 $mgm^{-2} yr^{-1}$, but how closely these values approximate net aeolian input is unknown. They could include a considerable proportion of P that is merely being redistributed within the catchment. This suggestion is supported by the work of Gomolka (1975) who sampled at a series of sites on land and on a small lake and found that although wet fallout was the same at all sites, dry fallout was only half as great at the lake sites as at the land sites. This meant that about a quarter of the P collected by the standard methods (Egnér and Eriksson, 1955) is not aeolian input, but is merely being redistributed within the catchment. Since the decrease in fallout occurred within 75 m of the shore, she could detect only the redistribution of relatively large particles. If very small particles containing P are also picked up by the wind, perhaps a larger fraction of dry fallout and part of the wet fallout can also be attributed to redistribution. Because of this uncertainty we do not know aeolian input and thus cannot easily estimate the contribution of weathering.

EXPORT IN STREAMS

In contrast to loss of P to the atmosphere, export in outflowing water is easily and frequently measured. Dillon and Kirchner recently analyzed their data and previously published values and showed a simple pattern of P export influenced by type of bedrock and land usage (Table I). The smallest annual export ($4.8 mgm^{-2} yr^{-1}$) is from forested igneous catchments. Sedimentary watersheds export roughly twice this amount. Even a limited amount of grazing doubles the amount of P exported from both types, and completely farmed catchments export twice as much again. A sedimentary, farmed catchment averages 46 $mgm^{-2} yr^{-1}$. The wide range of export values in every one of Dillon and Kirchner's categories shows that other variables must also influence phosphorus export. Keup (1968) indicated that as mean slope increases, export increases, and Kirchner (1975) showed that almost all of the variability in export from forested, igneous watersheds could be explained as a function of drainage density. This study should be followed up because Kirchner's sample of streams was small (18), and from a restricted area, and his hypothesis, if generally applicable, will be very useful. For example, Dillon and Rigler (1975) recommended using an average figure for export in their predictive model. This could result in a 50–100 percent error, much of which could be eliminated by applying a correction for drainage density if Kirchner is correct.

Large temporal changes in phosphorus concentration do

Table I
Export of Total Phosphorus in mgm^{-2} yr^{-1}
from Southern Ontario Catchments[a]

Land Use	Igneous	Sedimentary
Forest	4.8	10.7
	(2.5–7.7)[b]	(6.7–14.5)
Forest and Pasture	11.7	28.8
	(8.1–16.0)	(20.5–37.0)

[a]After Dillon and Kirchner (1975).

[b]Values in brackets indicate the range.

occur, and an awareness of them is necessary to obtain accurate estimates of P export from a catchment. Since these changes are also potentially informative about geochemical phenomena, a brief description follows.

In unpolluted headwater streams the lowest phosphorus concentrations frequently occur in winter, and the highest in summer (Figure 1). This cycle probably reflects the varying contributions of deep and superficial soil strata, with the contribution of deep strata predominating in winter. This hypothesis derives from the observation (Figure 2) that P concentration and water color are highly correlated, a correlation that would be expected if the higher phosphorus concentrations were characteristic of near-surface throughflow rich in humic compounds. Recently, Cross (personal communication) has shown that the concentrations of iron and phosphorus are also correlated in streams (Figure 3). One could further postulate from this that much of the P associated with color may be bound to an iron-humic complex similar to those studied by Levesque and Schnitzer (1967).

In addition to seasonal changes, there are also pronounced short-term effects on P concentration by flood events (Crisp, 1966). An example of this phenomenon in a granitic-moorland stream is shown in Figure 4. During the flood a small part of the increased P is soluble and correlated with increased color, a relation that would be predicted from my hypothesis to explain seasonal changes and Whipkey's (1965) demonstration that at peak discharge most of the stream water is derived from throughflow from the superficial soil strata.

Although the data in Figure 4 happen to come from a catchment that conforms closely to Freeze's (1972) requirements for throughflow to make a significant contribution to peak discharge, the contribution of water emerging from transient near-channel wetlands would probably be indistinguishable from that

of near-surface throughflow.   Both would be expected to be
richer in humic materials.

Most of the increased P concentration in Figure 4 was
due to particulate matter, probably particles that were re-
suspended from the stream bed by the increased turbulence.
This hypothesis requires that the stream bed accumulate P during periods of low flow, a process for which there is a great
deal of evidence (Keup, 1968).   This evidence is of two types.
Tracer studies with $^{32}PO_4$ show that the radioactivity disappears
from the water over a relatively short distance.   However, these

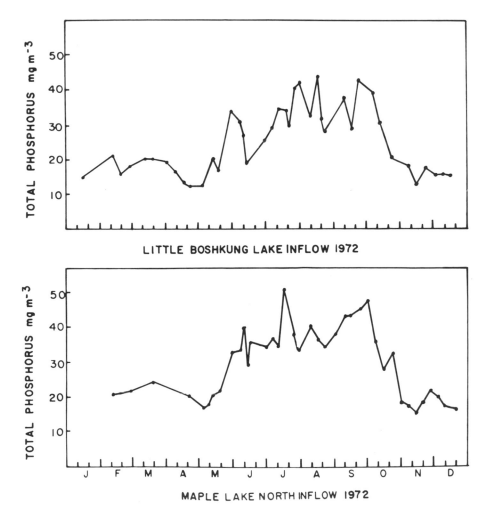

Figure 1.   Examples of the seasonal change in total phosphorus
   concentration in headwater streams in forested, igneous
   catchments, from Dillon (1974).

data, in the absence of chemical analyses, merely indicate an efflux of P. This efflux could be equaled or even exceeded by influx. Better evidence is given by analyses of total P that show a decrease downstream in a section receiving no additions of water. An example of such a decrease in a Dartmoor stream is given in Figure 5. The section between the confluence with the adit spring and sta 32 received no additional water inputs and was only 200 m long, yet in it the total P decreased from 16 to 13 μg. 1^{-1}. Although the absolute change was small, and would have been difficult to detect without the highly

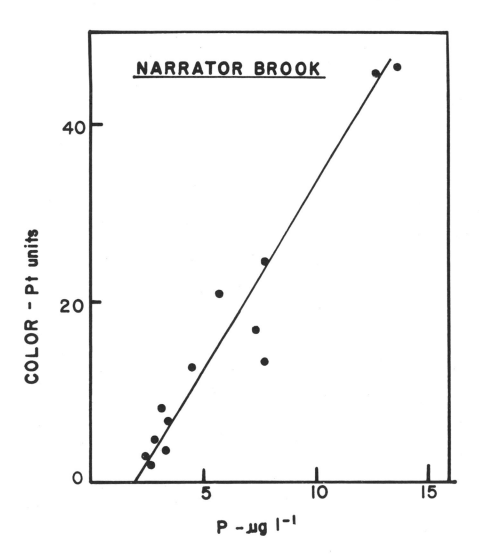

Figure 2. The relation between water color and total P in a Dartmoor stream in winter and during falling stage.

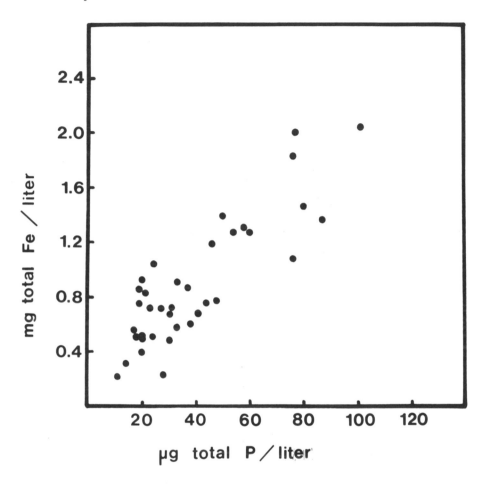

Figure 3. The relation between the concentration of total P
and total Fe in an Ontario stream as determined by P. M.
Cross (unpublished data).

reproducible ultraviolet digestion technique of Armstrong and
Tibbits (1968), it represents a considerable accumulation of
phosphorus in the stream bed during periods of low flow. The
result of these processes is to exaggerate the contribution of
P to lakes during peak discharge.

COMPARISON OF STREAM AND AEOLIAN LOADING

From the preceding sections it is obvious that, in the
absence of sources of pollution, the phosphorus load to a lake
will be influenced not only by the geology and land usage of its
catchment but also by the surface area of the lake relative to
the total surface area of its catchment. Table II illustrates
the interrelation of these variables and shows the surprisingly
great importance of aeolian P, particularly in lakes with a

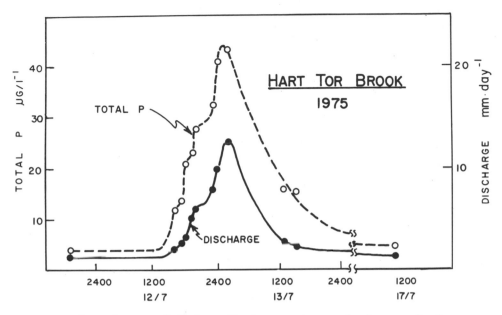

Figure 4. The total P in a Dartmoor stream during a single, brief flood.

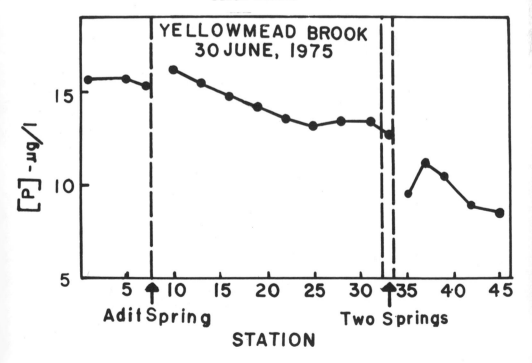

Figure 5. The total phosphorus concentration at different locations along a Dartmoor stream during a period of low flow.
The distance from the adit spring to Sta 32 is 200 m.

Table II
The Percentage Contribution of Aeolian Loading of P
to a Lake as it is Influenced by the Ratio
of $A_d : A_o$ if Aeolian Loading is Assumed
to be 37 mg m^{-2} yr^{-1}

$\dfrac{A_d}{A_o}$	% Aeolian P	
	Igneous-Forested Catchment	Sedimentary-Forested and Grazing Catchment
3	72	35
10	44	14
30	21	5
100	7	2

A_d is the area of the terrestrial part of the catchment and A_o is the area of the lake surface.

forested, igneous catchment. Only when the ratio of terrestrial area to lake surface area approaches 10 does the contribution of P from streams equal the aeolian contribution. Aeolian loading is relatively less important in partly grazed sedimentary systems, but even here cannot be ignored.

Although the form in which phosphorus is exported is of little importance to the terrestrial system, it may have a significant effect on the lake it enters. Orthophosphate is readily taken up by algae and bacteria, and thus can stimulate both production and decomposition. Although there is a good correlation between mean algal abundance and total P in lakes (Sakamoto, 1966), many lakes fall far off the regression line. One possible cause of this variability is differential availability of P from lake to lake. Consequently, it may be useful to know the fraction of available P as well as the total quantity of P entering a lake via terrestrial and aeolian sources.

Peters (in press and personal communication) has recently compared the fraction of readily available P in river waters and rain. Because chemical analysis can exaggerate the amount of available P in natural waters, he used a simple radiobiological assay based on measurement of the uptake of $^{32}PO_4$ by organisms in lakewater. When $^{32}PO_4$ is added to lakewater, it is taken up extremely rapidly by microorganisms (Figure 6). By subtracting the amount of ^{32}P remaining in solution when tracer equilibrium has been achieved (6.7 in Figure 6) from the curve describing the loss of ^{32}P from solution, a straight line is produced. From the slope of this line and the asymptote, the rate constant of uptake of PO_4 can be calculated (Riggs, 1963). Since this rate constant is very sensitive to small changes in the concentration of PO_4 in the lakewater, changes in it following small additions of stream water or rainwater can be used to measure the amount of PO_4 they contain.

   This method was used by Peters, and a summary of the
results he obtained with it is given in Table III. This shows
that despite the similarity in the total phosphorus in the rain
and stream samples there was a large difference in available
P. Almost half of the phosphorus in rain was readily available,
whereas less than one-tenth of the P in stream water was. If
the remainder of the phosphorus in stream water is unavailable,
the relative importance of aeolian P is much greater than suggested by Table II. Therefore, the fate of the remaining 92
percent is a serious gap in our knowledge. Does it sediment
out without being utilized or does it slowly become available
over a few weeks? Answers to questions such as these will
help us to refine models currently used to predict the relation
between phosphorus loading and trophic status of lakes.

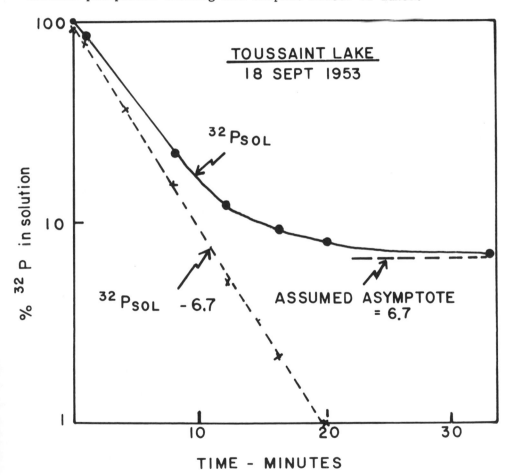

Figure 6. A typical example of the curve of loss of $^{32}PO_4$
   from solution in the water from the trophogenic zone of
   a lake in summer.

Table III
Orthophosphate Measured by Radiobiological Assay, and
Total P in Streams and Precipitation of
Lake Memphremagog, Quebec

	Total P $\mu g \cdot l^{-1}$	% as PO_4-P	Source
Six streams	29.5 (16–45)[a]	8.3 (3–18)	Peters, personal communication
Rain	39.6 (14–78)	48 (1–100)	Peters, 1977

[a]Range is given in brackets.

PHOSPHORUS CYCLE IN THE TROPHOGENIC ZONE OF LAKES

The phosphorus in the productive (trophogenic) zone of
most lakes is rapidly cycled from one group of organisms to
another. This rapid cycling is largely due to the small size
of organisms that inhabit the open water, but it also reflects
the fact that P is in short supply. Since PO_4 is the most
readily available form of P, the pool of PO_4 is incredibly
small, possibly less than 0.02 $\mu g.l^{-1}$ (Rigler, 1966) and is
turned over rapidly. In fact, the turnover time of phosphate,
given by measurements of the type that produced Figure 6, is a
good indication of the relative abundance of P in the lake.
Lakes in which phosphorus supply limits the growth of plants
will usually have an uptake rate constant of greater than 0.05
min^{-1}. Measurements of uptake rate constant (k) of PO_4 have
now been made for lakes in many parts of the world (Table IV),
and these show that in most lakes, from the subarctic to the
tropics, phosphorus is in great demand during the productive
season. In only a few (one of six in Europe and one of five
in Africa, and possibly L. Kinneret) did there appear to be a
surplus of phosphorus. In winter, when decomposition exceeds
production, there is a surfeit of available PO_4 and the rate
constants are generally extremely small.

The uptake of PO_4 from solution is primarily due to the
activities of the aquatic bacteria and the smallest planktonic
algae, although possibility of uptake by nonliving particles
(trypton) has not been eliminated (Rigler, 1973). Although
the microorganisms leach some PO_4 back into solution, and possibly also release organic phosphorus compounds that polymerize
extracellularly (Lean, 1973), the major loss of P from these
organisms is due to grazing by herbivorous zooplankton (Figure
7). In a rich lake, 27 percent of the phosphorus in the trophogenic zone may pass through the intestines of zooplankton
every day. More than half of this P is returned to the water

Table IV
Uptake Rate Constant of $^{32}PO_4$ Added to Surface Waters
of Lakes in Different Parts of the World

Region	No. of Lakes	Rate Constant (min^{-1})		Source
		Summer	Winter	
Chalk River, Ontario	3	0.038–0.28		Rigler, 1956
Alginquin Pk., Ontario	5	0.13–0.45	0.006–0.01	Rigler, 1964
Toronto region, Ontario	3	0.14–0.53	0.0001–0.14	Rigler, 1964
Kenora, Ontario	2	0.038–2.5	0.0001–0.008	Levine, 1975
Labrador	5	0.23–0.77		Ostrovsky, personal communication
Israel (L. Kinneret)	1	0.0035–0.09	0.002–0.025	Halmann and Stiller, 1974
Central Europe	6	0.001–0.24	0.0001–0.0002	Peters, 1975
Italy	1	0.09	0.0001	Peters, 1975
East Africa	5	0–1.5		Peters, 1976

as PO_4 and the rest returns as fecal material that is eaten
again, autolyzes or still contains living cells (Porter, 1976).
The phosphorus cycle in lake water is actually more complex than
indicated by Figure 7, but the details would add little here,
and, for anyone interested, have been reviewed by Rigler (1973).
    Although the rapidity with which phosphorus is cycled
is remarkable, the efficiency of recycling in a rich lake is
even more so (Peters and Rigler, 1973). Since tracer and sediment trap studies have shown that approximately 2 percent of
the phosphorus in the trophogenic zone sediments daily, whereas
25.4 percent is regenerated daily, the cycling efficiency
(100 x 25.4/27.4) is 93 percent. In fact this is a lower limit
since it assumes that all sedimenting P is due to losses in the
cycle, and none is due to, say, particulate unavailable P that
never took part in the cycle.
    Although the cycling rates of P fascinate biologists,
they are probably of less interest to geochemists than the rate
of loss to the sediments. This flux, although relatively small,

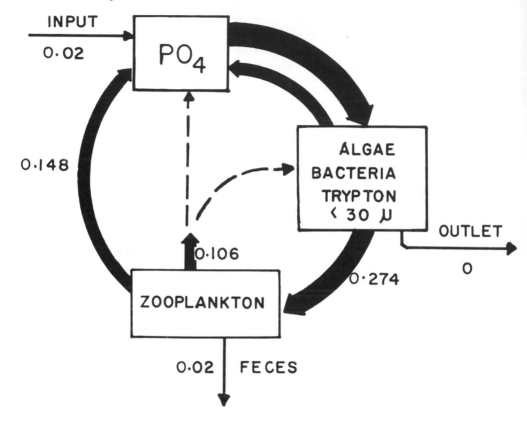

Figure 7.   Simplified diagram of the phosphorus cycle in the
trophogenic zone of a eutrophic lake modified from Peters and
Rigler (1973).   The numbers indicate phosphorus flux expressed
as the fraction of the total P in the trophogenic zone per
day.

is important because it will set a maximum limit to the fraction
of phosphorus received by a lake that is permanently retained
in the sediments.

RETENTION OF P IN LAKE SEDIMENTS

        Estimates of phosphorus retention in lakes are derived
from mass balance studies of inputs and the output, the annual
difference being taken as a measure of P retained in the sediments.   Because this final figure is derived from many individual determinations of stream discharge, phosphorus concentration in inlets and outlet, ground water flow and P content
(usually estimated), and aeolian loading, each of which is sus-
ceptible to error, it is difficult to obtain an accurate measure
of phosphorus retention.   Nevertheless, some simple generalizations about P retention have begun to appear.   Kirchner and

Dillon (1975) and Dillon and Kirchner (1975) analyzed the existing data on retention of P and discussed several empirical relations, the best of which was:

$$R_p = 13.2 \ /(13.2 + q_s)$$

where R_p is the retention coefficient of phosphorus (amount retained/amount loaded) and q_s is the areal water load to the lake in $m.yr^{-1}$.

This empirical model conforms very well to a conceptual model in which the sedimentation velocity of P is constant or the fraction of the total P sedimenting daily is constant. Therefore, it would be interesting to see what the annual pattern of sedimentation is. Unfortunately, the technology of collecting sedimenting materials is not developed to the point where we can have much faith in the data. A lot of work is still required in the design and calibration of sediment traps as well as in the interpretation of the values they give. As yet we cannot be certain that traps catch sedimenting material quantitatively, that the material is retained in the trap, that nonsedimenting material (*i.e.*, migrating plants or animals) is not caught, or the number of locations for any lake that should be sampled. Nevertheless, a comparison of two sets of data (Figure 8) suggests that we are not far from an answer. The data from Canadarago L. and Bob L. were obtained from very different traps (Fuhs, 1973; Rigler, MacCallum and Roff, 1974), yet they suggest a similar annual pattern. Sedimentation is highest in early summer and decreases until the lake begins to circulate in the autumn. At this time there is a sharp increase in the sedimentation in both lakes. This increase takes place when the thermocline is being depressed and almost certainly represents the redistribution of sediment that fell on relatively shallow bottom areas during the summer, where it was protected from turbulence by thermal stratification.

These data are incomplete, but they are supported by other types of data. For example, the lower two panels in Figure 8 show a typical annual pattern for the concentration of P in streams entering and leaving a lake. The concentrations are more similar in winter (little sedimentation) but diverge in summer. In fact, despite the large increase of concentration of P in the inflowing water, the P content of outflowing water actually decreases in summer. This effect would be expected if the sedimentation rate increased in the summer. Confirmation also comes from mass balance data (Schindler *et al.*, 1973). In E.L.A. lake #227, the percentage of net loss of phosphorus by sedimentation was highest during the summer. However, before mass balance studies can be fully interpreted, we need to know what fraction of the sedimenting P is returned to the water. At present we can take our pick of studies (Schindler *et al.*, 1973) that show little or no return and those (Lean and Charlton, 1976) that show a large return.

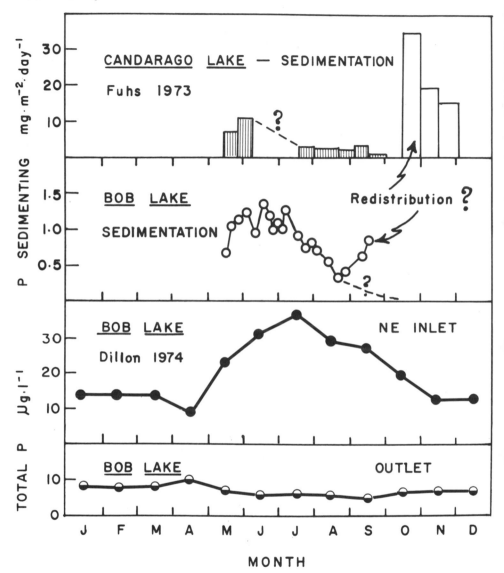

Figure 8.   Sedimentation rate of P in two lakes as determined
   from sediment traps and the concentration of total phosphorus
   in inflowing and outflowing water at Bob Lake.   The latter
   values were from Dillon (1974) and sedimentation in Bob Lake
   from the author's unpublished data.

        Regardless of the uncertainties about the causal mech-
anisms, there is no doubt that lakes generally retain a fraction of the incoming P that is a function of q_s and that the
effect of a lake in a drainage system is to decrease the average P concentration and to equalize the concentration over the
year.

ACKNOWLEDGMENTS

I am grateful to Robert Peters for his permission to cite unpublished values for available P in streams, and to Patsy Cross for permission to use data (on P and Fe concentrations in a stream) that will form part of her M.Sc. thesis at The University of Toronto.

REFERENCES

Armstrong, F.A.S., and S. Tibbitts. "Photochemical Combustion of Organic Matter in Sea Water, for Nitrogen, Phosphorus, and Carbon Determination," *J. Mar. Biol. Assoc. U.K.* 48: 143-152 (1968).

Crisp, D.T. "Input and Output of Minerals for an Area of Pennine Moorland: the Importance of Precipitation, Drainage, Peat Erosion and Animals," *J. Appl. Ecol.* 3:327-348 (1966).

Dillon, P.J. "The Prediction of Phosphorus and Chlorophyll Concentrations in Lakes," Ph.D. Thesis, University of Toronto (1974).

Dillon, P.J., and W.B. Kirchner. "The Effects of Geology and Land Use on the Export of Phosphorus from Watersheds," *Water Res.* 9:135-148 (1974).

Dillon, P.J., and W.B. Kirchner. "Reply," *Water Resources Res.* 11:1035-1036 (1975).

Dillon, P.J., and F.H. Rigler. "A Simple Method for Predicting the Capacity of a Lake for Development Based on Lake Trophic Status," *J. Fish. Res. Bd. Canada* 32:1519-1531 (1975).

Egnér, H., and E. Eriksson. "Current Data on the Chemical Sampling of Air and Precipitation," *Tellus* 7:134-139 (1955).

Freeze, R.A. "Role of Subsurface Flow in Generating Surface Runoff 2. Upstream Source Areas," *Water Resources Res.* 8: 1272-1283 (1972).

Fuks, G.W. "Improved Device for the Collection of Sedimenting Matter," *Limnol. Oceanog.* 18:989-992 (1973).

Gomolka, R.E. "An Investigation of Atmospheric Phosphorus as a Source of Lake Nutrient," M.Sc. Thesis, University of Toronto (1975).

Halmann, M., and M. Stiller. "Turnover and Uptake of Dissolved Phosphate in Freshwater. A Study in Lake Kinneret," *Limnol. Oceanog.* 19:774-783 (1974).

Keup, L.E. "Phosphorus in Flowing Waters," *Water Res.* 2:373–386 (1968).

Kirchner, W.B. "An Examination of the Relationship Between Drainage Basin Morphology and the Export of Phosphorus," *Limnol. Oceanog.* 20:267–269 (1975).

Kirchner, W.B., and P.J. Dillon. "An Empirical Method of Estimating the Retention of Phosphorus in Lakes," *Water Resources Res.* 11:182–183 (1975).

Lean, D.R.S. "Phosphorus Dynamics in Lake Water," *Science* 179:678–680 (1973).

Lean, D.R.S., and M.N. Charlton. "A Study of Phosphorus Kinetics in a Lake Ecosystem," in *Environmental Biogeochemistry,* vol. 2, J.O. Nriagu, Ed. (Ann Arbor, Michigan: Ann Arbor Science Publishers, 1976), pp. 283–294.

Levesque, M., and M. Schnitzer. "Organometallic Interactions in Soils: 6. Preparation and Properties of Fulvic Acid–Metal Phosphates," *Soil Sci.* 103:183–190 (1967).

Levine, S. "Orthophosphate Concentration and Flux within the Epilimnia of Two Canadian Shield Lakes," *Int. Ver. Theor. Angew. Limnol Verh.* 19:624–629 (1975).

Likens, G.E., and F.H. Bormann. "An Experimental Approach to New England Landscapes," in *Coupling of Land and Water Systems,* A.D. Hasler, Ed. (New York: Springer-Verlag, 1975), pp. 7–29.

Peters, R.H. "Orthophosphate Turnover in Central European Lakes," *Mem 1st. Ital. Idrobiol.* 32:297–311 (1975).

Peters, R.H. "Orthophosphate Turnover in East African Lakes," *Oecologia* 25:313–319 (1976).

Peters, R.H. "The Availability of Atmospheric Orthophosphate," *J. Fish. Res. Bd. Can.* 34, in press.

Peters, R.H., and F.H. Rigler. "Phosphorus Release by *Daphnia*," *Limnol. Oceanog.* 18:821–839 (1973).

Porter, K.G. "Enhancement of Algal Growth and Productivity by Grazing Zooplankton," *Science* 192:1332–1334 (1976).

Riggs, D.S. *The Mathematical Approach to Physiological Problems* (Baltimore: Williams and Wilkins, 1963).

Rigler, F.H. "A Tracer Study of the Phosphorus Cycle in Lake Water," *Ecology* 37:550-562 (1956).

Rigler, F.H. "The Phosphorus Fractions and Turnover Time of Inorganic Phosphorus in Different Types of Lakes," *Limnol. Oceanog.* 9:511-518 (1964).

Rigler, F.H. "Radiobiological Analysis of Inorganic Phosphorus in Lake Water," *Int. Ver. Theor. Angew. Limnol. Verh.* 16: 465-470 (1966).

Rigler, F.H. "A Dynamic View of the Phosphorus Cycle in Lakes," in *Environmental Phosphorus Handbook*, E.J. Griffiths, A. Beeton, J.M. Spence and D.T. Mitchell, Eds. (New York: John Wiley and Sons, 1973), pp. 539-572.

Rigler, F.M., M.E. MacCallum and J.C. Roff. "Production of Zooplankton in Char Lake," *J. Fish. Res. Bd. Can.* 31:637-646 (1974).

Sakamoto, M. "Primary Production by Phytoplankton Community in some Japanese Lakes and its Dependence on Lake Depth," *Arch. Hydrobiol.* 62:1-28 (1966).

Schindler, D.W., H. Kling, R.V. Schmidt, J. Prokopowich, V.E. Frost, R.A. Reid and M. Capel. "Eutrophication of Lake 227 by Addition of Phosphate and Nitrate: the Second, Third, and Fourth Years of Enrichment, 1970, 1971, and 1972," *J. Fish. Res. Bd. Can.* 30:1415-1440 (1973).

Whipkey, R.Z. "Subsurface Stormflow from Forested Slopes," *Int. Assoc. Sci. Hydrol. Bull.* 10:74-85 (1965).

CHAPTER 6

THE EFFECTS OF NUTRIENT ENRICHMENT ON THE CYCLING OF NITROGEN IN LAKE ECOSYSTEMS

CHRISTINA F. -H. LIAO

Canada Center for Inland Water
Burlington, Ontario, Canada

INTRODUCTION

The movement of nitrogen in lake ecosystems is extremely complex and little understood from a quantitative point of view. Though nitrogen and phosphorus have long been considered the two most important nutrients in regulating the productivity of aquatic ecosystems, the role of nitrogen in determining the algal biomass production in the lakes has often been neglected.

Several recent reports (*e.g.*, Oglesby, 1969; Weiss, 1970; Lueschow *et al.*, 1970) have suggested that nitrogen might become the limiting factor in aquatic biomass production more often than heretofore believed. This chapter will present the results of a study investigating the effects of nutrient enrichment on algal responses and the changes of nitrogen compartments in nonstratified lake ecosystems.

MATERIALS AND METHODS

Description of Lake

The Bay of Quinte, an eutrophic bay on the northern shore of Lake Ontario, was the site of the experiments (Lean *et al.*, 1975). In mid-June of 1973, three limnocorrals, each with an area of 25 m^2, were installed in water 4 m deep using sea curtains. The corral has a flotation collar to prevent water from mixing with the adjacent bay and the side curtain was extended from the water surface to about 0.5 m into the sediments.

No nutrient was added to Corral I. Corral II was enriched with P as H_3PO_4 at the rate of 7.07 µg P/1/wk, and

Corral III received the same amount of P plus nitrate at the
rate of 92 µg N/l/wk. Enrichment began at this rate on July 12,
1973, but the amount was doubled from August 3 to October 17,
1973. During 1974, enrichment began on May 24 and continued
to September 16 at the latter enrichment rate.

Sampling and Analytical Procedures

From July, 1973 through 1974, composite water samples
(0.5, 1, 2, 3 m) were collected from the bay and the corrals
and filtered through Whatman GH/C within two hours. The filtrate was acidified for preservation and later analyzed for
ammonium-nitrogen, nitrate + nitrite (Bremner and Keeney, 1965)
and total dissolved nitrogen by modified semimicro-Kjeldahl
procedure (Bremner, 1965). Particulate nitrogen was determined
by regular semimicro-Kjeldahl procedure (Bremner, 1965).
Undisturbed sediment cores (4.7-cm diam) were taken
with Kayak-Brinkhurst corer (Research Instruments Co., Guelph,
Ontario) and were subdivided into 2-cm sections. Interstitial
water was separated from the sediment by centrifugation,
filtered through GF/C and analyzed for nitrogen. The sediment
was air dried and ground for nitrogen analysis according to
the method used by Chen *et al.* (1972).

Laboratory Studies

Mineralization of nitrogen in both water and the sediment system were investigated under laboratory incubation. A
water sample was obtained from the bay only and incubated for
2 months at room temperature, with and without an air stream
flushing over, in an open air condition. Evaporation loss
was compensated and subsamples were withdrawn periodically to
analyze for inorganic nitrogen.
Sediment samples collected with Kayak-Brinkhurst corer
were divided into two portions, surface (0-5 cm) and bottom
(5-10 cm) sediments. The composited sediment samples from
each portion were incubated quiescent, in a wide-mouth open
container in a moisture-saturated room at 20°C. Samples were
withdrawn periodically and analyzed for inorganic nitrogen in
both pore water and in the sediment (Chen *et al.*, 1972). Microbial population of ammonifiers, Nitrosomonas and Nitrobacter
were estimated by MPN method (Alexander and Clark, 1965) in
both water and sediment samples.

RESULTS AND DISCUSSION

Nutrient Enrichment Effects on Algal Responses and Biomass
Nitrogen Production

Nutrient enrichment resulted in some species alteration
in the corrals. During 1974 summer observation, in Corral I,

which received no nutrient, the nitrogen-fixing species
Anabaena and *Aphanizomenon* were more predominant. In Corral
II, which received P only, nitrogen-fixing species also became predominant but more as *Gloetrichia* sp. with some *Anabaena. Microcystis,* the nonfixers, were the predominant
species in Corral III, which received both P and N.

Enrichment of the corrals with nutrients resulted in
only slight differences in particulate nitrogen (PT-N) production during the 1973 season (Figure 1). The PT-N reached maximum in late September, being highest in Corral III (850 µg N/1),
then in the bay (770 µg N/1) and only about 500 µg N/1 in
Corral I and II (maximum occurred in August). However, at the
end of the second year of enrichment, the PT-N in Corral III
was more than double the 1973 value (1870 µg N/1), and nearly
double in Corral II (750 µg N/1) but decreased slightly in
Corral I and the bay. The results would seem to suggest that
nitrogen might be more important in determining the algal biomass nitrogen in lake waters, especially those high in available phosphorus.

Dissolved Nitrogen Compartments in the Water

The seasonal changes of the various forms of nitrogen
in the water column are shown in Figure 1. During the summer
productive season nitrate was undetectable or present only in
trace amounts except in Corral III, which received nitrate enrichment. Nitrate started to accumulate slowly at the end of
September but the rate increased in the winter months. Maximum nitrate concentration was reached around the end of
February or the beginning of March. In Corral III, which received 2300 µg N/1 during 1973 enrichment, the maximum nitrate
concentration was only about 670 µg N/1. It is quite obvious
that the greater portion of the added nitrogen in Corral III
was lost to its environment, either through sedimentation and/or
to its atmosphere, since it could not be accounted for in the
other compartments.

Although ammonium-nitrogen was rapidly assimilated by
the plankton during the summer season (Liao, unpublished results), the concentration remained quite constant, ranging
from 100 to 250 µg N/1. Although the ammonium-nitrogen in the
surface water would be expected to be depleted, the concentration is usually much higher in the deeper water due to the decomposition of sedimentary materials above the sediment-water
interface (Serruya and Berman, 1969). Since the water samples
analyzed were the composited ones from various depth, the results shown in Figure 1 would reflect the ammonium-N in the
water when complete mixing could occur. Therefore, the values
might not be true ammonium-N concentration in the water during
the calm summer period. However, the regeneration of the
ammonium-N, mainly by microbial decomposition, might not be
able to account for such a high, steady concentration. The

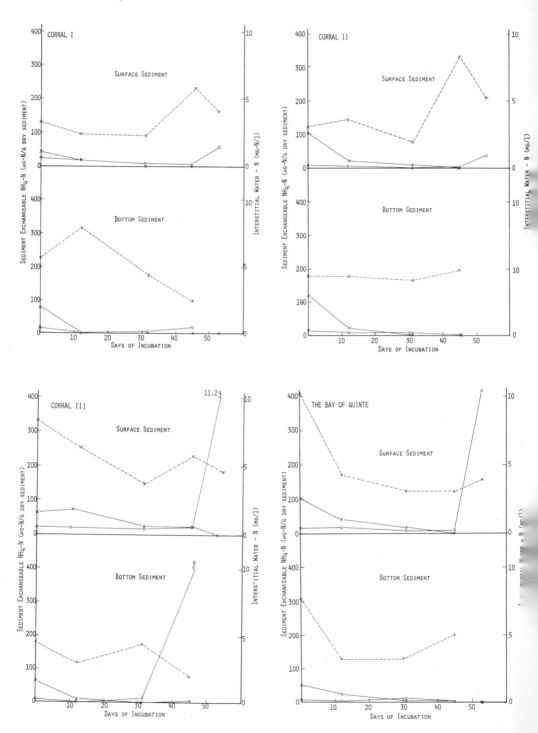

Figure 1.   Seasonal concentrations of particulate, nitrate, ammonium, and dissolved organic nitrogen for Corral I (o), Corral II (▲), Corral III (●) and the adjacent Bay of Quinte (△).

activities of zooplankton excretion might very well play an
important role in the ammonium-N regeneration in the water, as
suggested by Johannes (1968). Ammonium-N reached maximum in
November and the concentration in Corrals I and III (*ca.* 400
µg N/l) was about two-fold greater than those in the Bay and
Corral II.

Dissolved organic nitrogen (DON) was slightly higher
during the summer productive period and the amount is greater
in Corral II and III (*ca.* 600 µg N/l). This may be partially
due to the liberation of extracellular nitrogen into the water
by blue-green algae (Fogg, 1971) and the maximum biomass N
corresponded quite well with maximum DON in all corrals except
in the bay. The concentration of DON started to decrease in
late fall, stayed fairly constant in early winter and then decreased to a rather low concentration as the mineralization
proceeded simultaneously. The DON in Corral II, however, remained relatively high in comparison with others, even after
the winter months, possibly because DON is more refractory and
decomposes at a much slower rate (Mills and Alexander, 1974).

Changes of Nitrogen Concentration in Sediment Cores

Nitrogen concentrations in the pore water are shown in
Table I. Nitrate+nitrite were undetectable in pore water.
Both ammonium-N and total-N tended to increase in concentration with depth, and values were slightly higher during the
summer productive period than in winter. The results also
showed that ammonium-N and total-N were only slightly higher
in Corral III than in the others. The lower nitrogen concentration in the upper layer and in the winter months might be
the result of mixing with the overlying water.

Though nitrate+nitrite were never detected in the pore
water, a trace amount (*ca.* 5-30 µg N/g dry sediment) was always
present in the exchangeable fraction. Since nitrifying bacteria were found in depths to 10 cm of the sediment cores (see
laboratory studies), oxidation of ammonium-N might have occurred
after removal of the pore water and during sample preparation
through air drying.

There was a rather irregular distribution of exchangeable NH$_4$-N with depth (Table II), although in some instances
concentration tended to be higher in deeper zones. Exchangeable NH$_4$-N in the bay sediments was much higher (*ca.* two-fold)
than in the corrals during 1973, but concentration decreased
slightly in the winter and later to the levels similar to
those of the corrals in August of 1974. The exchangeable NH$_4$-N
in all three corrals was quite similar, with the concentration
lower in the summer and slightly higher in the winter but de-
creasing again after mixing occurred in the spring.

Total-N in the bay sediments was lower than in the corrals in summer of 1973 (ave 1.27% vs ave 1.50%), but it increased through the winter months, reaching the same levels as

Table I
Nitrogen Concentration in Interstitial Water Removed
from Various Depths of Sediment Profiles
on Dates of Sampling (mg N/1)[a]

Sample Dates	Corral I		Corral II		Corral III	
	NH$_4$-N	Total-N	NH$_4$-N	Total-N	NH$_4$-N	Total-N
August 21, 1973						
0-2 cm	1.4		1.7	2.8	3.2	5.0
2-4 cm	4.3	7.9	3.0	4.6	5.2	6.2
4-6 cm	3.2	7.5	5.6	6.5	6.3	7.4
February 25, 1974						
0-2 cm	0.8	2.2	1.4	1.4	1.8	4.2
2-4 cm	2.3	3.2	2.1	3.8	3.8	5.6
4-6 cm	3.1	5.8	3.5	5.1	4.4	6.7
6-10 cm	3.6	6.6	5.2	5.9	5.4	11.2
10-14 cm	5.6	8.6	6.9	7.8	7.6	10.9
14-18 cm	6.3	8.4	8.3	10.6	8.8	10.9

[a]Nitrate was not present in interstitial waters.

those of corrals in the summer of 1974. Total-N in all three
corrals was very similar and was higher in both summer seasons.
It decreased in the winter, however, because of some release
of the nitrogen to the water after decomposition and mixing.

Laboratory Studies

Potential nitrification activities in the water were
studied only from the bay. The results are shown in Table III.
In the aeration treatment, ammonium-N increased only after the
first week of incubation, and this could be either from organic-
N or reduction of the nitrate originally present in the water.
The reduction of $^{15}N_3$-N to NH$_4$-N was recently reported by
Stanford *et al.* (1975) in the soil system and could be a common
pathway in nitrogen cycle. Nitrate originally present in the
water disappeared during the first week of incubation, remained
negligible for more than 2 weeks and reached peak concentration
at 4 weeks, at a rate of *ca.* 9 µg N/1/day. After 2 months incubation, nitrate concentration was doubled, but total inorganic (NH$_4$ + NO$_3$)-N was only about 60 percent of the original concentration (*i.e.*, 40 percent was either lost or assimilated by
the microorganism).

In the nonaeration treatment, ammonium-N decreased gradually as the nitrification proceeded. However, after one month
incubation, there was an increase in NH$_4$-N, with the concurrent
decrease in NO$_3$-N that might have been transformed and reduced

Table II

Concentration of Total Nitrogen and Exchangeable-NH$_4$ at Various Depths of Sediment Core

	August 21/73		January 29/74		February 28/74		May 10/74		August 27/74	
	Total-N (%)	Exch-NH$_4$ µg/g	Total-N (%)	Exch-NH$_4$ µg/g	Total-N (%)	Exch-NH$_4$ µg/g	Total-N (%)	NH$_4$-N µg/g	Total-N (g)	NH$_4$-N µg/g
Corral I										
0– 2 cm	1.68	93	1.39	127	1.42	97	1.47	100	1.50	—
2– 4 cm	1.42	69	1.39	133	1.46	107	1.46	104	1.64	102
4– 6 cm	1.39	58	1.49	154	1.55	119	1.62	123	1.39	94
6–10 cm			1.48	127	1.49	129	—	—	1.44	—
10–14 cm			1.39	108	1.39	169	—	—	1.35	104
Corral II										
0– 2 cm	1.64	84	1.37	116	1.47	88	1.56	105	1.53	112
2– 4 cm	1.50	91	1.33	116	1.36	103	1.59	120	1.42	—
4– 6 cm	1.44	93	1.36	136	1.47	111	1.88	132	1.41	98
6–10 cm			1.37	155	1.40	123	—	—	1.28	—
10–14 cm			1.37	153	1.36	146	—	—	1.60	111
Corral III										
0– 2 cm	1.56	78	1.39	120	1.48	121	1.48	94	1.47	—
2– 4 cm	1.52	82	1.39	144	1.46	127	1.55	—	1.53	92
4– 6 cm	1.40	80	1.46	176	1.41	137	1.55	145	1.46	88
6–10 cm			1.39	148	1.42	119	—		1.39	—
10–14 cm			1.37	140	1.32	214			1.45	88
Bay										
0– 2 cm	1.29	155	1.37	146	1.55	140	—	—	1.55	79
2– 4 cm	1.27	174	1.39	138	1.47	140	—	—	1.58	90
4– 6 cm	1.26	179	1.51	136	1.48	140	—	—	1.42	94
6–10 cm	1.24	187			—	141	—	—	1.41	—
10–14 cm					1.45	140	—	—	1.37	94

Table III
Population of Nitrogen Cycle Bacteria in Lake Water
and Sediment Samples[a]

Sample Source	Ammonifier	Nitrosomonas	Nitrobacter
	(MPN/g dry sediment)		
Surface Sediment (0-5 cm)			
Corral I	50×10^5	13×10^3	5×10^3
II	17×10^5	9×10^4	4×10^4
III	36×10^6	11×10^3	12×10^4
Bay	36×10^5	14×10^3	4×10^4
Bottom Sediment (5-10 cm)			
Corral I	16×10^4	10×10^3	6×10^3
II	18×10^4	5×10^3	3×10^3
III	18×10^6	8×10^3	4×10^4
Bay	16×10^4	3×10^3	3×10^3

[a]Sampling date: June 26, 1974.

to NH_4-N. After 2 months incubation, nitrate-N was tripled,
though the nitrification rate was slower (ave 4.0 µg N/1/day),
and the overall loss of inorganic nitrogen was less, only 22
percent. These nitrification rates might be underestimated
since no continuous supply of the organic-N was made. However,
the slow rate might also be due to the heterotrophic nature of
the nitrifiers because the autotrophic nitrifiers were not found
in the water by the MPN procedure, as reported by Verstraete
and Alexander (1973). Population of ammonifiers in the water
was about 20×10^3/ml.

Nitrification potential in the sediment-water systems
was studied under quiescent, aerobic conditions; the results
are shown in Figure 2. Ammonium-N in pore water disappeared
in 10 days and remained negligible through 50 days incubation
period. Nitrate-N in the pore water did not start to appear
until after 45 days. At the end of 50 days, there was approximately 1.5 mg n/1 and 0.5 mg N/1 in the surface and bottom
sediment water of Corral I, respectively. In Corral II, about
1 mg N/1 appeared in the surface sediment water but none in the
bottom sediment water. In the bay, no nitrate was detected in
the bottom sediment water, but up to 10.5 mg/1 were found in
the surface sediment water; this could contribute about 108
µg N/1 to the overlying water if mixing occurred. In Corral III
about 11.2 mg and 19.1 mg of NO_3-N/1 were found in surface and
bottom sediment water, respectively. If mixing occurred within
the entire 10 cm of sediment, the total contribution would be
about 340 µg N/1.

Exchangeable nitrate+nitrite-N were not found in the sediment. Exchangeable ammonium-N decreased in most of the sediment samples, except in the sediment of Corral II and the surface sediment of Corral I.

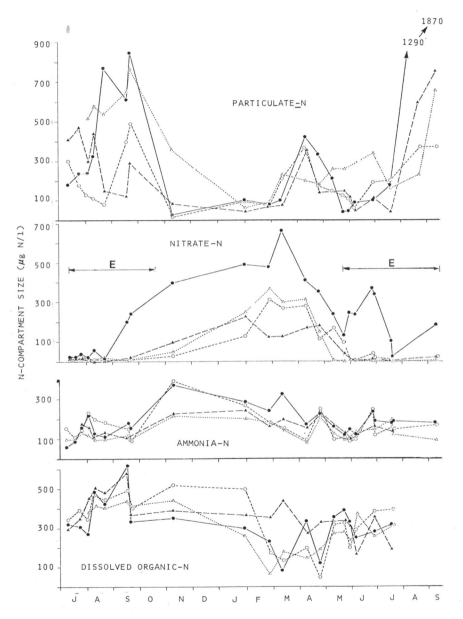

Figure 2. Mineralization of nitrogen in sediment—water system incubated in the laboratory at 20°C, for interstitial water ammonium-N (x————x) and nitrate-N (o————o) and for sediment exchangeable ammonium-N (x – – – x).

The populations of nitrogen cycle bacteria in the sediment are shown in Table IV. The number of ammonifiers is usually higher in the surface sediment than in the bottom. The ammonifiers in Corral III (*ca.* 36 x 10[6]) is ten-fold higher than those of others (*ca.* 35 x 10[5]) in surface sediment. In the bottom sediment, the number in Corral III (*ca.* 18 x 10[6]) is 100-fold higher than those of others (*ca.* 18 x 10[4]). The high ammonifier population in Corral III indicated that there was more organic substance available for decomposition. The number of *Nitrosomonas* and *Nitrobacter* is very similar in all the samples examined, with two exceptions. In Corral II surface sediment, the *Nitrosomonas* is slightly higher, and in Corral III sediment *Nitrobacter* is slightly higher.

Table IV
Nitrification Potential of Lake Water Collected from the Bay[a]

Days of Incubation	Aerated (μg-N/l)			Nonaerated (μg-N/l)		
	NH_4-N	NO_3-N	NH_4+NO_3	NH_4-N	NO_3-N	NH_4+NO_3
0	266	48	314	266	48	314
7	322	0	322	219	56	275
17	188	0	188	101	101	202
31	123	123	246	137	56	193
62	101	93	194	84	160	244

[a]Sampling Date: October 8, 1974.

SUMMARY AND CONCLUSION

The results of the study showed that the addition of nitrate and phosphorus to the water resulted in a significant increase in biomass nitrogen production when compared to adding phosphorus alone after two years experiment. However, not all the added nitrogen was retained in the water. The water that received nitrate amounting to 2.3 mg N/l during 1973 and 3.3 mg N/l during 1974 had only a maximum total-N in the water column of 1.6 mg N/l in 1973 and 2.7 mg N/l in 1974. It is estimated that approximately one-third of the added nitrogen was lost to the environment during first year and about one-half of that was lost during second year. Nitrogen could be lost from the system to the atmosphere via the formation of gaseous products during nitrogen transformation processes. However, if the nitrogen is lost to the sediment through seston biomass settlement, it would later be mineralized and released to the overlying water for later use.

REFERENCES

Alexander, M., and F. E. Clark. "Nitrifying Bacteria," in C. A. Black, Ed. *Methods of Soil Analysis. Part 2. Agronomy* 9:1477–1483. Am. Soc. of Agronomy, Madison, Wis.

Bremner, J. M. "Total Nitrogen," in Ç. A. Black, Ed. *Methods of Soil Analysis. Part 2. Agronomy* 9:1149–1178. Am. Soc. of Agronomy, Madison, Wis.

Bremner, J. M., and D. R. Keeney. "Steam Distillation Methods for Determination of Ammonium, Nitrate and Nitrite," *Anal. Chim. Acta* 32:485–495 (1965).

Chen, R. L., D. R. Keeney and J. G. Konrad. "Nitrification in Sediments of Selected Wisconsin Lakes," *J. Environ. Qual.* 1: 151–154 (1972).

Fogg, G. E. "Extracellular Products of Algae in Freshwater," *Arch. Hydrobiol. Beih. Ergebn. Limnol.* 5:1–25 (1971).

Johannes, R. E. "Nutrient Regeneration in Lakes and Oceans," *Adv. Microbiol. Sea* 1:203–212 (1968).

Lean, D. R. S., M. N. Charlton, B. K. Burnison, T. P. Murphy, S. E. Millard and K. R. Young. "Phosphorus: Changes in Ecosystem Metabolism from Reduced Loading," *Verh. Internat. Verein. Limnol.* 19:249–257 (1975).

Lean, D. R. S., C. F. -H. Liao, T. P. Murphy, and S. Painter. "The Importance of Nitrogen Fixation in Lakes," in *International Symposium on The Environmental Role of Nitrogen-Fixing Blue-Green Algae and Asymbiotic Bacteria,* September 20–24, 1976, Uppsala, Sweden (in press).

Lueshow, L. A., J. M. Helm, D. R. Winter and G. W. Karl. "Trophic Nature of Selected Wisconsin Lakes," *Wisc. Acad. Sci., Arts Lett.* 58:237–264 (1970).

Mills, A. L., and M. Alexander. "Microbial Decomposition of Species of Freshwater Planktonic Algae," *J. Environ. Qual.* 3:423–428 (1974).

Oglesby, R. T. "Effects of Controlled Nutrient Dilution on an Eutrophic Lake," *Adv. Water Poll. Res., Proc. 4th Int. Conf., Prague,* pp. 747–757 (1969).

Serruya, C., and T. Berman. "The Evolution of Nitrogen Compounds in Lake Kinneret," in *Developments in Water Quality Research,* pp. 73–78.

Stanford, G., J. O. Legg, S. Dzienia and E. C. Simpson, Jr. "Identification and Associated Nitrogen Transformation in Soils," *Soil Sci.* 120:147-152 (1975).

Verstraete, W., and M. Alexander. "Heterotrophic Nitrification in Samples of Natural Ecosystems," *Environ. Sci. Technol.* 7:39-42 (1973).

Weiss, C. M. "The Relative Significance of Phosphorus and Nitrogen as Algal Nutrients," *Water Resources Res. Institute Rep.* No. 34, Chapel Hill, North Carolina (1970).

CHAPTER 7

THE PHOTOOXIDATION OF LABORATORY CULTURES OF *MICROCYSTIS* UNDER LOW LIGHT INTENSITIES

J. N. ELOFF

  Botany Department
  University of the Orange Free State
  Bloemfonte, South Africa

INTRODUCTION

Photosynthetic organisms are generally sensitive to high light intensities in the presence of high O_2 concentrations and low CO_2 concentrations, suggesting that the lethal mechanism is a photooxidative effect. It has been postulated that photooxidation may be the causative agent in the sudden die-off of cyanobacterial blooms in nature (Abeliovitch and Shilo, 1972). It has been found that laboratory cultures are much more sensitive to high light intensities than natural blooms (Allison, Hoover and Morris, 1937). One isolate of *Microcystis* (strain 7005) was especially sensitive to high light intensity (Eloff, Steinitz and Shilo, 1976).

It has also been observed that cultures of *Microcystis* growing under relatively low light intensities frequently lyse without any apparent cause (Zehnder and Gorham, 1960). *Microcystis* blooms in nature frequently reach cell concentrations of 10^9 cells/ml, but laboratory cultures of *Microcystis* seldom reach cell densities in excess of 5×10^6 cells/ml.

This chapter will present results of experiments on the light sensitivity of different *Microcystis* isolates.

MATERIALS AND METHODS

The following *Microcystis* isolates were used: *Microcystis* 7005 from R. Y. Stanier, Institute Pasteur (axenic without gas vacuoles, nontoxic), *Microcystis* NRC-1 from P. R. Gorham, Research Council of Canada (nonaxenic with few gas vacuoles, toxic), *Microcystis* HVD from Hendrik Verwoerd Dam near Bethulie, South Africa (nonaxenic with gas vacuoles, nontoxic), and *Microcystis* HPB from the Hartebeespoort Dam near Pretoria, South Africa (axenic with gas vacuoles, toxic). The culture conditions

were as described by Eloff *et al.* (1976), with the difference
that Sylvania Grolux lamps were used at different light intensities at a temperature of 28 ± 1°C. By adding different concentrations of a mixture of pyrogallol and an equimolar mixture
of NaOH and Na_2CO_3 to a separate test tube within the culture
flask, oxygen was removed from Erlenmeyer culture flasks that
were closed with a rubber stopper (Eloff, 1977).

RESULTS

     The influence of different light intensities on the
growth of *Microcystis* 7005 as determined by turbidity measurements is shown in Figure 1. It is clear that at light intensities of 15.4 and 26.0 µEinsteins m^{-2} sec^{-1}, photoinhibition
took place and the cells lysed.

     Similar experiments were also carried out with *Micro-
cystis* NRC-1, *Microcystis* HVD and *Microcystis* HBP. The four
isolates differed in sensitivity to light intensity, the
Microcystis HBP being more resistant to photooxidation than
the other isolates. Figure 2 shows the highest yield obtained
within a growth period of 34 days at different light intensities
for the four *Microcystis* isolates.

     In a next series of experiments *Microcystis* 7005, the
most sensitive to light intensity of the isolates, were grown
in rubber-stoppered Erlenmeyer flasks at light intensities of
9 µEinstein m^{-2} sec^{-1}. The influence of a different carbonate

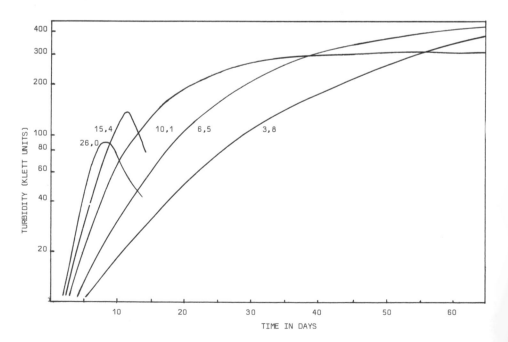

Figure 1. The influence of light intensity (µEinsteins m^{-2}
           sec^{-1}) on growth curve of *Microcystis* 7005.

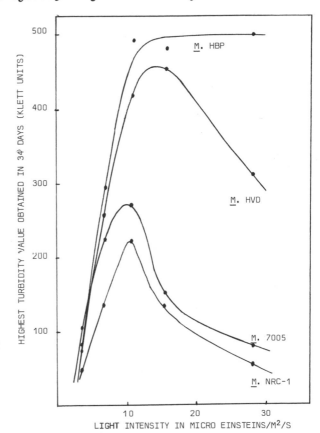

Figure 2. Influence of
light intensity on
optimal field of
four *Microcystis*
isolates.

content in the medium as well as the influence of a different
atmospheric oxygen concentration on the growth of *Microcystis*
7005 was determined by addition of alkaline pyrogallol to a
separate open test tube within the culture flasks. Figure 3
presents typical results obtained. The influence of varying
the alkali-pyrogallol mixture, *i.e.*, varying the concentration
O_2 on the yield of *Microcystis* in stoppered containers is shown
in Figure 4.

DISCUSSION

From Figure 1 it is clear that light intensities higher
than 10 µEinsteins m^{-2} sec^{-1} lead to inhibition of growth within 10 days at relatively low turbidity values corresponding to
cell densities of ± 7 x 10^5 cell/ml. This is in marked contrast to the cell densities of 10^9 cells/ml encountered in nature, with *Microcystis* growing under light intensities of up
to 2000 µEinsteins m^{-2} sec^{-1}.

In comparing the sensitivity of different *Microcystis*
isolates to high light intensities as shown in Figure 2, it is
clear that *Microcystis* HBP is most resistant, followed by *Microcystis* HVD. *Microcystis* 7005 and *Microcystis* NRC 1 are the
most sensitive. The light sensitivity does not correlate well
with parameters such as toxicity, presence of bacteria in the

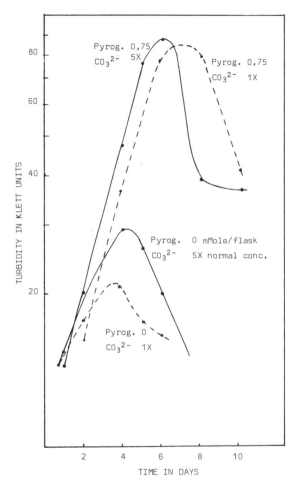

Figure 3.   Influence of alkaline pyrogallol and carbonate on the growth of *Microcystis* in closed containers.

culture and cell size, but there is a positive correlation between light sensitivity and absence of gas vacuoles. However, it has been shown that destruction of gas vacuoles by applying pressure does not change the sensitivity towards high light intensities (Eloff *et al.*, 1976) in a natural bloom of *Microcystis*.

If one compares the times that these cultures were kept under laboratory conditions (*Microcystis* HBP since 1976, *Microcystis* HVD since 1973, *Microcystis* 7005 since pre-1964 and *Microcystis* NRC-1 since 1954), there seems to be a good correlation between the time the cultures were kept under laboratory conditions and the sensitivity towards light. This probably means that the isolates have adapted to growing under low light intensities. This adaptation is accompanied by a change from colony to single-cell growth habit within a few months under our growth conditions and by the loss of gas vacuoles after a few years, in some cases. This clearly points to the hazards of extrapolating results obtained with laboratory cultures to a natural bloom.

From the data given in Figures 2 and 3 it is clear that removal of oxygen and, to a lesser extent, increasing the carbonate concentrations leads to protection against the lethal effect of light. Within limits, when the pH of the medium remains above pH 8, there is a stochiometric correlation between the alkaline pyrogallol concentration (*i.e.*, reciprocal of oxygen content) and optimal yield of *Microcystis* cells. The higher the oxygen content, the lower the resistance to the lethal effect of light. From these data one may deduce that the sensitivity to the light intensity is a photooxidative effect. It is remarkable that a pigmented photosynthetic organism is sensitive to photooxidation at light intensities as low as 10–15 µEinsteins m^{-2} sec^{-1}. This organism may be very useful in examining the mechanism of photooxidation in cyanobacteria. The basic knowledge gained in understanding the mechanism of photooxidation may be of value in explaining the die-off of cyanobacterial blooms in nature.

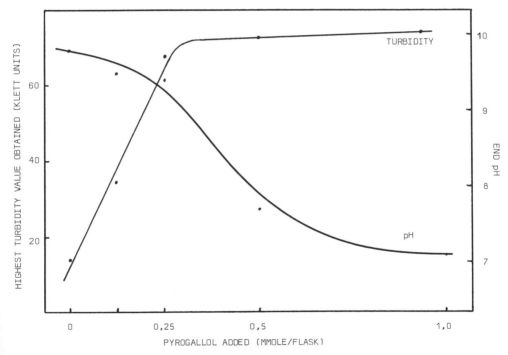

Figure 4. The influence of alkaline pyrogallol concentration on growth of *Microcystis* 7005 in closed containers.

REFERENCES

Aboliovich, A., and M. Shilo. "Photooxidative Death in Blue-Green Algae," *J. Bacteriol.* 111:682–689 (1972).

Allison, F. E., S. R. Hoover and H. J. Morris. "Physiological Studies with the Nitrogen-Fixing Alga *Nostoc muscorum,*" *Bot. Gaz.* 98:433-463 (1937).

Eloff, J. N. "The Use of Alkaline Pyrogallol with Liquid Cultures of *Microcystis,*" *J. Limnol. Soc. Stn. Afr.* 3 (in press).

Eloff, J. N., Y. Steinitz and M. Shilo. "Photooxidation of Cyanobacteria in Natural Conditions," *Appl. Environ. Microbiol.* 31:119-126 (1976).

Zehnder, A., and P. R. Gorham. "Factors Influencing the Growth of *Microcystis aeroginosa* Kütz. emend Elenkin," *Can. J. Microbiol.* 6:645-659 (1960).

CHAPTER 8

BACTERIOLOGICAL CHARACTERIZATION OF
PHYTOPLANKTON CELL SURFACES

DOUGLAS E. CALDWELL
SARAH J. CALDWELL

University of New Mexico
Albuquerque, New Mexico 87131   USA

INTRODUCTION

Henrici and McCoy (1938) were the first to report that
bacteria in phytoplankton occurred primarily within the microenvironment at algal surfaces. Current estimates are that
97 percent of the bacteria in phytoplankton are epiphytes and
only 3 percent are planktonic (Mikhaylenko, 1973). Given the
dilute nature of most natural waters, it is not surprising that
microbial heterotrophs are largely confined to this microenvironment. Studies of the bacteria attached to planktonic algae
and cyanobacteria are limited by the difficulties of plating
and observing them. They occur embedded in the mucilage of
cyanobacteria (Huetzel, 1969; Kessel, 1975) or attached directly to the cell surface (Paerl, 1975, 1976) using a holdfast
(Hirsch, 1972). There is also evidence that productivity measurements are affected by these bacteria (Nalewajko, 1976;
Caldwell, 1977) and that the bacteria may determine algal community structure by producing chelates (Murphy, 1976), inhibitors (Vance, 1965) or other compounds (Caldwell, 1977).
The distribution of phytoplankton in the epilimnion has
been positively correlated with the distribution of bacteria
(Straskrabova, 1974, 1975; Guseva, 1951; Lin, 1972; Maksimova,
1973; Mikhaylenko, 1973; Hagedorn, 1969; Ohwada, 1972, 1973).
These bacteria are Gram-negative (Berland *et al.*, 1970;
Godlewska, 1972; Simidu, 1964; Zagallo, 1953; Taylor, 1938,
1942). Chrost (1975) has shown that this may be due to the
inhibition of Gram-positive bacteria by algal inhibitors. The
investigation described in this chapter used electron microscopy as a means of studying the density and spatial distribution of bacteria, algae and cyanobacteria in the macro-and
microenvironments of plankton. The bacteria were found to be

associated primarily with gas-vacuolate cyanobacteria rather than the algae. A bacterial isolate from an *in situ* association of Anabaena and bacteria was found to be dependent upon the microenvironment of cyanobacterial mucilage for growth.

METHODS

During an *Anabaena* bloom in Quemado Lake, New Mexico, the gas-vacuolate cyanobacteria and attached heterotrophic bacteria were separated from the other components of plankton by density gradient centrifugation. A 20-ml lake sample was layered on 20 ml of a sterile 20% (w/w) ficoll solution (mol wt 70,000, Sigma F-2878) and centrifuged at 3,000 G for 20 min at 4°C. The gas-vacuolate cyanobacteria and attached bacteria formed a pellicle on the surface. The use of continuous ficoll gradients, sucrose gradients, 20% ficoll alone, or lake water alone caused the gas vacuoles to collapse. At higher speeds, the bacterial epiphytes were partially released from the mucilage.

The homogenization procedure of McCurdy (1974), based on homogenization with glass beads, was then used to disperse the attached bacteria. Serial dilutions in Moss's algal medium (Moss, 1972) supplemented with 0.8 g/l nutrient broth were made. At higher dilutions the bacteria associated with *Anabaena in situ* were found embedded in mucilage of the laboratory strain of *Anabaena*. Initially, the bacteria were difficult to cultivate on standard media. However, by adjusting the pH to 9.0 (1 ml 1 N NaOH/100 ml nutrient agar) growth was consistently obtained on solid media. No liquid medium was capable of supporting the isolate (T-isolate) in the absence of *Anabaena*.

Electron micrographs were used to calculate *in situ* biovolume with the following equation:

$$B = \frac{(f)(c)}{v}$$

where:

    f = collection filter area (cm^2)
    v = sample volume (ml)
    c = cross-sectional area of the cells in thin
           section per cm along the collection filter
           (cm)
    B = biovolume of the cells per ml (cm^3/ml).

The biovolume of an average bacterial and cyanobacterial cell was calculated (*Anabaena* 7.5 x 7.5 μm, T-isolate 1.9 x 0.5 μm) and used to estimate cell numbers from biovolume measurements.

The axenic *Anabaena* sp. used in laboratory studies of the bacteria-*Anabaena* association was supplied by Howard McCurdy (University of Windsor, Ontario). It was not gas-vacuolate and was isolated as described by McCurdy and Hodgson (1973). Stocks of the isolate were maintained on Moss's medium supplemented with 0.8 g/l nutrient broth (Difco) to detect bacterial contamination.

Moss's medium (Moss, 1972) was used for most experiments. Nutritional tests were conducted using Difco (Detroit) media.

RESULTS

Electron microscopy of *in situ Anabaena*-bacterial aggregates revealed that virtually all of the bacteria present were embedded in *Anabaena* mucilage and were Gram-negative. These occurred in clusters resembling microcolonies. Quantitative electron microscopy revealed that the biovolume of the *Anabaena* cells and associated bacteria were $2.3 \pm 1.3 \times 10^{-5}$ (95 percent confidence interval) and $3.5 \pm 2.0 \times 10^{-7}$ cm^3/ml of lake water, respectively. The density of the bacterial cells in the macroenvironment of lake water was $7.4 \pm 4.1 \times 10^5$ cells/ml. In the microenvironment of *Anabaena* mucilage $2.6 \pm 1.4 \times 10^{11}$ cells/ml were found. There were 13.4 ± 7.3 embedded bacterial cells per *Anabaena* cell.

Although 72 bacterial isolates were obtained from plankton during the course of the summer, only one isolate (T-isolate) could be obtained immediately preceding the peak of the *Anabaena* bloom. This isolate possessed a number of cultural characteristics suggesting that it was associated with *Anabaena in situ*. When growing in two-member liquid culture with *Anabaena* on Moss's medium, it formed *Anabaena*-bacterial aggregates identical in morphology to those seen *in situ*. It would not grow in liquid culture in the absence of *Anabaena* but would grow alone on a variety of solid media. When grown on solid media, it produced soft colonies analogous to those formed by other Gram-negative, rod-shaped organisms. However, when sterile filtrates from *Anabaena* cultures were used instead of distilled water, the isolate produced tough colonies that could be removed, suspended in distilled water, and shaken without being disrupted.

The isolate was Gram-negative, rod-shaped to vibrioid and 1.9×0.5 μm in size. It occurred in two growth forms in culture, either within the mucilage covering the cell chains of *Anabaena* or as a flagellated swarmer cell, which showed an obvious positive chemotactic response to *Anabaena*.

DISCUSSION

The Gram-negative bacteria present during the *Anabaena* bloom were almost entirely embedded within the mucilage of *Anabaena* cell chains at a density of 2.6×10^{11} cells/ml. Thus, any future bacteriological studies of similar cyanobacterial blooms should consider the microenvironment of the cell surface where most bacterial activity occurs. These bacteria

can be quantified using phase microscopy and agar slides
(Caldwell, 1975) or using transmission electron microscopy of
thin sections. In the latter case, cell numbers, cell biovol-
umes and cell microcolonies can be determined. In the former,
only cell numbers can be determined. Plating methods can be
used if the sample is adequately homogenized, the pH is at 9.0
and an autoclaved *Anabaena* culture with 8 g/l nutrient broth
is used as the plating medium. Under these conditions the
bacteria associated with *Anabaena in situ* will produce tough
colonies that can be easily distinguished from the soft colonies of most other rod-shaped bacteria.

Since these bacteria cannot be grown in liquid, it is
probable that the flagellated swarmer cell will not divide
unless it is in contact with a gel of some type. *Anabaena* mucilage and 1.5 percent agar both fill this requirement. Within the epilimnion, the swarmer cell's only function appears to
be the dispersal of the organism, while growth occurs only at
extremely high cell densities in the mucilage microenvironment.
These high *in situ* densities (2.6×10^{11} cells/ml) can be obtained in culture only at high nutrient concentrations on solid media. This suggests that the bacteria of phytoplankton
are not living in a dilute macroenvironment but rather in a
relatively rich microenvironment. Thus, a carbon cycle must
exist in which the processes of production and decomposition
occur within *Anabaena*-bacterial aggregates. As a result, data
resulting from the addition of labeled organic substrates and
CO_2 to bottled samples are difficult to interpret since the
rate at which carbon is cycled within these aggregates is not
measured. This hypothetical nutrient cycle in the microenvironment is thus a significant problem, since the functional relationship between cyanobacteria and heterotrophic bacteria
may play a role in determining the distribution, abundance,
and structure of phytoplankton communities.

ACKNOWLEDGMENTS

We wish to acknowledge the General Ecology Section of
the National Science Foundation for grant DEB 76-01226, which
supported this work. We also wish to thank Brian Ohler for
technical assistance.

REFERENCES

Berland, B. R., D. J. Bonin and S. V. Maestrini. "Study of
Bacteria Associated with Marine Algae in Culture. III. Organic Substrates Supporting Growth," *Mar. Biol.* 5:68-76 (1970).

Caldwell, D. E., and J. M. Tiedje. "A Morphological Study of
Anaerobic Bacteria from the Hypolimnia of Two Michigan Lakes,"
Can. J. Microbiol. 21:362-376 (1975).

Caldwell, D. E. "The Planktonic Microflora of Lakes," *CRC Critical Reviews in Microbiology* (in press).

Chrost, R. J. "Inhibitors Produced by Algae as an Ecological Factor Affecting Bacteria in Water Ecosystems. I. Dependence Between Phytoplankton and Bacterial Development," *Acta Microbiol. Pol., Ser. B* 7:125-133 (1975).

Chrost, R. J. "Inhibitors Produced by Algae as an Ecological Factor Affecting Bacteria in Water. II. Antibacterial Activity of Algae During Blooms," *Acta Microbiol. Pol., Ser. B* 7:167-176 (1975).

Godlewska-Lipowa, W. A., and I. Jablonska. "Spatial Differentiation Abundance of Bacteria in the Water of Mikolajskie Lake," *Pol. J. Ecol.* 20:367-371 (1972).

Guseva, K. A. "Interrelation of Phytoplankton and Saprophyte Bacteria in a Reservoir," *Zoologicheskiy Institute. Trudy Problemnykh: Tematiches Kikh Soveshchaniy No. 1.* (National Technical Information Service-AD-650-805), pp. 34-38 (1951).

Henrici, A. T., and E. McCoy. "The Distribution of Heterotrophic Bacteria in the Bottom Deposits of some Lakes," *Trans. Wisc. Acad. Sci.* 31:323-361 (1938).

Hirsch, P. "New Methods for Observation and Isolation of Unusual or Little Known Water Bacteria," *Z. Allg. Mikrobiol.* 12:203-218 (1972).

Hagedorn, V. H. "The Verticle Distribution of Thiamine Bacteria," *Ber. Dtsch. Bot. Ges.* 82:223-234 (1969).

Kuentzel, L. E. "Bacteria, Carbon Dioxide, and Algal Blooms," *J. Water Poll. Control Fed.* 41:1737-1747 (1969).

Kessel, M., and J. N. Eloff. "The Ultrastructure and Development of the Colonial Sheath of *Microcystis marginata*," *Arch. Microbiol.* 106:209-214 (1975).

Lin, K. "Phytoplankton Succession in an Eutrophic Lake with Special Reference to Blue-Green Algal Blooms," *Hydrobiologia* 39:321-334 (1972).

Maksimova, E. A. "Annual Dynamics of the Vertical Distribution of Heterotrophic Bacteria in Southern Baikal," *Mikrobiologiya* 42:469-474 (1973).

McCurdy, D., and W. F. Hodgson. "Method for the Selective Enumeration of Blue-Green Bacteria in Water," *Appl. Microbiol.* 26:682-686 (1973).

McCurdy, H. D., and W. F. Hodgson. "The Isolation of Blue-
Green Bacteria in Pure Culture," *Can. J. Microbiol.* 20:
272-273 (1974).

Mikhaylenko, L. Ye., and I. Ya. Kulikova. "Interdependence of
Bacteria and Blue-Green Algae," *Hydrobiol. J.* 9:32-38 (1973).

Moss, B. "The Influence of Environmental Factors on the Dis-
tribution of Freshwater Algae: an Experimental Study. I.
Introduction and the Influence of Calcium Concentration,"
J. Ecol. 60:917-932 (1972).

Murphy, T. P., D. R. S. Lean and C. Nalewajko. "Blue-Green
Algae: Their Excretion of Iron-Selective Chelators Enables
them to Dominate other Algae," *Science* 192:900-902 (1976).

Nalewajko, C., T. G. Dunstall and H. Shear. "Kinetics of Extracellular Release in Axenic Algae and in Mixed Algal-Bacterial Cultures: Significance in Estimation of Total (gross)
Phytoplankton Excretion Rates," *J. Phycol.* 12:1-5 (1976).

Ohwada, K., and N. Taga. "Vitamin B_{12}, Thiamine, and Biotin
in Lake Sagami," *Limnol. Oceanog.* 17:315-320 (1972).

Ohwada, K., and N. Taga. "Seasonal Cycles of Vitamin B_{12},
Thiamine and Biotin in Lake Sagami, Patterns of Their Distribution and Ecological Significance," *Int. Revue ges. Hydrobiol.* 58:851-871 (1973).

Paerl, H. W. "Microbiol Attachment to Particles in Marine and
Freshwater Ecosystems," *Microbiol. Ecol.* 2:73-83 (1975).

Paerl, H. W. "Specific Associations of the Blue-Green Algae
Anabaena and Aphanizomenon with Bacteria in Freshwater
Blooms," *J. Phycol.* 12:431-435 (1976).

Simidu, U., K. Ashino and E. Kaneko. "Microbiol Formation and
Degradation of Minerals," *Adv. Appl. Microbiol.* 6:153-157
(1964).

Straskrabora, V. "Seasonal Occurrence of Several Groups of
Heterotrophic Bacteria in two Reservoirs," *Int. Rev. ges.
Hydrobiol.* 59:9-16 (1974).

Straskrabova, V. "Seasonal Variations in the Production and
Biomass of Bacterial Plankton in the Klicava Reservoir and
Their Relation to the Production of Algae," *Folia Microbiol.*
20:76 (1975).

Taylor, C. B., and H. G. Lochhead. "Qualitative Studies of
Soil Microorganisms. II. A Survey of the Bacterial Flora of
Soils Differing in Fertility," *Can. J. Res. Ca.* 16:162 (1938).

Taylor, C. B. "Bacteriology of Freshwater. III. The Types of Bacteria Present in Lakes and Streams and Their Relationship to the Bacterial Flora of Soil," *J. Hyg.* 42:284–296 (1942).

Simidu, U., and E. Kaneko. "Bacterial Flora of Phyto- and Zooplankton in the Inshore Water of Japan," *Can. J. Microbiol.* 17:1157–1160 (1971).

Vance, B. D. "Composition and Succession of Cyanophycean Water Blooms," *J. Phycol.* 1:81–86 (1965).

Zagallo, A. C. "Oxidative Metabolism of some Bacteria and Blue-Green Algae, Alone and in Association," *Agronomia Lusitana.* 15:315–345 (1953).

CHAPTER 9

PHOTOTROPHIC SULFUR BACTERIA OF SALT MEROMICTIC LAKES AND THEIR ROLE IN SULFUR CYCLE

V. M. GORLENKO

Institute of Microbiology
USSR Academy of Sciences
Moscow, USSR

The salt meromictic lakes are a suitable object for studies of biological processes of sulfur turnover. The water column in such lakes is stratified according to the degree of salinity. As a rule, the deep unmixed strata contain hydrogen sulfide formed as a result of sulfate-reducing bacterial activity. The high production of hydrogen sulfide is determined by large amounts of sulfates and organic matter in salt lakes.

Different microorganisms are involved in oxidation of hydrogen sulfide: phototrophic sulfur bacteria, thiobacteria and colorless sulfur bacteria. The exact role of each group of bacteria is unclear. In addition few data are available on the species composition of phototrophic sulfur bacteria, which intensely multiply in the plankton of meromictic salt lakes.

We have studied the vertical distribution, the species composition and the role of phototrophic sulfur bacteria in oxidation of hydrogen sulfide in four meromictic salt lakes of different origin. The results of these studies are presented in this chapter.

OBJECTS AND METHODS

Description of Lakes

Lake Pomyaretskoye, with a maximum depth of 5.5 m, is situated near the health resort Truskavetz. It was formed on the site of an old ozocerite mine. Lake Repnoye (depth 6.5 m) and Lake Veissovo (depth 17 m) belong to the group of Slavyansk Lakes (town Slavyansk, Donetz Province). They appeared as a result of karst formation due to leaching of gypsum-anhydrite

and salt strata on the Permian system. Lake Mogilnoye, of sea
origin, is located on Kildin Island in the Barents Sea. Separated from the sea by a narrow 70-m strip of land, its maximum
depth is 17 m.

Chemical analyses were done and the vertical distribution of microorganisms and the intensity of sulfur turnover
processes were determined in the deepest points of these lakes.
Samples of water were drawn with a one-liter Rutner bathometer,
and silt monoblocks were taken with a stratometer equipped with
a tube of organic glass. Water temperature was measured with
a mercury thermometer inserted into the bathometer. The acidity and the redox potential were determined with a ПМ-03 po-
tentiometer using a glass electrode for pH analysis and a
smooth platinum electrode coupled with a chlorine-silver electrode for assessing Eh. Eh in water was measured in special
small glass receptacles (Sorokin, 1966).

Water transparency was assessed on a Secci disk, and
illumination was estimated by means of a luxmeter equipped with
an underwater transducer. Hydrogen sulfide in water was measured iodometrically immediately after sampling. Oxygen was
measured after Winkler, chlorides, by argentometric titration
(Reznikov *et al.*, 1970), and sulfates by the alizarine method
(Zavarov, 1957). The total number of microorganisms was estimated on erythrosine-stained membrane filters. The photosynthesizing bacteria were estimated on unstained membrane filters
in transmitted and reflected light (Gorlenko *et al.*, 1973) and
by the method of final dilutions on the Pfennig agarized medium
(Pfennig, 1965; Trüper, 1970). The number of thiobacteria was
assessed on the Beyerinck medium (Romanenko and Kuznetsov, 1974).
The intensity of bacterial sulfate reduction was measured by an
isotope method using $Na_2S^{35}O_4$ (Ivanov, 1964), photosynthesis
and the dark assimilation of carbon dioxide, by the radiocarbon
method (Sorokin, 1959).

The capacity of bacteria for dark and light assimilation
of carbon dioxide was measured by the method of process stimulation in individual samples *in situ* adding $Na_2S \cdot 9H_2O$ or hypo-
sulfide together with $NaHC^{14}O_3$. The relation between the rate
of bacterial photosynthesis and underwater illumination was
measured after Sorokin (1966). For this purpose light and dark
receptacles with lake water containing photosynthesizing bacteria
and hydrogen sulfide were suspended at different levels beginning with the surface. The maximum value of photosynthesis was
taken for 100 percent. The amount of hydrogen sulfide oxidized
under the action of phototrophic sulfur bacteria was estimated
by the well-known Van Niel formula for bacterial photosynthesis
on the basis of CO_2 assimilation values *in situ*. The amount of
hydrogen sulfide utilized by the thiobacteria was estimated by
the Baas-Becking and Parks formula, assuming the effectivity
of free energy utilization to be 15 percent (Baas-Becking and
Parks, 1927).

RESULTS

Physicochemical Conditions in the Studied Lakes

In all the lakes studied chemocline and thermocline were pronounced, and the hypolimnion waters contained hydrogen sulfide. In Lake Pomeretskoye thermocline and chemocline coincided and were found at a depth of about 3 m (Figure 1), at which point the boundary of the hydrogen sulfide layer was located. In the bottom layers there were 340 mg/l of hydrogen sulfide. The upper 3 m of the water body were markedly demineralized, while the mineralization of hypolimnion waters reached up to 1.6 percent.

In Lake Repnoye hydrogen sulfide remained only in the bottom part (maximum 119 mg/l). The upper limit of its distribution was at a depth of 5–5.5 m and coincided with the thermocline and chemocline zone (Figure 2). The mineralization of the surface waters was 0.9 percent, and of the bottom waters, 1.4 percent.

In Lake Veissovo two salt and temperature stops were recorded. The limit of hydrogen sulfide distribution was situated at the upper gradient, at a depth of 1.25 m (Figure 3). Waters rich in hydrogen sulfide were in direct contact with oxygen waters. In the bottom region hydrogen sulfide concentration attained 790 mg/l, and mineralization was 11.5 percent of salts. The surface oxygen–containing waters had 2.9 percent of salts.

In Lake Mogilnoye chemocline began at a 5-m depth, whereas thermocline was at a depth of 8–10 m (Figure 4), where the hydrogen sulfide level was found also. Up to a 5-m depth the lake was markedly demineralized; below 5 m mineralization increased abruptly and attained the salinity of sea water. Hydrogen sulfide concentration near the bottom was 176 mg/l.

Vertical Distribution and Species of Phototrophic Bacteria

In all the lakes massive growth of phototrophic sulfur bacteria was demonstrated. They formed a colored layer 0.5 to 1.0 m thick at the upper limit of hydrogen sulfide distribution (Figures 1–4).

Some general consistencies were recorded in all the lakes. Phototrophic sulfur bacteria were strictly localized at the upper limit of hydrogen sulfide distribution (Figures 1–4). The level of their concentration was determined by the depth of light penetration and the rate of hydrogen sulfide supply from the lower horizons. Only one species predominated in each lake, attaining enormous numbers of 30–40 million cells/ml, according to direct counts. In all cases, these were brown or green chlorobacterial species. Purple bacteria were present as concomitant species and their numbers did not exceed 100 thousand/ml.

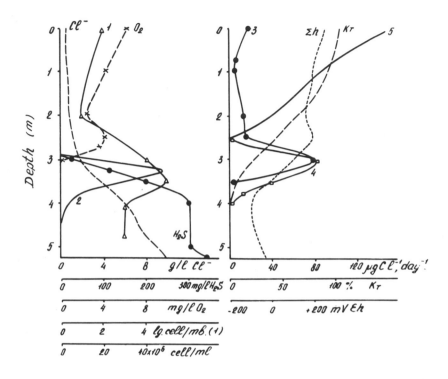

Figure 1. Vertical distribution of phototrophic bacteria in Lake Pomjaretskoye and their activity.

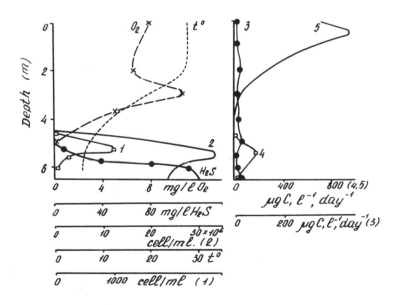

Figure 2. Vertical distribution of phototrophic bacteria in Repnoye and their activity.

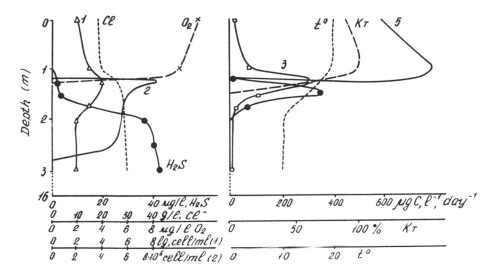

Figure 3.   Vertical distribution of phototrophic bacteria in
Lake Veissovo and their activity.

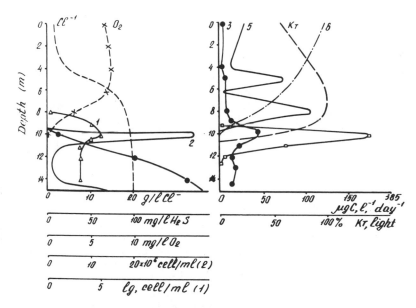

Figure 4.   Vertical distribution of phototrophic bacteria in
Lake Mogilnoye and their activity.

(1=*Thiobacillus* sp.; 2=phototrophic bacteria [Figure 1. *Chlorobium chlorovibrioides*; Figure 2. *Chlorobium phaeovibrioides*;
Figure 3. *Polodictyon phaeum*; Figure 4. *Chlorobium phaeovibrioides*]. 3=dark CO_2 assimilation; 4=bacterial photosynthesis; 5=phytoplankton photosynthesis; 6=light penetration.)

In different lakes, populations of phototrophic bacteria
varied. However, the number of species in these populations
was limited. Among chlorobacteria (family *Chlorobiaceae*) were
found: *Chlorobium phaeovibrioides*, *Chlorobium chlorovibrioides*
nov. sp., *Pelodictyon luteolum*, *Pelodictyon phaeum* and *Prosthecochloris phaeoasteroidea*. Among purple bacteria (family
Chromatiaceae), *Thiocapsa roseopersicina*, *Thiodictyon bacil-
losus*, *Lamprocystis* sp., *Chromatium* sp. Only in Lake Repnoye
were there small amounts of members of the *Rhodospirillaceae-
Rhodopseudomonas sulfidophila* family. Most species were isolated in a pure culture and their morphology and physiology
were investigated.

All the strains required a medium with a high content
of NaCl, *i.e.*, 0.5 to 3 percent, and the salinity necessary for
the growth of the predominant species was close to that prevailing in their natural environment.

In lakes with identical salinity, the preferential development of a species depends on many factors. Of special
importance are underwater illumination and the quality of light
penetrating into the layer of phototrophic bacteria. In lakes
Repnoye, Veissovo and Mogilnoye, brown chlorobacteria enriched
with carotinoid pigment predominated. Due to their pigmenta-
tion, these bacteria have no competitors at great depths and
use efficiently the dim green light reaching deep waters
(Pfennig, 1967; Trüper and Genovese, 1968). Brown chlorobacteria can also predominate at small depths, but only in waters
with low transparency due to the growth of phytoplankton or
the presence of suspended particles.

Curiously enough, the isolated phototrophic bacterial
species, including the bacteria with gas vacuoles of the
Pelodictyon and *Lamprocystis* genera, were tolerant to high
hydrogen sulfide concentrations. It should be remembered that
Pfennig, who studied mainly freshwater strains, separated the
phototrophic bacteria with gas vacuoles into a special ecologic
subgroup, classifying them as oligosulfidophils (Pfennig, 1967).
According to Pfennig's terminology, the saltwater species *Pelodictyon* and *Lamprocystis* may be named eurisulfidophils. Interestingly enough, the single species of nonsulfur purple bacteria that has been found turned out to be tolerant to very high
sulfide concentrations. All the strains studied grew better
under moderate illumination, the optimal temperature being
about 25° and pH in the range of 6.5-7.6.

Counts of individual species over a short interval of
0.25 cm revealed their exact localization within the colored
layer. Species stratification is an expression of their ecologic capabilities. As a rule, brown species of chlorobacteria
occupied the horizon below the green ones, and species with
gas vacuoles showed a peak above the immobile chlorobacteria
devoid of gas vacuoles. *Thiocapsa roseopersicina* and *Rhodopseudomonas sulfidophilla*, *i.e.*, bacteria capable of aerobic
metabolism, occupied the uppermost horizon and did not grow
massively.

The count of thiobacteria oxidizing thiosulfate and
hydrogen sulfide did not exceed 10^3-10^5 cells per ml. These
aerobic microorganisms were concentrated in close proximity
to phototrophic bacteria in a zone of low oxygen concentrations.
In Lake Veissovo significant numbers of unicellular colorless
sulfur bacteria *Thiovolum* and *Thiospira* were also identified.

Microbiological Processes of Sulfur Turnover

Experiments with radioactive sodium sulfate, $Na_2S^{35}O_4$,
have shown that the microbiological process of hydrogen sulfide formation was most intensive in the superficial layer of
silt deposits in the deepest parts of the lakes (Table I).
The activity of sulfate-reducing bacteria was 100-1000 times
lower in the water, and beneath the layer of phototrophic bacterial growth sulfate reduction was always increased. The
generated hydrogen sulfide occupied the deep, more mineralized
water layers. Hydrogen sulfide-containing waters and oxygen-
containing waters came in contact at the chemocline or thermocline level (Figures 1-4). In this zone, which was accessible
to light, bacterial photosynthesis proceeded with maximal intensity. In Lake Mogilnoye bacterial photosynthesis (0.48
mg C, liter^{-1}, day^{-1}) exceeded phytoplankton production almost
three-fold. In other lakes light assimilation of carbon dioxide by phototrophic bacteria was somewhat lower and ranged
from 0.09 to 0.36 mg C, liter^{-1}, day^{-1}.

As a rule, the carbon dioxide dark assimilation peak
was located above bacterial photosynthesis, and to a significant extent it was due to chemosynthesis by thiobacteria or
colorless sulfur bacteria. In three lakes chemosynthesis was
low: 0.02-0.04 mg C, liter^{-1}, day^{-1}. Lake Veissovo was an
exception in this respect; more than 0.3 mg C, liter^{-1},
day^{-1} was synthesized in the dark from carbon dioxide in the
zone of contact between waters rich in oxygen and those containing hydrogen sulfide. In Lake Veissovo hydrogen sulfide
aerobic oxidation processes proceeded violently with the formation of a molecular sulfur suspension.

A comparison of data on light and dark carbon dioxide
assimilation in the oxidation zone of different lakes suggests
that phototrophic bacteria not only outnumber aerobic sulfur
bacteria, but are also considerably more active. It has been
calculated that the activity of phototrophic sulfur bacteria
in the chemocline-thermocline zone accounts for the oxidation
of up to 2.6 mg H_2S/l/day. The contribution of thiobacteria
to sulfur turnover in salt meromictic lakes is much lower.
These bacteria could oxidize daily no more than 0.1-0.2 mg
H_2S/l/day. A different situation arose if the boundary of the
hydrogen sulfide zone was immediately under the aerated lake
surface. Thus, in Lake Veissovo the contribution of thio-
and colorless sulfur bacteria to the oxidation of hydrogen
sulfide is comparable to that of phototrophic bacteria.

Table I

Intensity of Bacterial Photosynthesis, Chemosynthesis and Sulfate Reduction in Lakes

Lake and Main Species of Phototrophic Bacteria	Intensity of Bacterial Sulfate Reduction (mg S/H₂S/1/day)		Photosynthesis of Algae (µg C/1/day)	Bacterial Photosynthesis			Chemosynthesis	
	Silt	Water		(µg C/1/day)	(mg S/H₂S/1/day)	(mg S/H₂S/1/day)	(µg C/1/day)	(mg S/H₂S/1/day)
Pomyaretskoye (*C. chlorovibrioides*)	28.4	0.33	0.15	0.09	0.12	0.47	0.02	0.1
Repnoe (*C. phaeovibrioides*)	15.6	0.12	0.95	0.16	0.21	0.85	0.035	0.17
Veissovo (*P. phaeum*)	19.2	0.08	0.8	0.36	0.48	1.92	0.32	1.6
Mogilnoye (*C. phaeovibrioides*)	10.4	0.03	0.17	0.48	0.64	2.6	0.04	0.2

Factors Limiting the Activity of Sulfur Turnover Bacteria

Favorable conditions for sulfate-reducing bacterial activity exist in salt meromictic lakes. These microorganisms
do not lack.

DISCUSSION

Salt meromictic reservoirs as compared to freshwater
display highly intensive biological processes of sulfur turnover. Typically, the individual stages of the transformation
of sulfur compounds are strictly localized and spatially dis-
sociated. Hydrogen sulfide formation takes place mainly in the
thin superficial layer of silt deposits, whereas the oxidative
processes are concentrated in the narrow boundary zone between
hydrogen sulfide and oxygen waters. The main role in hydrogen
sulfide oxidation belongs to the phototrophic sulfur bacteria
forming the colored layer, where 1 ml contains tens of millions
of cells. The role of thio- and colorless sulfur bacteria in
sulfur turnover is secondary.

Specific conditions existing in salt meromictic lakes
explain the fact that only certain species of phototrophic bacteria grow in these reservoirs. Most of them do not dwell in
freshwater stratified lakes and estuaries. This applies to
the brown chlorobacterial species *Chlorobium phaeovibrioides*,
Pelodictyon phaeum and *Prosthecochloris phaeoasteroides*, as
well as to the green species *Chlorobium chlorovibrioides* and
Pelodictyon luteolum and the purple bacteria *Lamprocystis* sp.
Such phototrophes as *Thiocapsa roseopersicina*, *Chromatium* sp.
and *Rhodopseudomonas sulfidophila*, due to their universal physiology, can grow also as benthos forms in estuaries.

Phototrophic sulfur bacteria and thiobacteria growing
at the boundary between the reduced and oxidized zones compete
for hydrogen sulfide. The former require hydrogen sulfide as
a donor of electrons for photosynthesis, while the latter needs
it as an energy-rich substrate. Depending on their physiologic
features, these bacteria occupy specific ecologic niches, and
this is expressed in the spatial dissociation of the two groups.
Oxygen-dependent thiobacteria display maximal activity in mi-
croaerophilic conditions, where hydrogen sulfide is present in
limited amounts, and suffer permanently from a deficit of energy-rich substrate. Experiments have fully confirmed this conclusion. The addition of hydrogen sulfide or thiosulfate to
the samples *in situ* increased $C^{14}O_2$ assimilation in the dark
more than three-fold. Limited growth of thiobacteria is determined also by a low rate of oxygen supply from the upper
horizons.

Phototrophic bacteria, as anaerobes, grow below the
thiobacteria. The level of their massive growth depends on the
depth of light penetration and the rate of hydrogen sulfide
supply from the hypolimnion. More often than not the colored

layer is formed at the lower limit of light penetration. As
a result, the phototrophic bacteria in salt meromictic reservoirs are limited by the amount of light, but do not suffer
from a lack of hydrogen sulfide. In isolated samples transferred to the upper horizons with brighter illumination, the
intensity of bacterial photosynthesis rose ten-fold and more.
At the same time, addition of hydrogen sulfide to the samples
in situ did not stimulate bacterial photosynthesis.

REFERENCES

Baas-Becking, L. G., and G. S. Parks. "Energy Relations in
   Metabolism of Autotrophic Bacteria," *Physiol. Rev.* 7:85 (1927).

Gorlenko, V. M., E. N. Chebotaryev and V. I. Kachalkin. "Microbiological Processes of Hydrogen Sulphide Oxidation in
   Lake Repnoye (Slav lakes)," *Microbiologia* 42:723-728 (1973)
   (in Russian).

Gorlenko, V. M., E. N. Chebotaryev and V. I. Kachalkin. "Microbiological Processes of Hydrogen Sulphide Oxidation in
   Lake Veissovo (Slav lakes)," *Microbiologia* 43:610-615 (1974a)
   (in Russian).

Gorlenko, V. M., E. N. Chebotaryev, and V. I Kachalkin, "Participation Microorganisms in Sulphur Turnover in Pomyaretskoye Lake," *Microbiologia* 43:908-914 (1974b)(in Russian).

Gorlenko, V. M., M. B. Vainstein and V. I. Kachalkin. "Microbiology of the Lake Mogilnoye. I. Microbial Processes," in
   Relict Lake Mogilnoye (Leningrad: Nauka, 1975, pp. 188-197
   (in Russian).

Ivanov, M. V. *The Role of Microorganisms in Genesis of Sulphur
   Deposits* (Moscow: Nauka, 1964), p. 38 (in Russian).

Pfennig, N. "Anreicherungskulturen für rote und grüne Schwef-
   elbakterien," *Zbl. Bakt.* I Abt., Suppl. 1:179-189 (1965).

Pfennig, N. "Photosynthetic Bacteria," *Ann. Rev. Microbiol.*
   21:285-325 (1967).

Reznikov, A. A., E. P. Mulikovskaya and I. V. Sokolov. *Methods
   of Analysing Natural Waters* (Moscow: Nauka, 1970)(in Russian).

Romanenko, V. I., and S. I. Kuznetsov. *Ecology of Microorganisms in Freshwater Reservoirs* (Leningrad: Nauka, 1974)(in
   Russian).

Sorokin, Yu. I. "Interrelation of Microbial Processes of Sulphur and Carbon Metabolism in the Meromictic Lake Belovod," *Institut biologii vnutrennich vod. Trudy* 12(15):332-347 (in Russian).

Sorokin, Yu. I., and N. Donato. "On the Carbon and Sulphur Metabolism in the Meromictic Lake Faro (Sicily)," *Hydrobiologia* 47:241-252 (1975).

Trüper, H. G., and S. Genovesa. "Characterisation of Photosynthetic Sulfur Bacteria Causing Red Water in Lake Faro (Messina, Sicily)," *Limnol. Oceanog.* 13:225-232 (1968).

Trüper, H. G. "Culture and Isolation of Phototrophic Sulfur Bacteria from the Marine Environment," *Helgoländer wiss. Meeresunters* 20:6-16 (1970).

Zavarov, G. V. "Determination of Sulfate," *Zavodskaja laboratoria* 1:48-57 (1957)(in Russian).

CHAPTER 10

SULFUR CYCLE IN MEROMICTIC LAKES
(MICROBIOLOGICAL AND ISOTOPIC DATA)

A. G. MATROSOV
A. M. ZYAKUN
M. V. IVANOV

Institute of Biochemistry and
Physiology of Microorganisms
USSR Academy of Sciences
Puschino, USSR

INTRODUCTION

The study on the processes of the sulfur cycle in meromictic lakes is of great interest since these water basins provide the possibility of studying differently directed processes
of the sulfur cycle in one ecosystem. It has been known that
the vital activity of sulfate-reducing microorganisms results
in the intensive microbiological formation of hydrogen sulfide
in the bottom sediments of the lakes mentioned, and the mass
development of phototrophic bacteria oxidizing the reduced
sulfur compounds is observed often in the upper border of the
anaerobic zone.

The vital activity of both sulfate-reducing and sulfur-
oxidizing microorganisms participating in the sulfur cycle
leads to the change in the isotopic composition of its reduced
and oxidized forms. The character of the distribution of sulfur isotopes in the process of sulfate reduction to H_2S has been
fairly well investigated in the laboratory experiments on pure
and accumulating cultures of sulfate-reducing bacteria (Kemp and
Thode, 1968). It has been shown that during microbiological
sulfate reduction the separation of sulfur isotopes takes
place, followed by the increase in the contents of heavy isotope ^{34}S in the residual sulfate and light isotope ^{32}S in the
biogenic hydrogen sulfide. Considerably less is known about
the direction and value of isotopic effects in the processes
of hydrogen sulfide oxidation by phototrophic bacteria (Kaplan and
Rittenberg, 1964). The few results available reveal the slight
increase in contents of light isotope ^{32}S in the residual

hydrogen sulfide (Mekhtieva and Kondratjeva, 1966, in Russian).
In the case of the combination of reducing and oxidative cycles,
the distribution of sulfur isotopes represents the more complicated picture. It is easy to model the cycles separately in
the laboratory, but it is more advisable to study the regularities of the distribution of sulfur isotopes in the combined
cycles by the example of natural ecosystems under the conditions
of the closed sulfur cycle.

　　Pursuance of this research allows for solving two important biogeochemical problems. First, on the base of the distribution of sulfur isotopes one can restore the ecological
conditions both in the modern and ancient water basins. Second,
the change in the isotope content of microbial exometabolites
may serve as a criterion of the geochemical activity of microorganisms. However, to solve these problems successfully, it is
necessary to reveal the regularities of the isotope fractionation for the main specific groups of bacteria of the sulfur
cycle.

　　This chapter will present the results of our work to
study the regularities of the distribution of sulfur isotopes
in the products of the vital activity of microorganisms participating in the sulfur cycle in meromictic lakes. The investigations were carried out on meromictic lakes with different
sulfate contents of water and silts. The distribution of sulfur isotopes in zones of the mass development of sulfate-reducing and phototrophic sulfur bacteria was studied in detail, as
were hydrochemical conditions, the intensity of microbiological
processes of the sulfate reduction and photooxidation of hydrogen and sulfide by means of the radioactive label (Ivanov, 1964,
in Russian).

　　The preparation of samples for the sulfur isotopic analysis was carried out according to Ustinov and Grinenko (1965),
and the isotope content measurements were made on a mass-spectro-
meter MI-1305 engineered to take precise measurements. $\delta^{34}S$
values were calculated with the following formula:

$$\delta^{34}S = \left(\frac{(^{34}S/^{32}S/)\ \text{sample}}{(^{34}S/^{32}S)\ \text{standard}} - I \right) \cdot 1000\%o$$

The Sikhote-Aline meteorite sulfur was used as a standard. Re-
producibility of isotopic measurements made up 0.2-0.4%o.

RESULTS AND DISCUSSION

　　According to the results obtained, all the water basins
were divided into three groups: freshwater, salt continental
and marine lagoons. The data on the first group water basins
are tabulated in Tables I and II. The results obtained characterize the peculiarities of the distribution of sulfur isotopes
under the conditions when the sulfate concentration in the lake
is the limiting factor. First of all, one should note insignif-

Table I
Results of Chemical, Microbiological and Isotope
Analyses in the Freshwater Lakes

Basin	Depth: Water(M) Silt(cm)	Intensity of Sulfate Reduction (mg$_s$2-/1/hr)	S (mg/1)		δ^{34}S,%o	
			S^{2-}	SO$_4^{2-}$	S^{2-}	SO$_4^{2-}$
Black Kichier	4.5	–	0.3	18.2	–	+22.6
Water	5.5	0.0153	21.2	20.2	-2.0	+25.2
	8.0	0.0132	54.4	33.2	+2.0	+25.6
	8.7	0.0283	61.5	33.0	+5.9	+24.8
Silt from the depth	0-6	13.3	322	44.1	+2.0	+10.0
9 m	6-18	1.38	330	27.0	+2.5	–
Large Kichier	7.0	0.019	4.4	15.4	+13.6	+17.5
Water	9.0	0.004	7.4	15.9	+11.5	+17.6
Silt from the depth	14.5	0.004	13.1	17.8	+17.1	+19.6
15 m	0-18	6.18	146	14.4	+4.9	+10.5
Kononjer						
Silt-22 m	0-6	5.2	445	13.6	+4.3	+9.0
Silt-12 m	0-18	3.94	700	10.0	+10.0	+14.8
Ruznechikha						
Silt-20 m	0-25	3.64	210	12.1	+11.2	+12.0
Silt-11 m	0-6	0.45	130	12.0	+9.6	+12.0
Myshinjer						
Silt	–	–	514	9.0	+8.2	+9.3
Okha-Lyampi						
Silt	–	–	340	15.0	+6.7	+10.6

icant variations and the light isotope content of sulfur of silty water sulfates in the deep water part of the basin (δ^{34}S = +9.0 – +13.4%o). Evidently, this points to the fact that these basins are supplied with subsoil waters bringing the sulfates from the Permian sediments. In the unmixed anaerobic zone of the lakes the sulfates from the water thickness and silts from the coastal zones are markedly enriched in the heavy isotope (δ^{34}S = +14.8 – +25.6%o), and hydrogen sulfide dissolved in water and sulfides from silty sediments are approximate in isotope content to sulfates from the same samples (δ^{34}S from +4.3%o to +17.1%o). We think that the enrichment in heavy isotopes ^{34}S of sulfates is caused by the microbiological sulfate reduction detected by means of the radioisotopic label(Ivanov, 1964). However, the value of the sulfur isotope separation is different.

Table II
Results of Hydrochemical, Microbiological and Isotopic
Analyses of the Lake Sakovo Water and Silts

Sampling Site	Depth: Water(M) Silt(cm)	Intensity of Sulfate Reduction $(mg^2 S/1/hr)$	S (mg/1) S^{2-}	S (mg/1) SO_4^{2-}	$\delta^{34}S,\%o$ S^{2-}	$\delta^{34}S,\%o$ SO_4^{2-}
Water	2.0			51.2	–	+13.1
	5.0	0.0005	6.7	256	15.0	+14.2
	7.0	0.0016	8.2	242	–10.8	+15.4
	10.0	0.0006	9.2	264	–	+14.6
	15.0	0.0006	10.4	272	–	+14.3
Silt from the depth 15 m	0–6	4.5	348	250	–29.7	+10.3
	6–12	3.38	114	280	–25.4	+13.1
	12–18	2.76	169	276	–23.8	+13.4
Silt from the depth 6 m	0–6	0.707	158	217	–18.6	+15.4
	6–12	2.57	154	218	–25.2	+16.4
	12–18	–	174	218	–	+15.0

The difference between the isotope content of the sulfur of sulfates and hydrogen sulfide formed by the sulfate reduction is minimal (1–5%o) at the low sulfate concentrations (10–12 mg sample/1) and maximal (26–40%o) at the high $^2SO_4$ content in Lake Sakovo (210–280 mg sample/1).

The analogous distribution of sulfur isotopes is characteristic of the saltish Slavonik lakes (Donetsk Region) where sulfates regularly increase their heavy isotope ^{34}S content from $\delta^{34}S = +12.5\%o$ on the surface to $\delta^{34}S = +18.3 - +20.7\%o$ in the bottom water (Table III). The isotope content of sulfides varies within the limits $\delta^{34}S = -16.6 - -2.2\%o$.

The other distribution of sulfur isotopes is characteristic of the salt lagoons separated from the sea. The isotope content of different sulfur forms from the Mogilnoye Lake situated on the Kildin Island at the entrance to the Gulf of Murmansk is tabulated in Table IV. Because the Barentsovo Sea is the source of sulfates there, a different distribution of sulfate sulfur isotopes occurs than in the continental lakes supplied by the underground waters. Indeed, the heaviest sulfate was found in the silty water from the deep water station ($\delta^{34}S = +30.4\%o$). The reduced sulfur forms are considerably enriched in light isotopes ^{32}S and have values of $\delta^{34}S = -18.0-27.3\%o$.

Correlation between the results of the determination of the sulfate reduction intensity and isotope content of different

Table III
Results of Chemical, Microbiological and Isotopic
Analyses in Salt Lakes

Basin	Depth: Water(M) Silt(cm)	Oxidized H_2S Phototrophic Bacteria	S (mg/1)		$\delta^{34}S,\%o$	
			S^{2-}	SO_4^{2-}	S^{2-}	SO_4^{2-}
Repnoe	0.5	–	–	–	–	+12.7
Water	5.5	+	32	657	−16.6	+14.2
	6.0	+	105	691	−16.2	+15.7
Silt from	6.3	+	112	706	−12.3	+18.3
the depth	0–6	–	912	666	−9.7	+15.6
6 m	7–18	–	757	580	−8.4	+15.7
Silt from						
the depth	0–6	–	493	703	−11.2	+12.3
5 m	7–12	–	160	633	–	+12.8
Veissovo	1.5	+	4.0	1170	–	+12.5
Water	2.2	+	37	1130	–	+13.1
	4.0	–	43	1320	–	+14.1
	8.0	–	298	1280	−2.2	+16.6
	12.0	–	739	980	−4.7	+20.7

sulfur forms in ten hydrogen sulfide lakes makes it possible to
affirm that under the conditions of the lakes investigated the
main process responsible for the fractionation of sulfur–stable
isotopes is the microbiological reduction of sulfates, resulting in the depletion of the heavy isotope ^{34}S content of hydrogen sulfide and sulfides and the enrichment of the residual
sulfate in this isotope. However, in freshwater basins the
separation process depends much on the sulfate mineralization
in the medium.
    In zones of the mass development of phototrophic sulfuro-
bacteria this main process of separation may coincide with the
other process of fractionation connected with the anaerobic
oxidation of hydrogen sulfide. It has been shown that in the
zone of the mass development of phototrophic sulfurobacteria
hydrogen sulfide is isotopically lighter than that sampled from
the site of its generation (Tables III and IV). On the other
hand, the elemental sulfur of the surface horizon of the silts
in the Mogilnoye Lake (Table IV) is markedly heavier as compared to hydrogen sulfide from the same samples. There and in
the upper borderline of the hydrogen sulfide zone of the water
thickness the large build-ups of photosynthetic bacteria were
found depositing sulfur extracellularly (Gorlenko *et al.*, 1975).
These results are a sufficient demonstration of the availability

Table IV
Isotopic Content of Sulfur in the Lake Mogilnoye
Water and Silt

Sampling Site	Depth: Water(M) Silt(cm)	H₂S (ml/kg)	Isotopic Sulfur Content, δS^{34}			
			SO_4^{2-}	S°	FeSO₂	H₂S
Water	8.0	–	+15.6	–	–	–
	10.0	41.5	+21.0	–	–	–
	12.0	89.1	+22.7	–	–	-20.4
	14.0	155.4	+24.4	–	–	-22.3
Silt from 15 m depth	0–5	740	+28.0	-15.4	–	-18.0
	5–10	452	+29.0	-18.3	-19.2	-18.4
Silt from 5 m depth	10–20	277	+30.4	-21.0	-17.4	-21.0
	0–10	39.1	+14.0	-20.2	–	-25.0
Silt from 10 m depth	0–6	–	+17.0	–	-20.0	-26.0
	10–20	–	+23.2	-26.0	-27.3	-25.3

of the process of fractionation of sulfur isotopes in the natural ecosystem under the influence of photosynthetic and sulfurobacteria. However, the final conclusion about the value
and direction of isotope effects under the oxidation of dissolved hydrogen sulfide has been drawn on pure cultures of
phototrophic bacteria *Ectothiorhodospira Shaposhnikovii*, which
deposit elemental sulfur into the medium and *Chromatium minu-
tissimum*, which deposit sulfur in cells (Table V).

The results of bench experiments allow also for speaking
about the pronounced increase in the weight of elemental sulfur,
which is the first product of hydrogen sulfide photooxidation.
It should be noted that the maximal difference between the isotope contents of hydrogen sulfide and elemental sulfur in the
bench experiments and in Lake Mogilnoye is 5‰.

The direction of the sulfur isotope separation to the
increase in the content of heavy isotopes [34]S of the photooxidation product coincides by the sign with the well-known Dole's
effect for oxygen. This assumes the possible analogy in mechanisms of the separation of sulfur and oxygen—stable isotopes
during photosynthesis. Therefore, there is a basic difference
between the processes of the separation of isotopes of sulfur
oxidative and reducing cycles. Clearly, the reducing cycle
predominance in the ecosystem of the residual sulfate and later
hydrogen sulfide generations will similarly enrich the heavy
isotope [34]S content as the part of sulfate uptaken increases.
For the oxidative cycle one can assume the increase in the
light isotope [32]S content of the residual hydrogen sulfide in

Table V
Fractionation of Sulfur Isotopes by
Phototrophic Sulfurobacteria

Bacteria	Time(h)	S (mg/1)				δS^{34}, ‰ [a]			
		H_2S	$S°$	$S_xO_y^{2-}$	SO_4^{2-}	H_2S	$S°$	$S_xO_y^{2-}$	SO_4^{2-}
Ectothiorho-	0	102	–	–	–	–	–	–	–
dospira	10	53	9.0	–	30.5	–0.8	+2.9	–	+0.4
Shaposhniko-	11	44	10.8	–	36.5	–1.2	+3.6	–	+1.5
vii	13	24	9.4	–	57.6	–1.6	+3.8	–	+2.3
	24	0	6.0	–	80.0	–	+1.8	–	+1.5
Chromatium	0	146	–	–	–	–	–	–	–
minutissium	9	108	5.2	17.1	15.7	0	+2.5	–2.6	0
	11	72	10.6	16.8	44.8	0	+0.6	–2.3	0
	14	24	8 1	9.2	89.6	0	+1.7	–1.9	0

[a] Measurements were carried out with respect to the initial hydrogen sulfide.

the anaerobic zone as compared to the hydrogen sulfide from the place of its generation, the enrichment in the heavy isotope ^{34}S content of the elemental sulfur and the enrichment of sulfates in ^{32}S light isotope in the basin as compared to sulfates of containing rocks.

REFERENCES

Dole, M, and G. Jenks. *Science* 100:409–411 (1944).

Gorlenko, V. M. *et al. The Relict Mogilnoe Lake* (Leningrad: AN USSR Press, 1975), p. 188.

Ivanov, M. V. *Role of Microbiological Processes in the Genesis of Native Sulphur Deposits* (Moscow: "Nauka" Press, 1964).

Kaplan, J. A., and S. C. Rittenberg. *J. Gen. Microbiol.* 34:195 (1964).

Kemp, A. L. W., and H. C. Thode. *Geochim. et Cosmochim. Acta* 32:71 (1968).

Mekhtieva, V. L., and E. N. Kondratjeva. *Doklady AN USSR* 166: 465 (1966).

Ustinov, V. I., and V. A. Grinenko. *Precise Mass-Spectrometry Technique of Sulphur Isotope Content Definition* (Moscow: "Nauka" Press, 1965).

CHAPTER 11

MICROENVIRONMENTS FOR SULFATE REDUCTION AND METHANE PRODUCTION IN FRESHWATER SEDIMENTS

TH. E. CAPPENBERG
E. JONGEJAN

Limnological Institute "Vijverhof"
Nieuwersluis, The Netherlands

INTRODUCTION

Previous investigations have indicated an ecological relationship between sulfate-reducing and methane-producing bacteria in mud of Lake Vechten (Cappenberg, 1974a,b; 1975;
Cappenberg and Prins, 1974). It was demonstrated that maximum
numbers of the two bacterial groups occur at different depths,
$i.e.$, the sulfate reducers at a depth of 0-2 cm in the mud and
the methanogenics at a depth of 4-6 cm in the mud. Results of
selective inhibition of sulfate-reducing and methanogenic processes in mud samples indicated that lactate is the main source
of energy for sulfate reduction and acetate is the main precursor for methane. From experiments with ^{14}C-labeled substrates
in mud samples and studies of mixed continuous cultures of sulfate-reducing and methane-producing bacteria, a commensalism
between the two species can be described, $i.e.$, the acetate-
fermenting methanogenic benefits from the acetate released by
the sulfate reducer, which is, in turn, not affected in the
presence of the former.
Further information on the breakdown kinetics of lower
fatty acids was needed in our studies of the anaerobic mineralization of organic matter, as part of the carbon cycle in a
lake. These acids, for instance, acetate and lactate, are intermediate metabolites in methanogenesis. Their pool sizes do
not change appreciably in mud and, therefore, the rate of their
dissimilation must equal their rate of formation. The dissimilation rate of an intermediate is the product of the turnover
rate constant and its pool size. Some experiments using radio
gas chromatography as a tool to obtain accurate data in this
respect will be described in this chapter. Emphasis will be

laid on the breakdown pathways of intermediates towards CH_4 and CO_2 in mud in experiments using uniformly and nonuniformly ^{14}C-labeled substrates, and conclusions are drawn from the label distribution between CO_2 and CH_4.

MATERIALS AND METHODS

Mud Sampling

Undisturbed mud cores were taken from the deepest part (12 m) of Lake Vechten by means of a modified Jenkin surface-mud sampler. Subsamples were taken in the laboratory immediately after sampling with a syringe through previously drilled holes 2 mm in diameter in the perspex sampling tubes. The holes were covered with Scotchtape no. 471.

Incubation Technique

The samples were incubated anaerobically at the environmental temperature (8-10°C) in 1.5-ml Suba-Seal-stoppered vials placed in a shaking water bath. The vials were flushed with oxygen-free nitrogen to maintain anaerobic conditions. The nitrogen gas was freed from oxygen by leading it through a column of BASF catalyzer R3-11 at 150°C. At appropriate intervals, the samples were centrifuged at 4000 rpm for 5 min at 0°C, and 25-μl aliquots were taken for ^{14}C-acetate analysis.

Analysis of Acetic Acid

The analysis of acetic acid in aqueous solution was performed on a Packard-Becker 417 gas chromatograph fitted with a flame ionization detector (FID) using helium as the carrier gas. The method used was that of Cochrane (Cochrane, 1975) with some modifications. A 6-ft x 2-mm i.d. glass column loaded with 20% neopentyl-glycol adipate on Chromosorb W-AW-DMCS (80-100 mesh) was used. The carrier gas (24 ml/min) was passed over formic acid (Merck Suprapur) contained in a stainless steel vessel before it entered the column. The following temperatures were chosen: column 115°C, injector 150°C, detector 220°C. A stable baseline was obtained with attenuation setting 4 x 1 (10^{-11} A f.s.d.) and higher. Injections of 10 μl of standard solutions containing from 15 to 240 μmol/l of sodium acetate (corresponding to 0.9 to 14.4 mg/l of acetic acid) were made. A plot of the peak height against the concentration was perfectly linear over the entire range. If necessary, preconcentration of the samples was achieved by evaporation at 120°C.

Analysis of ^{14}C-Labeled Acetic Acid, Carbon Dioxide and Methane

Acetic Acid

The effluent of the gas chromatographic column was divided by a 1:1 splitter into two streams: one leading to the FID, the other via a 1/16"-o.d. stainless steel tube to a Packard 894 gas proportional counter. Optimal results were obtained keeping this connection at ambient temperature. Before entering the counting tube, the organic compounds in the gas stream were oxidized over CuO at 750°C. The total helium gas flow through the counter was increased to 120 ml/min, while 12 ml/min propane was added as quench gas. With a counting range of 1000 cpm and a time constant of 1 s approximately, 1 nCi of ^{14}C-acetate could be measured with a counting efficiency of 70 percent. The signals of the FID and of the proportional counter were recorded on a W+W Tarkan 600 dual channel recorder, while the latter signal was integrated using a Kipp en Zonen BC 1 numerical integrator.

Carbon Dioxide and Methane

Prior to analysis of $^{14}CO_2$ and $^{14}CH_4$, 50 µl of formic acid was added to liberate the dissolved CO_2. The gases were allowed to expand into a 5-ml gas-tight syringe. Gas samples (100 µl) were analyzed with a Perkin-Elmer F 11 gas chromatograph equipped with a katharometer detector. The exit of the detector was connected to the gas proportional counter by a 1/16-in.-o.d. stainless steel tube. If desired, both gas chromatographs could be connected to the gas proportional counter simultaneously. The following conditions were used: column 6 ft x 1/8 in. stainless steel loaded with Porapak Q 50-80 mesh, carrier gas 15 ml/min helium; temperatures: column ambient, injector 100°C, detector 200°C. The labeled substrates were purchased from the Radiochemical Centre, Amersham, England.

RESULTS AND DISCUSSION

Turnover and Breakdown of Acetate

A mud sample (about 1 g) was removed from a mud core at a depth of 5 cm and transferred anaerobically to a 1.5-ml vial. At zero time, 200 µl of 2-^{14}C-acetate (1 µCi/ml) was injected into the vial, the contents were rapidly mixed, and incubated at 10°C. At appropriate times 25-µl aliquots of the supernatant were removed for radio gas chromatographic analysis (see Materials and Method section).

The ^{10}log of the cpm (counts per minute) in the acetate fraction was plotted against time, giving a straight line with a correlation coefficient of 0.955. From this a turnover rate constant (k) was calculated as $k = 0.244 \pm 0.015$ hr^{-1}. An analogous experiment with mud from a depth of 1 cm gave $k = 0.07$ hr^{-1}. The turnover of an intermediate such as acetate is the product of its turnover rate constant and its concentration. Preliminary experiments indicate an acetate concentration of

0.6 mg/l at 5-cm depth and of 0.3 mg/l at 1-cm depth, giving a
turnover of 0.1 mg/l.hr^{-1} and 0.02 mg/l.hr^{-1} respectively.
These findings, pointing to a much higher turnover of acetate
in lower layers in the mud of Lake Vechten, agree with our earlier observation that the maximum abundance of acetate-ferment-
ing methanogenic bacteria is found at a depth of 4-6 cm
(Cappenberg, 1974a,b).

In earlier experiments (Cappenberg, 1976), we studied
the formation of $^{14}CO_2$ and $^{14}CH_4$ from 1-^{14}C-, 2-^{14}C- and U-^{14}C-
acetate in mud. These results are summarized in Table I.

Table I
Label Distribution Between $^{14}CO_2$ and $^{14}CH_4$ from ^{14}C-Acetate
in Mud from a Depth of 5 cm in the Mud Core

Substrate	$F_{CO_2} = \dfrac{^{14}CO_2}{^{14}CO_2 + {}^{14}CH_4}$
1-^{14}C-acetate	0.86 ± 0.03
2-^{14}C-acetate	0.24 ± 0.01
U-^{14}C-acetate[a]	0.57 ± 0.01

[a]U-^{14}C-Acetate is a 1:1 mixture of 1-^{14}C- and 2-^{14}C-acetate.
Therefore, the calculated value of F_{CO_2}, based on the values
from the specifically labeled acetates, is (0.86 + 0.24)/2 =
0.55 ± 0.02, which is in excellent agreement with the observed
value of 0.57 ± 0.01.

From these results it can be concluded that of the methane
formed from acetate, 84 percent originates from the methyl carbon and 16 percent from the carboxyl carbon. Conversely, of
the carbon dioxide formed from acetate, 78 percent originates
from the carboxyl carbon and 22 percent from the methyl carbon.
The formation of methane from the carboxyl carbon of acetate is
probably due to CO_2/H_2-fermenting bacteria, which can use the
CO_2 produced by acetate-splitting bacteria as a substrate. It
is not yet known what kind of organisms play a role in the
anaerobic conversion of the methyl carbon of acetate into CO_2.
By radio gas chromatographic analysis we found that incubation
with $^{14}CH_4$ of mud samples or of pure cultures of *Desulfovibrio
desulfuricans* does not result in formation of $^{14}CO_2$. It is
possible that acetate is converted into two molecules of CO_2
by the anaerobic sulfur-reducing, acetate-oxidizing *Desulfuromonas acetoxidans*, an organism recently isolated by Pfennig
and Biebl (1976). If this occurs in the mud of Lake Vechten,
the following scheme of the breakdown of acetate can be described:

$$CH_3\text{---}CO_2H \xrightarrow{\;k_1\;} CH_4 \quad + \quad CO_2$$

$$\downarrow k_2$$

$$2\ CO_2$$

(with k_3 arrows connecting back to CH_4)

For specifically labeled substrates this leads to the following schemes and relations:

$$CH_3\text{---}{}^*CO_2H \xrightarrow{\;k_1\;} CH_4 \quad + \quad {}^*CO_2$$

$$\downarrow k_2 \qquad\qquad\qquad \downarrow k_3$$

$$CO_2 + {}^*CO_2 \xrightarrow{\;\;\;\;k_3\;\;\;\;} {}^*CH_4$$

with
$$
_1F_{CO_2} = \frac{^{14}CO_2}{^{14}CO_2 + {}^{14}CH_4} = \frac{k_1 + k_2}{k_1 + k_2 - k_3} \cdot \frac{e^{-k_3 t} - e^{-(k_1 + k_2)t}}{1 - e^{-(k_1 + k_2)t}}
$$
(1)

$${}^*CH_3\text{---}CO_2H \xrightarrow{\;k_1\;} {}^*CH_4 \quad + \quad CO_2$$

$$\downarrow k_2 \qquad\qquad \downarrow k_3$$

$${}^*CO_2 + CO_2$$

with
$$
_2F_{CO_2} = \frac{^{14}CO_2}{^{14}CO_2 + {}^{14}CH_4} = \frac{k_2}{k_1 + k_2 - k_3} \cdot \frac{e^{-k_3 t} - e^{-(k_1 + k_2)t}}{1 - e^{-(k_1 + k_2)t}}
$$
(2)

From the relations 1 and 2, it follows that $_1F_{CO_2}/_2F_{CO_2} = 1 + k_1/k_2$. From Table I, at 5 cm depth $_1F_{CO_2}/_2F_{CO_2} = 0.86/0.24 = 3.6$, thus leading to $k_1/k_2 = 2.6 \pm 0.3$. Combination of this result with the turnover rate constant of acetate at 5 cm depth $(k_1 + k_2 = 0.244\ hr^{-1})$ indicates a value of $k = 0.068 \pm 0.009$ hr^{-1} and of $k_2 = 0.18 \pm 0.02\ hr^{-1}$. A value for k_3 can be found by substitution in (1) of the known values for $_1F_{CO_2}$ and $k_1 + k_2$; thus, a $k_3 = 0.24\ hr^{-1}$ is obtained. Alternatively, k_3 can be determined from an experiment wherein mud is incubated with $^{14}CO_2$.

From the above data the following conclusions can be drawn concerning the breakdown of acetate in mud of Lake Vechten at 5 cm depth: one mole of acetate is split into one mole of CH_4 and one mole of CO_2 with $k = 0.068\ hr^{-1}$; one mole of acetate is oxidized to two moles of CO_2 with $k_2 = 0.18\ hr^{-1}$ and one mole of CO_2 is reduced by H_2 to one mole of CH_4 with $k_3 = 0.24\ hr^{-1}$.

We further studied the label distribution between $^{14}CO_2$ and $^{14}CH_4$ in relation to the depth in the mud. Samples from different depths from one mud column were incubated with 2-^{14}C-acetate, and the $^{14}CO_2$ and $^{14}CH_4$ formed were analyzed radio gas chromatographically (see Materials and Methods section). From these results (Figure 1) it is clear that oxidation of the methyl carbon of acetate to CO_2 is more important in the upper layers of the mud. Therefore, it seems likely that part of the carbon of acetate is converted to CO_2 by anaerobic, sulfur-reducing, acetate-oxidizing organisms, as free sulfur is available in the upper layers of the mud in Lake Vechten by oxidation of FeS (personal communication H. Verdouw). Taking into account that the turnover rate constant and the concentration of acetate both increase with depth, it may be concluded that the complete picture of the breakdown of acetate in mud of Lake Vechten is rather complex. Further experiments concerning these aspects are in progress.

Turnover and Breakdown of Lactate

We reported earlier on the formation of $^{14}CO_2$ and $^{14}CH_4$ from U-^{14}C-lactate in mud samples (Cappenberg and Prins, 1974). In an experiment (Cappenberg, 1976) we studied the breakdown of lactate in mud of Lake Vechten. Mud (46 g, upper 5 cm sediment) was incubated at 10°C with 0.0125 µCi Na-U-^{14}C-L-lactate. At appropriate times, 1-2-g samples were drawn and analyzed for lactate and acetate by partition chromatography. Radioactivity was assessed by liquid scintillation counting. The results of this experiment are presented in Figure 2, in which the log of cpm of the acetate and lactate fractions is plotted against time (the cpm value of acetate is multiplied by 1.5 because only 2/3 of the lactate radioactivity can theoretically be present in the acetate fraction).

Apparently lactate is broken down according to first order kinetics with $k = 2.37$ hr^{-1}. The acetate curve shows a rapid formation during the first hour and a slow decrease later on, with a maximum occurring after approximately 2 hours.

If the lactate breakdown can be described according to:

$$\text{lactate} \xrightarrow{\;k_1\;} \text{acetate} \xrightarrow{\;k_2\;} \text{products}$$
$$\quad A \qquad\qquad\qquad B$$

then Equations 3 and 4 are valid.

$$A/A_o = e^{-k_1 t} \tag{3}$$

$$B/A_o = \frac{k_1}{k_1 - k_2} (e^{-k_2 t} - e^{-k_1 t}) \tag{4}$$

with A_o as the lactate activity at $t = 0$. When $k_1 > k_2$,

Equation 4 after some lapse of time is reduced to Equation 5:

$$B/A_o = \frac{k_1}{k_1 - k_2} e^{-k_2 t} \qquad (5)$$

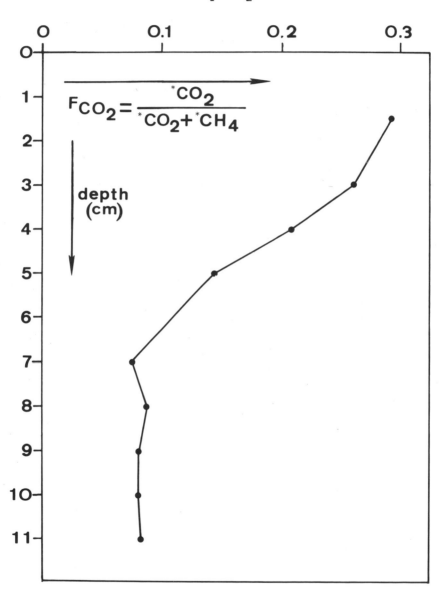

Figure 1. Label distribution between CO_2 and CH_4 $(F_{CO_2} = \frac{{}^*CO_2}{{}^*CO_2 + {}^*CH_4})$ in relation to the depth in the mud after after incubation of mud samples with $2-{}^{14}C$-acetate during 1 h at 10°C.

This means that after some time the acetate curve in Figure 2
must become a straight line with a slope of −0.434 k_2. As can
be seen from Figure 2, this is indeed the case. From the tan-
gent to the acetate curve (−.−.−) we calculate k_2 = 0.48 hr^{-1}.
However, when these values for k_1 and k_2 are substituted into
Equation 4, the resulting curve (....) does not fit the observed

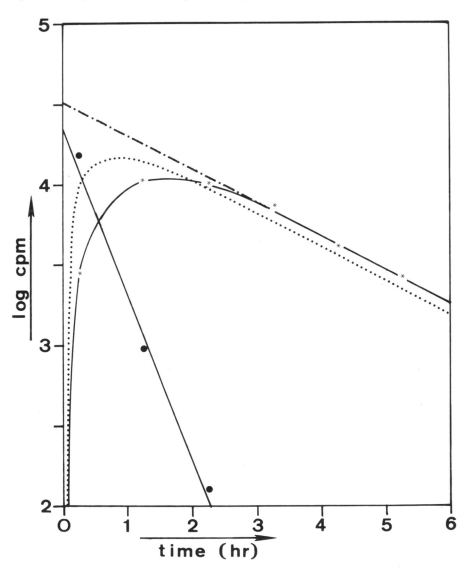

Figure 2.   Breakdown of Na–U–^{14}C–L–lactate in mud.
    •———• = log (cpm) in the lactate fraction
    ——— = log (cpm x 1.5) in the acetate fraction
    •———• = tangent to the acetate curve
    •••••= calculated curve using Equation 4.

values. Notably, the maximum is too high and occurs too early.
The time at which the maximum of the acetate curve is
reached (t_{max}) can be derived from Equation 4 by differentiation. This gives:

$$t_{max} = \frac{\ln k_1/k_2}{k_1 - k_2} \tag{6}$$

If lactate is broken down to acetate and to some other
product simultaneously, then the following set of equations
can be derived:

$$\text{lactate} \xrightarrow{k_1} \text{acetate} \xrightarrow{k_2} \text{products}$$
$$A \qquad\qquad B$$
$$\downarrow k_3$$
$$\text{products}$$

$$A/A_o = e^{-(k_1 + k_3)t} \tag{7}$$

$$B/A_o = \frac{k_1}{k_1 + k_3 - k_2} (e^{-k_2 t} - e^{-(k_1 + k_3)t}) \tag{8}$$

With $(k_1 + k_3) > k_2$, Equation 8 becomes after some time:

$$B/A_o = \frac{k_1}{k_1 + k_3 - k_2} e^{-k_2 t} \tag{9}$$

and

$$t_{max} = \frac{\ln (k_1 + k_3)/k_2}{k_1 + k_3 - k_2} \tag{10}$$

Then from Figure 2 it follows that $k_1 + k_3 = 2.37$
and $k_2 = 0.48$ hr^{-1}. This means that in this case the maximum
in the acetate curve occurs at the same time as in the former
case. Therefore, we conclude that the breakdown of lactate is
more complicated than in these simple models. Further investigation of this problem is necessary to be able to draw more
definite conclusions.
    The gas chromatography gas proportional counting system
described here provides an accurate tool for the simultaneous
analysis of turnover and breakdown of lower fatty acids in bottom deposits, but stresses the complexity of this system. The
data indicate a substrate relationship between sulfate-reducing
and methane-producing bacteria, since labeled methane is obtained from mud incubated with labeled lactate. However, the
kinetic aspects of this phenomenon are difficult to describe
at this moment. Not only is this a kinetically complex system,
but also the kinetic parameters are depth-dependent in the mud.
For instance, the turnover rate constant and concentration of

acetate both increase with depth, and the breakdown of acetate
into CO_2 and CH_4 follows different pathways at various levels
in the mud. Similar phenomena can be expected with the turnover and breakdown of lactate in this habitat. Therefore, one
must be careful in drawing conclusions from the label distribution between CO_2 and CH_4 from the anaerobic breakdown of
complex labeled organic substrates such as glucose and cellulose (*e.g.*, Nelson and Zeikus, 1974; Weng and Jeris, 1976).

REFERENCES

Cappenberg, Th. E. "Interrelations Between Sulfate-Reducing
and Methane-Producing Bacteria in Bottom Deposits of a
Freshwater Lake, I. Field Observations," *Antonie van Leeuwenhoek* 40:285-295 (1974a).

Cappenberg, Th. E. "Interrelations Between Sulfate-Reducing
and Methane-Producing Bacteria in Bottom Deposits of a Freshwater Lake, II. Inhibition Experiments," *Antonie van Leeuwenhoek* 40:297-306 (1974b).

Cappenberg, Th. E. "A Study of Mixed Continuous Cultures of
Sulfate-Reducing and Methane-Producing Bacteria," *Microb.
Ecol.* 2:60-72 (1975).

Cappenberg, Th. E. "Methanogenesis in the Bottom Deposits of
a Small Stratifying Lake," in *Microbial Production and Utilization of Gases (H_2, CH_4, CO)*, Symposium Procedures. H. G.
Schlegel, N. Pfennig and G. Gottschalk, Eds. (Göttingen:
E. Goltze-Verlag, 1976).

Cappenberg, Th. E., and R. A. Prins. "Interrelations Between
Sulfate-Reducing and Methane-Producing Bacteria in Bottom
Deposits of a Freshwater Lake, III. Experiments with [14]C-
labeled Substrates," *Antonie van Leeuwenhoek* 40:457-469 (1974).

Cochrane, G. G. "A Review of the Analysis of Free Fatty Acids
(C_2-C_6), *J. Chrom. Sci.* 13:440-447 (1975).

Nelson, D. R., and J. G. Zeikus. "Rapid Method for the Radioisotopic Analysis of Gaseous End Products of Anaerobic Metabolism," *Appl. Microbiol.* 28:258-261 (1974).

Pfennig, N., and H. Biebl. "*Desulfuromonas acetoxidans* gen.nov.
and sp.nov., a New Anaerobic, Sulfur-Reducing, Acetate-Oxidizing Bacterium," *Arch. Microbiol.* 110:3-12 (1976).

Weng, Cheng-nan, and J. S. Jeris. "Biochemical Mechanisms in
the Methane Fermentation of Glutamic and Oleic Acids,"
Water Res. 10:9-18 (1976).

CHAPTER 12

AMINO ACIDS AS A MEASURE OF ENVIRONMENTAL STRESS: A WINTER STREAM AS A REACTOR MODEL

G. W. HODGSON
B. L. BAKER
S. A. TELANG

The Environmental Sciences Centre
The University of Calgary
Calgary, Alberta, Canada

INTRODUCTION

Environmental stress is a term used to describe natural geochemical processes encountered in a natural system, *e.g.*, a natural water course, to indicate the degree of degradation that might be expected for substances in the stream. As such, it is related to processing capacity, and may be useful in predicting the detailed behavior of substances entering the stream. A variety of stream models have been developed for stream systems in general (Biswas, 1976; Boling *et al.*, 1975; Brebbia, 1976; Cummins, 1974; Harris, 1976; Hynes, 1970; Likens, 1970; Telang *et al.*, 1976; and Williamson *et al.*, 1976). For the present discussion, a model of the stream based primarily in analogy with a chemical process reactor is proposed. In this case, the stream water is pictured as flowing through a reaction chamber characterized by certain conditions of temperature, turbulence, pH, redox and catalysis. Amino acids and other components in the stream are affected by the processing conditions, and the degree of change in the relative abundance of the amino acids presents an integrated measure of the severity of those conditions.

For streams that are active biologically, the reactor may be pictured as having a catalytic surface over which the reactants are carried by the stream flow. This is particularly appropriate when it is recognized that the biological component frequently comprises a layer of sessile bacteria on the stream bed (Telang *et al.*, 1976; Harris and Hansford, 1976). This "catalytic" surface is part of the total reactor system, and

measurements of water quality involving amino acids in the flowing stream present a total view of the environmental stress of
the stream.

MOLECULAR DEPLETION

Consider, as in the case of stable isotope studies
(Krouse, 1974), a reaction involving two reacting species:

$$A \xrightarrow{\quad k_A \quad} products$$
$$B \xrightarrow{\quad k_B \quad} products$$

If $k_A \neq k_B$, a depletion of one of the reactants will occur relative to the other. Using concentration terms, after some exposure to the given environmental stress, a depletion factor
may be written

$$DF_{AB} = \frac{(A/B) \text{ sample} - (A/B) \text{ standard}}{(A/B) \text{ standard}}$$

For convenience of comparison of depletion factors for various
pairs of amino acids, "A" and "B" are assigned as members of a
given pair that are more stable and less stable, respectively.
Accordingly, the depletion-factor scale starts at zero and is
open ended as A/B increases.

The "standard" value for determining the depletion factor
involves knowledge of the ratio of the members of the acid pair
in some closely related circumstances. An appropriate choice
would be the ratio for the major source material, preferably
the biota from which the amino acids are derived, or from some
secondary source material, as in the following sequence:

$$\text{Biota} \longrightarrow \text{Combined amino acids} + \text{free amino acids}$$
$$\text{Combined amino acids} \longrightarrow \text{Free amino acids}$$
$$\text{Free amino acids} \longrightarrow \text{Products.}$$

Since the nature of the original biota was not well known in
the present study, the data for (A/B) standard were taken from
the ratio for individual amino acid pairs in the combined acid
form as measured in the stream waters. Thus, for example, the
depletion factor for the glycine/serine pair was given by

$$DF_{G/S} = \frac{(Gly/Ser) \text{ free} - (Gly/Ser) \text{ combined}}{(Gly/Ser) \text{ combined}}$$

STREAM SYSTEM

The stream in the present study was the Medicine River
of west central Alberta. It is a small tributary (about
35,000 kl per day) of the Red Deer River draining some 220,000

hectares of farmland devoted to cropping and forage production. In addition, a substantial proportion of the drainage region comprises muskeg in which mineral soil is overlaid with accumulations of peat. Figure 1 shows the general location of the river and Table I indicates several qualitative and quantitative aspects of the stream system. The river was examined at four points in a reach of 80 km. Studies of this river system were part of a larger study involving the Red Deer River and a number of other tributaries to that river (Baker *et al.*, 1976).

The data used to illustrate the depletion principle in environmental stress were for a point source in time. Samples of river water were collected at four points in a 24-hr period in midwinter (January 26/27). At that time the stream was almost completely covered with ice. Access to the flowing water was gained by drilling holes through the ice (50 cm thick) using

STUDY AREA

Figure 1. Map of study area--Medicine River drainage basin, central Alberta, Canada

Table I
General Aspects of Medicine River Drainage Basin

| | \multicolumn{4}{c}{Sampling Location} | | | |
Medicine River Drainage Basin—January 27, 1977	Rimbey	Gilby	Benalto	Innisfail
Cumulative Drainage Area (hectares)	40,000	82,000	167,000	220,000
Flow	2.5	5.1	10.3	13.6
Volume of Flow (1)	6.1×10^6	12.5×10^6	25.2×10^6	33.3×10^6
Water Analyses				
DO(mg/1)	10.3	7.9	7.5	2.2
BOD(mg/1)	2.7	1.7	1.3	0.6
COD(mg/1)	26.2	34.0	51.5	32.0
Transport Per Day				
DO(kg)	62.8	98.8	189.0	73.3
BOD(kg)	16.5	21.3	32.8	20.0
COD(kg)	160	425	1289	1066

a power auger.

The general condition of the stream water was that it was unsaturated with oxygen, one of the reasons for selecting this particular stream. Of particular importance is the observation that the dissolved oxygen fell steadily from 10.3 mg/1 (*cf.*, 11 mg/1 for water saturated with oxygen), to 2.2 mg/1, 80 km downstream. It is commonly agreed that undersaturation with oxygen is directly related to high contents of oxygen-consuming organic matter in this particular stream and the nearly complete ice cover which prevented efficient reoxygenation of the water.

AMINO ACID ANALYSES

Amino acids in the sampled stream water were determined by conventional gas chromatographic methods (Telang *et al.*, 1976). The sample was first passed through an ion exchange column to adsorb the free acids. The column eluate was then hydrolyzed to recover the "combined" amino acids. For quantitative estimation, the amino acid fractions were derivatized with *n*-butanol and trifluoroacetic anhydride for analysis by gas chromatography. Peak heights were measured, compared with standards, and reported as μg/1 of river water for the individual amino acids.

RESULTS

Data generated in the amino acid analyses of waters from each of the four sites on the Medicine River, summarized in Table II, indicate that total free amino acids were about 20 µg/1 and combined amino acids were much more abundant at about 100 µg/1. These levels and the ratios between combined and free forms of amino acids agree well with previous studies of waters in the Red Deer River System (Baker *et al.*, 1976) and in the Mackenzie River basin (Peake *et al.*, 1972).

Table II
Summary of Data for Individual Amino Acids
in Medicine River—January 27, 1977
(in µg/1)

Site	Free	Combined	Total
Rimbey	18.6	174.7	193.3
Gilby	20.0	37.2	57.2
Benalto	10.5	64.0	74.5
Innisfail	16.4	72.0	88.4

REACTOR MODEL

The stream system of the Medicine River, with four sampling points (Figure 1), can be conveniently treated as a simple "reactor" model. The model features inputs and outputs, and the processes involved can be inferred from the differences between output and input in the stream.

The basic concept of the model is the mass flow of amino acids in the stream system. Amino acids enter the model section by:

1. being present in the inflowing water of the Medicine River
2. being present in surface runoff and tributary water entering the Medicine River between the sampling points
3. being generated *de novo* in the model section by stream biota, and by
4. being leached or freed from allocthonous substances (leaves, etc.) in the stream.

Similarly, amino acids leave the section by:

1. being carried out by the main stream flow
2. being carried out by water seeping from the stream into the stream bed, recharging subsurface aquifers

3. being converted (degraded) in the stream (for example, by oxidation or metabolism), and by
4. being deposited on the stream bed (for example, on sedimenting particles).

The above system of inputs and outputs refers to both free and combined amino acids.

The analytical data of the present study were treated in terms of the model for an understanding of the processes occurring in the Medicine River. Application was made to a 32-km portion of the Medicine River downstream from Rimbey.

The reactor model was evaluated for the mass flow of several individual amino acids. Thus, for example, the input of combined aspartic acid was calculated, from input concentrations and water flow rates, as 118 g/day. The corresponding input of free aspartic acid was 5 g/day. The measured outputs of combined and free aspartic acid were 70 and 15 g/day, respectively. The local input of aspartic acid was inferred to be 118 and 5 g/day, combined and free respectively, in keeping with the abundance of aspartic acid in the main stream input. From these combined inputs and stream output, it was possible to infer that the local conversion in the 32 km of stream accounted for 154 and 7 g/day of combined and free aspartic acid, respectively.

From corresponding data for five other individual amino acids, it was possible to arrive at the generalized data displayed in Figure 2 for the mass transfer of amino acids in that segment of the Medicine River. In this schematic drawing the data for each of six individual amino acids were normalized to 100 units per day mass inflow of combined acid. The other numerical data in Figure 2 were averages of the corresponding normalized data for each of the other inputs and outputs in the model. The amino acids involved were glycine, phenylalanine, 4-hydroxyproline, aspartic acid, threonine and serine. The The significant findings in the evaluation of this model (keeping in mind its limitations) are: (1) that roughly half of the "combined" amino acid component entering the stream reactor is lost within the reactor, and (2) that free amino acids are generated within the reactor, presumably by conversion (hydrolysis) of combined amino acids.

Further examination of the normalized data revealed that the mainstream output (mass flow) of the individual acids in the combined acids was reasonably constant relative to the input, ranging from 55-68 units for the indicated average of 60 units in Figure 2. On the other hand, as might be expected, the variability in mass flow for free amino acids leaving the reactor was extremely great, with values ranging from 2 to 112 units for the "average" of 40 units shown in Figure 2. This variability was a direct function of the stability of the respective acids, and it led directly to the ranking of the acids presented in Table III. The ranking so developed corresponds

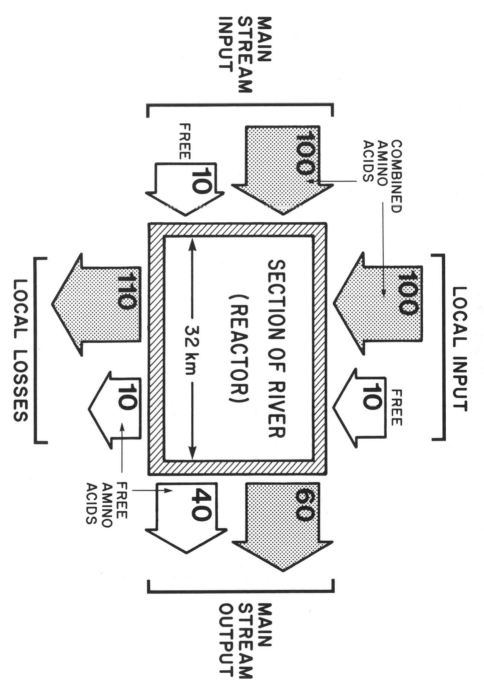

Figure 2. Normalized mass balance for individual amino acids in a winter stream.

Table III
Stability Ranking for Individual Amino Acids
Based on Survival in Stream "Reactor"

	Stream Section		
	I	II	III
Most Stable	4-OH Proline	Phenylalanine	4-OH Proline
	Phenylalanine	Glycine	Phenylalanine
	Glycine	Threonine	Threonine
	Threonine	4-OH Proline	Glycine
	Aspartic acid	Aspartic acid	Aspartic acid
Least Stable	Serine	Serine	Serine

generally with that developed by Abelson (1959), Hare and
Mitterer (1969), Khan and Sowden (1971), and Vallentyne (1969).
        Amino acid data for the other two segments of the stream
produced similar results. The ranking of the individual amino
acids for relative stabilities was confirmed in most cases, as
indicated in Table III. This was true even though the mass
loading of the downstream sections was significantly greater
due to local inputs with appreciably higher concentrations of
combined amino acids.

DEPLETION FACTOR

        The ranking developed by the output of free amino acids
drew particular attention to those and other individual amino
acids. Accordingly, data for a variety of pairs of amino acids
were treated to evaluate the depletion factors for those pairs.
Data for pairs involving alanine, valine, glycine, leucine,
isoleucine, proline, threonine, serine, 4-hydroxyproline, phenylalanine, aspartic acid and glutamic acid were reasonably consistent, while those for sulfur-containing acids tended to be
erratic. Table IV shows typical data for seven pairs of individual amino acids. The results show clearly that some acid
pairs exhibited small but real depletion, *e.g.*, glycine/valine,
while others showed profound changes, *e.g.*, 4-hydroxyproline/
aspartic and threonine/serine.
        The foregoing data in general are demonstrative of the
stream under particular environmental stress, *e.g.*, sharply
restricted oxygen supply and substantial organic load.

Table IV
Depletion Factors for Selected Pairs of Amino Acids
Calculated from Field Data for the Medicine
River Under Ice Cover

Acid Pair	Depletion Factor
4-OH Proline/aspartic acid	7.8
Threonine/serine	6.2
Phenylalanine/aspartic acid	2.6
4-OH Proline/phenylalanine	1.9
Isoleucine/leucine	1.0
Glycine/serine	0.9
Glycine/valine	0.7

ACKNOWLEDGMENTS

The authors wish to acknowledge the technical assistance provided by Jenny Wong and Walter Binder throughout the study. Funding for this project was provided by Environment Canada and Alberta Environment.

REFERENCES

Abelson, P. H. "Geochemistry of Organic Substances," in *Researches in Geochemistry*, P. H. Abelson, Ed. (New York: J. Wiley and Sons, 1959), pp. 79–103.

Baker, B. L., S. A. Telang and G. W. Hodgson. *Organic Water Quality Studies in the Red Deer Basin: Baseline Data for Effects of Dam Construction and Muskeg Leaching* (Calgary: Environmental Sciences Centre [Kananaskis], Publication 76-6, The University of Calgary, 1976).

Biswas, A. K., Ed. *Systems Approach to Water Management* (New York: McGraw-Hill Publishing Company, 1976).

Boling, R. H., F. D. Goodman, J. A. VanSickle, J. O. Zimmer, K. W. Cummins, R. C. Peterson and S. R. Reice. "Towards a Model of Detortus Processing in a Woodland Stream," *Ecology* 56:141–151 (1975).

Brebbia, C. A. "Mathematical Models for Environmental Problems," *Proceedings of the International Conference,* University of Southampton, England, September 8–12 (London: Pentech Press, 1976).

Cummins, K. W. "Structure and Function of Stream Ecosystems," *Biosci.* 24:631–640 (1974).

Hare, P. E., and R. M. Mitterer. "Laboratory Simulation of Amino Acid Diagenesis in Fossils," *Carnegie Inst. Wash. Yearbook* 67:205–210 (1969).

Harris, N. P., and G. S. Hansford. "A Study of Substrate Removal in a Microbial Film Reactor," *Water Res.* 10:935–943 (1976).

Hynes, H. B. N. *The Ecology of Running Waters* (Toronto: University of Toronto Press, 1970).

Khan, S. N., and F. J. Sowden. "Thermal Stabilities of Amino Acid Components of Humic Materials under Oxidative Conditions," *Geochim. Cosmochim. Acta* 35:854–858 (1971).

Krouse, H. R. "Sulfur Isotope Abundances and Environmental Assessment—Application to Sulfur Gas Research in Alberta," *Proceedings of Alberta Sulfur Gas Research Workshop,* Edmonton, November 1973. Northern Forest Research Center Information Report NOC-X-72 (1974).

Likens, G. E., F. H. Bormann *et al.* "Effects of Forest Cutting and Herbicide Treatment on Nutrient Budgets in the Hubbard Brook Watershed Ecosystem, " *Ecol. Monog.* 40:23–47 (1970).

Peake, E., B. L. Baker and G. W. Hodgson. "Hydrogeochemistry of the Surface Waters of the Mackenzie River Drainage Basin, Canada. II. The Contribution of Amino Acids, Hydrocarbons and Chlorines to the Beaufort Sea by the Mackenzie River System," *Geochim. Cosmochim. Acta* 36:867–883 (1972).

Telang, S. A., B. L. Baker, J. W. Costerton and G. W. Hodgson. *Water Quality and Forest Management: the Effects of Clear-Cutting on Organic Compounds in Surface Waters of the Marmot Creek Drainage Basin,* Publication 76-5 (Calgary: The University of Calgary, The Environmental Sciences Centre [Kananaskis], 1976).

Vallentyne, J. R. "Pyrolysis of Amino Acids in Pleistocene Mercenaria Shelf," *Geochim. Cosmochim. Acta* 33:1453–1458 (1961).

Williamson, K., and P. L. McCarty. "A Model of Substrate Utilization by Bacterial Films," *J. Water Poll. Control* 48: 9–24 (1976).

CHAPTER 13

POLLUTION HISTORY OF TRACE METALS IN SEDIMENTS, AS AFFECTED BY THE RHINE RIVER

W. SALOMONS

Delft Hydraulics Laboratory
Delft, The Netherlands

A. J. DE GROOT

Institute for Soil Fertility
Haren (Gr.), The Netherlands

INTRODUCTION

In industrialized countries the trace metal concentrations in fluvial sediments reflect the industrial activity in the drainage areas of the relevant rivers. In Western Europe the river Rhine is an outstanding example of a stream in which large quantities of metals are discharged. In its lower courses the dissolved and particulate metals are transported to some artificial freshwater lakes, which are a result of enclosure works (see Figure 1, Haringvliet and Lake IJssel), to the Rotterdam harbor area, and to the North Sea. In recent years numerous studies have dealt with the concentrations of trace metals in the sediments (De Groot, 1973; De Groot and Allersma, 1975), as well as with the dissolved and particulate trace metals (Duinker *et al.*, 1974; Duinker and Nolting, 1976, 1977). In this chapter we shall describe the development of the trace metal concentrations in the sediments with time and discuss briefly some processes of these metals in freshwater bodies.

OCCURRENCE OF TRACE METALS IN SEDIMENTS

The grain size composition of the sediments in sedimentation areas may vary considerably. Because trace metals are associated with the finely grained particles, a wide range in trace metal concentrations is found, too. The concentrations correlate positively with the amount of finely grained particles,

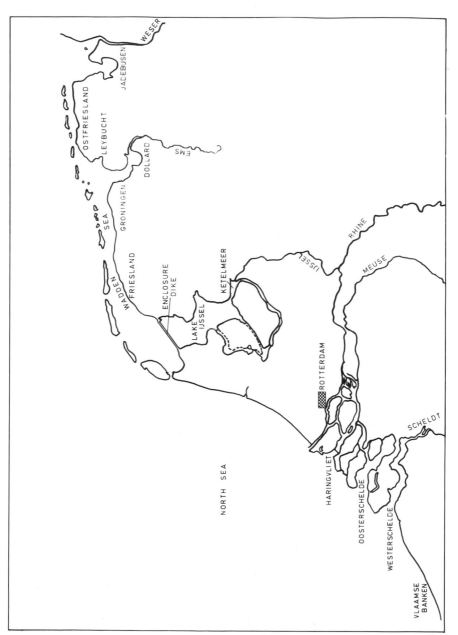

Figure 1.   The area studied.

as expressed by the percentage of particles less than 16 μm in diameter (Figure 2C). The mineralogical composition (Figure 2B) as well as the major element composition (Figure 2A) also correlate with this parameter.

To compare the composition of sediments from different sedimentation areas and to determine the development of trace element concentrations with time, the concentrations at 50% <16 μm will be used. This value corresponds with the mean grain size composition of estuarine sediments from the Rotterdam harbor, a major sedimentation area in The Netherlands.

The distribution of trace metals over the various chemical compounds and minerals in sediments (including discrete minerals, which may be formed by the metals themselves) is described as elemental partition. Various leaching techniques have been used to determine the elemental partition of trace metals in sediments. Our routine procedure consists of two successive extraction procedures by which three different fractions of heavy metals can be distinguished:

1. Acid-reducible fraction. An extraction with 0.1 M hydroxylamine-HCl (pH 2) is carried out. This extraction releases presumably those metals which are associated with hydrous oxides of manganese and those which occur as carbonates, hydroxides and sulfides. By substitution of hydroxylamine-HCl for HCl at the same pH of 2, acetic acid (33%) or a mixture of 1 M hydroxylamine-HCl and 25% (v/v) acetic acid comparable results for the relevant sediments have been found.
2. Acid-oxidizable fraction. An extraction is performed with a solution of hydrogen peroxide (30%) at a pH of 2.5. This extraction probably releases that part of the metals which is associated with organic solids.
3. Resistant fraction. This fraction is obtained by subtracting from the total amount of trace metal in the sample, the amounts found in the two preceding extractions.

Results have been obtained in this respect for the metals manganese, zinc, copper, lead, cadmium and nickel in fluvial sediments from the rivers Rhine, Meuse, Ems and Scheldt and in marine sediments from the Wadden Sea and the Oosterschelde (Figure 3).

Although the distribution of the trace metals over the various fractions is variable, some trends can be recognized. Compared with the fluvial sediments, the trace metals in marine sediments tend to occur to a larger extent in the resistant fraction. The amounts of the trace metals (except Cu), which are associated with the acid-oxidizable fraction, is relatively constant; this trend is quite pronounced in the fluvial sediments.

In both marine and fluvial sediments nickel is predominantly associated with the resistant fraction. Zinc occurs in

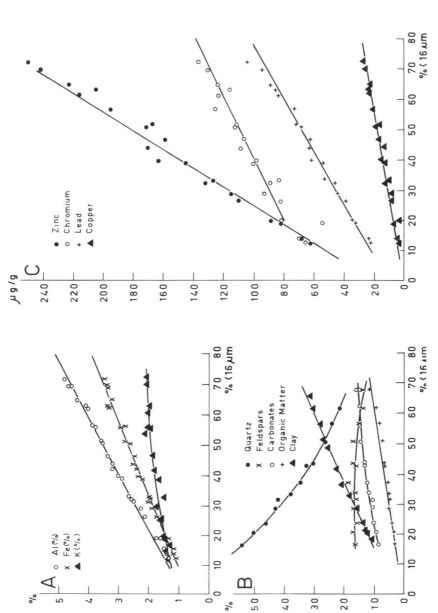

Figure 2. Composition of the sediments studied. Correlations with the amount of finely grained particles in sediments (% < 16 μm) and (A) major element composition, (B) mineralogical composition, (C) trace metal composition.

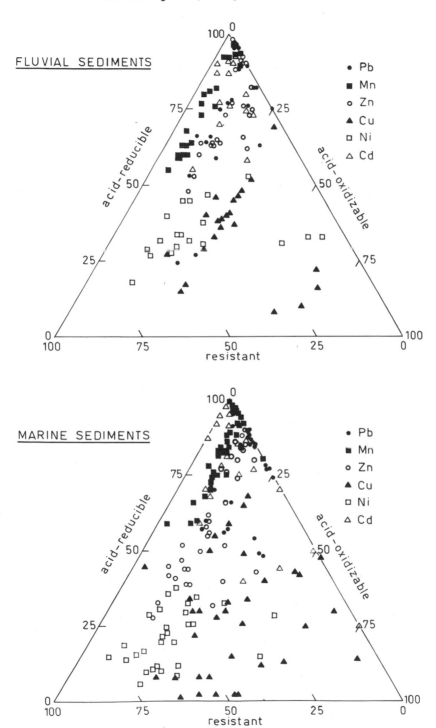

Figure 3. Mode of occurrence of trace metals in fluvial and in marine sediments.

the acid-reducible fraction and partly in the resistant fraction. Lead and cadmium occur mainly in the acid-reducible fraction. The distribution of copper over the various fractions is extremely variable in marine sediments. The data show, however, that this metal appears to be more associated with the acid-oxidizable fraction than the other metals studied.

RESULTS AND DISCUSSION

Generally, the concentrations of trace metals in river sediments reflect the occurrence and abundance of certain rocks or mineralized deposits in the drainage area of the river. At present, however, the anthropogenic input of certain trace metals into the environment equals or exceeds the amounts released by weathering. Often it is difficult to make a direct quantitative estimate of the anthropogenic contribution to the trace metal concentrations in sediments. By analyzing sediments actually collected about 50 years ago, we have been able to trace the development of trace metal concentrations in fluvial, marine and lagoon sediments. Samples from the following three areas have been investigated for trace metals:

1. Fluvial samples from the river Rhine taken on its flood plain in 1922 (Masschaupt and Hissink, 1924). Two areas have been sampled, one area regularly flooded by the Rhine and without vegetation (area A), the other irregularly flooded and grown over with willows (area B). In both areas, samples from depths of 0–25 cm and 25–50 cm had been taken. The regularly flooded area represents the most recent material; the layer 0–25 cm was deposited probably around 1920. The samples from the irregularly flooded area were deposited close to the beginning of the 20th century.
2. Marine sediments from the Dollard (Figure 1) collected in 1921. Both the tidal flat and the salt marsh have been sampled up to depths of 100 cm (Masschaupt, 1923). No differences in trace metal concentrations were found along the profiles and between the tidal flat and salt marsh samples.
3. Lagoon sediments from the Zuiderzee, sampled in 1933.

Trace Metals in Sediments from the River Rhine

The development of trace metal concentrations in sediments from the river Rhine could be studied by means of samples collected on its flood plain in 1922 and of bottom sediments collected in 1958, 1970 and 1975. Additionally, soil samples have been analyzed from polders reclaimed in 1788 and in the 15th and 16th centuries. The results of the analyses are given in Table I.

If we take into account the spread in the calculated

Table I

Trace Metal Concentrations in µg/g (values at 50% < 16 µm)
in Sediments from the River Rhine

	Cu	Zn	Ni	Pb	Cr	Cd	Hg	As
Rhine Polders Reclaimed in:								
15th–16th century	21	93	33	31	77	0.5	0.14	12.2
1788	25	100	39	29	85	0.3	0.21	12.5
River Flood Plain Sampled in 1922:								
Area A 0–25 cm	68	1051	36	273	107	4.4	2.6	45.9
25–50 cm	69	779	32	232	106	4.7	–	–
Area B 0–25 cm	41	378	36	141	84	1.6	0.91	32.7
25–50 cm	33	174	36	87	85	0.7	–	–
Bottom Sediments Sampled in:								
1958	294	2420	54	533	642	14	10.5	198
1970	323	1855	62	447	785	27	14.5	136
1975	325	1905	81	399	820	31	10.1	54

values, which in this case is about 10 percent, the differences
in trace metal concentrations between the two polders is not
significant (Table I). With the exception of copper, the trace
metal concentrations are comparable with those found in sediments from the Dollard (1921) and from the Zuiderzee (1933).
As can be concluded from Table II the similarity suggests that
these concentrations are close to the original contents in Rhine
sediments and may be regarded as a baseline level.

The samples from the river flood plain have high concentrations of copper, zinc, lead, cadmium and mercury. The nickel and chromium values are close to the baseline. Apparently,
the concentrations of copper, zinc, lead, cadmium and mercury
were already anthropogenically influenced at that time. This
fact is further substantiated by the variations in trace metal
concentrations with depth and by the differences between the
younger depositions area A and the overgrown area B. With increasing age of the sediments the trace metal concentrations
decrease. We may conclude, therefore, that already in the beginning of the 20th century the river Rhine was polluted with
a considerable number of trace metals.

Between 1920 and 1958 all trace element concentrations
studied have increased in the sediments from the river Rhine
(Figure 4). Between 1958 and 1975 this rise in the concentrations continued for cadmium, phosphorus, copper and chromium.
The concentrations of lead, zinc and mercury, however, decreased,
and the concentration of copper tended to level off. The de-
cline in the arsenic concentrations is striking, and is probably caused by a ban on the use of arsenic-containing pesti-
cides.

The anthropogenic contribution to the total metal concentrations in sediments from the Rhine exceeds the background
value by an order in magnitude, in some cases. It can even be
estimated that less than 1 percent of the cadmium found in
Rhine sediments in 1975 originated from natural sources.

Trace Metals in Nearshore Sediments

Nearshore sediments have been sampled along the Belgian,
the Dutch and part of the German coast. The localities sampled are shown in Figure 1. Sources for the sediments in this
area are the rivers Rhine, Meuse and Scheldt, as well as material transported by a northward current through the English
Channel. The overall transport of sediments in the coastal
areas of Belgium and The Netherlands is directed to the north.
The contribution of fluvial material to the sediments deposited in the nearshore environment is relatively small (Salomons,
1975; Salomons et al., 1975).

The trace metal concentrations (values at 50% < 16 µm)
in the relevant sediments are given in Table II and shown for
some metals in Figure 5. The metal contents in the Dollard
sediments from 1921 can be regarded as baseline levels in this

Table II
Trace Metal Concentrations in µg/g (values at 50% < 16 µm)
in Near Shore Sediments and in Sediments from
Lake IJssel (Zuiderzee)[a]

	Cu	Zn	Ni	Pb	Cr	Cd
Wadden Sea						
Dollard 1921	10	88	26	32	74	0.3
Dollard 1958	24	150	27	47	85	0.7
Dollard 1975	10	135	27	45	91	0.6
Groningen 1957	25	175	21	65	100	0.6
Groningen 1970	17	180	22	68	105	0.9
Groningen 1975	22	160	25	67	92	0.9
Friesland 1958	29	235	22	80	100	0.8
Friesland 1970	32	250	29	86	115	0.9
Leybucht 1975	18	140	27	53	89	0.6
Ost-Friesland 1969	17	150	25	55	104	0.6
Jadebusen 1969	13	125	25	43	88	0.4
Southern Areas						
Oosterschelde	25	160	25	55	90	0.9
Westerschelde	29	170	23	62	97	1.0
Vlaamse Banken	26	190	19	75	92	0.6
Zuiderzee (Lake IJssel)						
1933	19	133	39	39	88	0.4
1974	39	460	37	88	106	2.8

[a]The sampled localities are shown in Figure 1.

respect. Except for Cu, these values are close to the metal contents that were regarded as baseline levels for the river Rhine (compare Rhine polders in Table I). Compared with the Dollard sediments from 1921, the chromium and nickel concentrations in 1970 increased only slightly. The concentrations of cadmium, zinc, lead and copper, on the other hand, increased considerably.

No clear-cut trend in trace metal concentrations is observed during the last 20 years in the Wadden Sea area. A slight increase is found in Friesland, whereas the concentrations remained at a constant level in the Dollard and in the Groningen area. The concentrations found in the areas south of the Rhine-Meuse estuary (Oosterschelde, Westerschelde and Vlaamse Banken) are comparable to those found in the Groningen area. The trace metal concentrations in the Dutch Wadden Sea

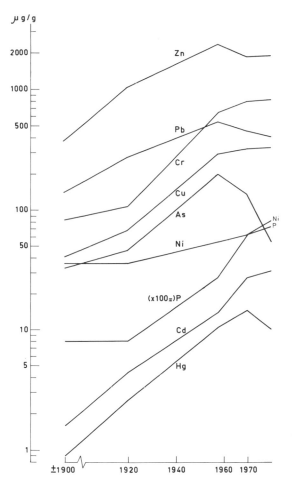

Figure 4.   History of
trace metals in
Rhine sediments.

decrease in an easterly direction (Figure 2), apparently caused
by a diminishing influence of the river Rhine.   A similar trend
is found along the German coast (Leybucht, Ost-Friesland and
Jadebusen).

Several processes are responsible for the relatively
small increase, as compared with the river Rhine, in trace metal concentrations:

1.   The sediments from the river Rhine, the most important
     source of highly contaminated sediments, are deposited
     for the greater part in the Rotterdam harbor area and
     in the artificial freshwater lakes.   The sediments from
     the Rotterdam harbors are continuously dredged and used
     partly for landfilling.   The latter sediments and those
     deposited in the Haringvliet and in Lake IJssel are taken
     out of the "system" permanently.
2.   Studies on the origin of sediments found in the Wadden
     Sea area have shown that the rivers Rhine and Meuse are

not the major source for these sediments (Salomons, 1975; Salomons *et al.*, 1975). In the North Sea the contaminated fluvial sediments are mixed with large amounts of relatively clean marine sediments.

3. In the Wadden Sea area an erosion and mixing of older, relatively uncontaminated sediments with more recent polluted material takes place, causing a dilution of trace metal contents.

4. The erosion of deposited layers and the subsequent release of heavy metals, which are present in the pore waters, to the surface water may also contribute to a decrease in the heavy metal contents of the sediments (Duinker *et al.*, 1974).

Trace Metals in Lake IJssel (Zuiderzee)

Lake IJssel came into existence in 1933, when the Zuiderzee was shut off from the Wadden Sea by the Enclosure Dike. Since then the lake's main source for sediments is the river IJssel, a distributary of the Rhine. The water discharge of the river IJssel is estimated at 8.5 km^3/yr, the sediment load at 400,000 tons/yr, and the water discharge of Lake IJssel to the Wadden Sea is about 12 km^3/yr. The residence time of the water in the lake is about six months. The main depositional area for the contaminated sediments of the river IJssel is the Ketelmeer (Figure 1); the remainder is spread out over the

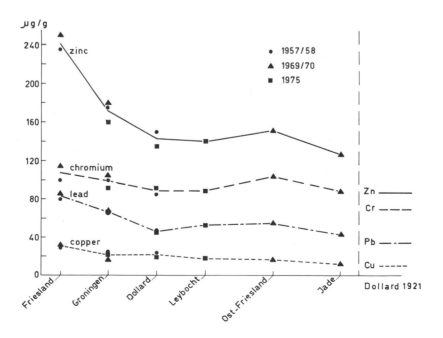

Figure 5.   Trace metals in the Wadden Sea.

lake. The shallowness of the lake allows frequent erosion of
bottom sediments to occur. The recent, contaminated sediments
are mixed intensively with the older sediments. Consequently,
hardly any gradients in trace metal concentrations in the sediments of Lake IJssel are found.

The pH of the water in the lake increases from about 7.2
(river IJssel) to more than 8.5 at the Enclosure Dike. Two
processes are responsible for this. First, the partial pressure
of CO_2 in river water from the IJssel exceeds the partial pressure of CO_2 in the atmosphere. As a consequence, in the
Ketelmeer and in Lake IJssel the excess of carbon dioxide escapes to the atmosphere, giving rise to an increase in pH.
Second, the high phosphorus load of the river IJssel causes algal blooms in Lake IJssel. The consumption of CO_2 by these
organisms causes an additional rise in the pH. The latter process is probably the most important.

Due to the high pH of Lake IJssel, calcium carbonate
precipitates. The stable carbon isotopic composition of these
newly formed carbonates differs from that of the carbonates in
the sediments from the river IJssel, as can be seen from the
data in Table III. In this way the carbon isotopic composition
can be used to distinguish between sediments from Lake IJssel
and those from the river IJssel.

Hydrodynamical and geochemical processes, as described
before, determine trace metal concentrations in Lake IJssel.
In order to illustrate these processes, we will discuss the
trace metal concentrations in sediments from the Ketelmeer
(the interface between the river IJssel and Lake IJssel).

If the dissolved and particulate trace metals behave
conservatively and if there is no transport of sediments from
Lake IJssel into the Ketelmeer, the composition of the sediments
in the Ketelmeer will be similar to that of the Rhine. However,
both in 1972 and in 1974 this was not the case (Table III).
The stable carbon isotopic composition of the carbonates of the
sediments sampled in 1972 shows that these are derived mainly
from the river IJssel (Rhine). The concentrations of cadmium,
zinc and nickel are higher than expected, whereas the concentrations of chromium, lead and copper are lower. The low

Table III
Trace Metal Concentrations in the Ketelmeer and Lake IJssel
(Rhine 1970 = 100). The Stable Carbon Isotopic
Composition of the Carbonates in the Rhine is
$-2.7 \pm +0.4$.

	Cu	Zn	Ni	Pb	Cr	Cd	$\delta^{13}_{PDB} (^o/oo)$
Ketelmeer 1972	92	114	111	81	86	115	-2.6
Ketelmeer 1974	62	90	100	54	56	89	-1.4
Lake IJssel 1974	12	25	63	20	13	10	$+0.8 \pm 1.0$

concentrations for these latter metals are probably caused by a small admixture of sediments from Lake IJssel. In 1974 the stable carbon isotopic composition shows that the sediments are composed of about equal mixtures of sediments from the lake and from the river. This mixing ratio explains the concentrations of copper, chromium and nickel. However, the concentrations of zinc, cadmium and nickel are higher.

Detailed investigations in progress (Salomons, unpublished results; Duinker, personal communication) show significant decreases in the concentrations of some dissolved trace metals. Apparently, adsorption or precipitation processes are taking place. These processes are able to influence the composition of the sediments only if a large part of a trace metal is transported in solution. The metals chromium and lead are transported for about 20 percent in solution; adsorption of these metals onto the sediments influences their composition only to a small extent. The concentrations of chromium and lead, therefore, could be explained by a simple mixing of sediments from the river IJssel with sediments from Lake IJssel.

Copper, cadmium, zinc and nickel, on the other hand, are transported for 40, 50, 60 and 70 percent, respectively, in solution. An adsorption of these metals causes a significant increase in the concentrations in the sediments. This increase is indeed found for cadmium, zinc and nickel, but not for copper. This discrepancy is probably caused by the dependence of the adsorption process on the pH.

Laboratory experiments have shown that the adsorption of zinc (O'Conner and Renn, 1964; Murray and Murray, 1973) and of cadmium and nickel (Salomons, unpublished results) is strongly dependent upon pH, especially over the pH range observed in the Ketelmeer and Lake IJssel. The adsorption of copper, however, is not dependent upon the pH between pH values of 7 and 9, which is the range observed in Lake IJssel (O'Conner and Kester, 1975; Grimme, 1968).

The results of these laboratory experiments are in qualitative agreement with the metal concentrations observed in the Ketelmeer. It appears from our data that the carbon cycle of Lake IJssel and of the Ketelmeer determines, indirectly, the concentrations of metals in the surface waters and in the sediments.

REFERENCES

Duinker, J. C., and R. F. Nolting. "Dissolved and Particulate Trace Metals in the Rhine Estuary and the Southern Bight," *Marine Poll. Bull.* 8:65-69 (1977).

Duinker, J. C., and R. F. Nolting. "Distribution Model for Particulate Trace Metals in the Rhine Estuary, Southern Bight and Dutch Wadden Sea," *Neth. J. Sea Res.* 10:71-102 (1976.

Duinker, J. C., G. T. M. van Eck, and R. F. Nolting. "On the Behaviour of Copper, Zinc, Iron and Manganese and Evidence for Mobilization Processes in the Dutch Wadden Sea," *Neth. J. Sea Res.* 8:214-239 (1974).

Grimme, H. "Die adsorption von Mn, Co, Cu und Zn durch Goethit aus verdünnten Lösungen," *Z. Pflanzenernähr. Düng. Bodenkunde* 121:58-65 (1968).

Groot, A. J. de. "Occurrence and Behaviour of Heavy Metals in River Deltas with Special Reference to the Rivers Rhine and Ems," *North Sea Science,* M.I.T. Press, 308-325 (1973).

Groot, A. J. de, and E. Allersma. "Field Observations on the Transport of Heavy Metals in Sediments," *Prog. Water Technol.* 7:85-95 (1975).

Maschhaupt, J. G. "Verslag van een onderzoek naar de gesteldheid van den bodem in den Dollard met het oog op inpoldering. Bijdragen tot de kennis van de Provincie Groningen en omgelegen streken," *Nieuwe Reeks, Tweede druk* (1923).

Maschhaupt, J. G., and D. J. Hissink. "Gesteldheid van den bodem in den Zuid-Hollandschen Biesbosch," *Versl. Landbouwk. Onderz.* 24:110-136 (1924).

Murray, C. N., and L. Murray. "Adsorption-Desorption Equilibria of some Radionuclides in Sediment-Fresh Water and Sediment-Seawater Systems," in *Radioactive Contamination of the Marine Environment,* IAEA Vienna, 105-124 (1973).

O'Conner, T. P., and D. R. Kester. "Adsorption of Copper and Cobalt from Fresh and Marine Systems," *Geochim. Cosmochim. Acta* 39:1531-1543 (1975).

O'Conner, J. T., and C. E. Renn. "Soluble-Adsorbed Zinc Equilibrium in Natural Waters," *J. Am. Water Works Assoc.* 56:1055-1061 (1964).

Salomons, W. "Chemical and Isotopic Composition of Carbonates in Recent Sediments and Soils from Western Europe," *J. Sediment. Petrol.* 45:440-449 (1975).

Salomons, W., P. Hofman, R. Boelens and W. G. Mook. "The Oxygen Isotopic Composition of the Fraction less than 2 microns (Clay Fraction) in Recent Sediments from Western Europe," *Mar. Geol.* 18:M23-M28 (1975).

SECTION III

SHALLOW PHOTIC WATERS AND SEDIMENTS WITH SPECIAL
REFERENCE TO STROMATOLITIC ENVIRONMENTS

CHAPTER 14

BIOGEOLOGIC RELATIONSHIPS OF ANCIENT
STROMATOLITES AND MODERN ANALOGS

STANLEY M. AWRAMIK
CONRAD D. GEBELEIN

  Department of Geological Sciences
  University of California
  Santa Barbara, California 93106 USA

PRESTON CLOUD

  U.S. Geological Survey and
  Department of Geological Sciences
  University of California
  Santa Barbara, California 93106 USA

INTRODUCTION

        Much that has been written about stromatolites sought
the application of models developed from studies of modern stromatolites and their analogs to the ancient stromatolitic record.
However, the Recent, particularly in regard to stromatolites,
is not an exact replica of the past (Hoffman, 1973, p. 188).
Several features in the history of stromatolites are unlike
known Recent stromatolite phenomena: (1) complex branching patterns in columnar stromatolites as seen in *Linella* Krylov and
Jacutophyton Shapovalova; (2) conical-columnar stromatolites
with diameters approaching 10 m (Donaldson, 1976); (3) stromatolitic bioherms tens of meters thick and biostroms traceable
for tens of kilometers; (4) an abundance and distribution of
stromatolites during the Paleophytic (Cloud, 1976). Nevertheless, studies on presently forming stromatolites and their analogs provide us with an observational framework within which to
understand and interpret ancient stromatolites (Table I).
        The study of ancient stromatolites is a science of form,
and has depended on the interpretation of morphology based on
modern analogs. In order to provide a workable framework for
this interpretation, we will review present understanding of

Table I
Biogeology of Ancient and Recent Stromatolites

	Recent	Ancient (observed)	Ancient (inferred)
Biology			
Built by blue-green algae	yes	yes	yes
Bacteria present	yes	yes	yes
Eucaryotes present	yes	yes	?
Vertical differentiation	yes	no	?
High diversity	yes	yes	?
Dominated by few species	yes	yes	?
Environmental Setting			
Normal marine	yes	yes	yes
Hypersaline marine	yes	yes	yes
Lagoonal marine	yes	yes	yes
Depth below photic zone	yes	?	yes
Marsh	yes	yes	yes
Freshwater lakes	yes	?	?
Alkaline lakes	yes	yes	yes
Streams	yes	yes	yes
Thermal springs	yes	?	no
Terrestrial environment	no	no	?
Intertidal	yes	yes	yes
Supratidal	yes	yes	yes
Subtidal	yes	yes	yes
Mechanism of Formation			
Trapping and binding	yes	yes	yes
Mineral precipitation	yes	yes	yes
No detritus (bio-mat)	yes	?	?
Composition			
Carbonate	yes	yes	yes
Silicoclastic	yes	yes	yes
Organic matter	yes	?	?
Microstructure			
Biologically influenced	yes	yes	yes
Abiologically influenced	no	?	?
Combination of above	?	?	?
Macrostructure			
Biologically influenced	yes	yes	yes
Abiologically influenced	yes	yes	yes
Combination of above	?	?	yes

the microbiology, ecology, composition, distribution, microstructure, macrostructure and morphogenesis of Recent biogenic
stromatolites, their analogs, and how these factors apply to
the biogeologic record.

RECENT BIOGENIC STROMATOLITES AND THEIR ANALOGS

Biogenic analogs to ancient stromatolites are known to
be forming in a variety of Recent environments (Figure 1;
Serebryakov, 1975; Golubic, 1976; Semikhatov *et al.*, in preparation). Cardinal to our present understanding of stromatolites are the modern analogs forming in Shark Bay, Bermuda,
southern Florida, Bahamas, Persian Gulf, and Yellowstone National Park. Twelve generalizations emerge from studies of these
areas.

1. Biogenic stromatolites and algal mats are produced
by the growth and metabolic activity of blue-green algae (cyanophytes or cyanobacteria) with local eucaryotic or bacterial associates. Eucaryotic algae can participate in algal mat formation, particularly in subtidal or permanently submerged environments (Hommeril and Rioult, 1965; Gebelein, 1969; Neumann
et al., 1970; Horodyski *et al.*, in press; Playford and
Cockbain, 1976). Bacteria are commonly viewed as decomposers
of accreted algal mat organics (Golubic, 1973). The role of
bacteria in "algal" mat growth is poorly understood. Bacteria
contribute to formation of laminae at the surface of some biomats and can actually form additional laminae at depth within
an accreted mat (Doemel and Brock, in press). These pioneering
studies and subsequent studies on the role of bacteria in algal
mat growth and laminae formation may alter some of our prior
widely held assumptions. But although algal mats can be built
by diverse procaryotes and eucaryotes, it does appear that blue-
green algae dominate in their construction.

2. Many algal mat and stromatolite building communities
are vertically differentiated along microenvironmental gradients,
with cyanophytes at the top and bacteria at the bottom of laminae (Sorensen and Conover, 1962; Golubic, 1973). Within aerobic portions of an algal mat lamina, biological stratification of the microbiota occurs along physical and chemical gradients within the lamina (Golubic, 1973, p. 457).

3. The diversity of species in Recent algal mats and
stromatolites may approach 50 (Golubic, 1976) but the community
is usually dominated by one or a few species (Golubic, 1973).
Many of the subordinate species live within the mat, while
others may simply be washed in and deposited there. "Inflated"
diversities may also be a product of vertical differentiation.
An algal mat is a miniature ecosystem. During its early growth
and development, an alga or some algae (usually a low diversity)
establish themselves on a substrate. Through the growth and
development of these pioneer species, a modified microenvironment is created below the surface mat in which other microorganisms

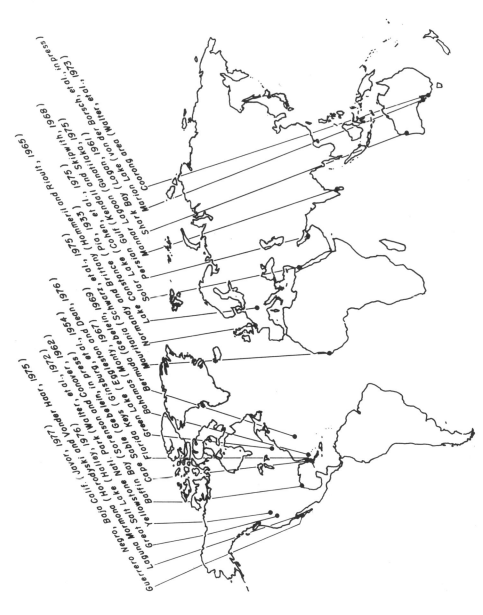

Figure 1.   General distribution of some Recent biogenic stromatolites and their analogs.

grow. Algae at the fluid-biosediment interface probably are the microorganisms critical to the understanding of stromatolite shape, for they respond most readily to prevailing environmental factors.

4. Microstructure refers to grain-to-grain and crystal-to-crystal relationships, lamina thickness, relief along a single lamina (amplitude) and the distribution of organic matter and elements associated with organic matter (Semikhatov *et al.*, in preparation). It is controlled by the microbiota of the mat, and as Gebelein (1974, pp. 579-581) has pointed out, it appears that the surface algae (at the fluid-biosediment interface) are responsible for the nature of the trapped and bound particles, their grain-to-grain relationships and relief along a single lamina. Changes in lamina morphology may occur at depth with microbial growth, increasing laminar thickness (Monty, 1976, p. 219) and crystal-to-crystal relationships or altering grain-to-grain relationships by microbial activity.

5. The chemical and physical limits and tolerances of cyanophytes and bacteria-producing Recent stromatolites and biomats are extremely wide (Brock, 1976, p. 142).

6. Recent biogenic analogs, although most commonly found in environments of carbonate sedimentation, are not restricted to them but are also found in silicoclastic regions (Walter, Bauld and Brock, 1972, 1976; Horodyski and Vonder Haar, 1975; Schwarz *et al.*, 1975).

7. All known environments for biogenic stromatolite formation are aqueous. Stromatolite analogs have been reported from shallow normal marine (Gebelein, 1969); shallow hypersaline to periodically exposed marine (Logan, 1961; Logan, Hoffman and Gebelein, 1974); lagoonal marine (Horodyski and Vonder Haar, 1975); freshwater marsh (Monty, 1967); meromictic lakes (Eggleston and Dean, 1976); saline lakes (Eardley, 1938; Halley, 1976); streams (Golubic and Fischer, 1975); and thermal springs (Walter, Bauld and Brock, 1972). Stromatolites and modern analogs formed by biogenic processes appear to require some period of aqueous submergence or wetting; they are not known from exclusively terrestrial environments (that is, without the action of water).

8. Nonmarine stromatolite analogs commonly lithify while growing (Monty, 1971, 1973). Marine analogs may lithify during or after growth.

9. Algal mats and stromatolites flourish in environments that exclude or restrict metazoans and higher plants (Brock, 1967; Garrett, 1970; Monty, 1973). Eucaryotic algae outcompete blue-green algae under some specific circumstances (Monty, 1973). The prevalence of blue-green algae vs eucaryotic algae may be a function of the chemical environment such as salinities and pH but also allelopathy. Precipitation and mineral matter forming hard structures during growth eliminate burrowing activity by organisms unable to penetrate a hard substrate and seriously affect destruction by higher plants and

turbulence. Endoliths, however, become active.
    10. Algal communities forming stromatolite analogs in
intertidal zones are commonly arranged on a sloping surface
perpendicular to the shoreline along desiccation gradients
(Logan, Hoffman and Gebelein, 1974). These communities, their
horizontal zonation, and their microstructure are similar in
comparable environments (Gebelein, 1974, in press; Golubic and
Awramik, 1974).
    11. As presently understood, macrostructure in Recent
stromatolite analogs is dominantly controlled by the degree of
turbulence or other physical factors with little control exercised by the component microbiology (Gebelein, 1969; Logan,
Hoffman and Gevelein, 1974). However, morphogenesis of some
small-scale macrostructure, domes and columns, a few centimeters
to millimeters in size, can be a consequence of the biological
growth habit of the algae (Golubic, 1973, 1976; Walter, Bauld
and Brock, 1976). Thus, an interplay of biological controls on
microstructure and small-scale macrostructure with environmentally controlled macrostructure no doubt occurs, but too little
data are yet available to assess the relative significance of
these different factors.
    12. In addition to ecological succession on a micro-
scale as outlined in generalization 3, algal mats may be part
of a larger ecological succession that results in substrate
stabilization by algae, followed by halophytes and subsequent
plant communities as seen in lagoons along the west coast of
Baja California, Mexico. The final stage in such a succession
would be plants whose roots and attendant animal burrowers would
destroy much and perhaps all evidence of algal mat activity.

ANCIENT STROMATOLITES

    The preceding section on modern stromatolites and their
analogs emphasizes data relevant to our understanding of stromatolites in the past. This section on ancient stromatolites combines the results of this analysis with data from the geologic
record to advance further toward the same end. Our discussion
of ancient stromatolites relies heavily on the pre-Phanerozoic
record primarily because we are most familiar with it. Reports
that deal with the distribution, associations and stratigraphic
succession of pre-Phanerozoic stromatolites are too numerous to
summarize here (see Bibliography compiled by Awramik *et al.*,
1976), but they establish that stromatolites are known from
every major nondeformed unmetamorphosed pre-Phanerozoic plat-
form deposit. We believe there are 12 generalizations indicated by these records.
    1. Ancient stromatolites are presumed to be entirely or
almost entirely of biogenic origin based on comparison with
Recent analogs. Indeed, blue-green algae are inferred to be
the dominant stromatolite builder (for a review see Awramik,
in press). In rare instances where microfossils are preserved

in silicified ancient stromatolites, the most abundant forms
have been considered to be blue-green algae. Microfossils interpreted as eucaryotes are infrequently found in ancient stromatolitic laminae (Awramik *et al.*, 1976). Fossil morphotypes
interpreted as bacteria are also known (Schopf and Blacic, 1971;
Awramik and Barghoorn, in press), but their role in the processes associated with stromatolitic growth or degradation is not
known. Walter *et al.* (1972) and Doemel and Brock (in press)
have postulated that photosynthetic bacteria may have played a
major role in the construction of early pre-Phanerozoic stromatolites. Although appealing, this claim remains unsubstan-
tiated and is inconsistent with our present understanding of
the prevalent microorganisms and processes affecting the formation of stromatolites.

2. Fairchild (in press) was unable to detect any evidence of vertical differentiation of microbial components within the lamina of the Boorthanna stromatolitic cherts. Awramik
(unpublished) has repeatedly searched for evidence of this
phenomenon in stromatolitic cherts from the Gunflint Iron Formation, Beck Spring Dolomite, and Bitter Springs Formation with
no encouraging results. Were ancient stromatolite-building
microbial communities vertically differentiated? We do not
know.

3. Microbial diversity in ancient stromatolites paral-
lels that found in modern analogs (Awramik *et al.*, 1976). Microbial population diversity studies within individual stromatolites are known only from: (a) the Gunflint stromatolites
in which 2 morphotypes constitute over 95 percent of the microbiota with 12 other morphotypes occurring in minor abundance
(Awramik, 1976; Awramik and Barghoorn, in press) and (b)
Vendian *Conophyton gaubitza* from South Kazakstan (Schopf and
Sovietov *et al.*, 1976). Studies on ancient microbiotas have
been concerned primarily with the documentation of the presence
of different morphotypes, not with their relative abundances
or as components of a microbial population.

4. Some distinctive microstructures found in ancient
stromatolites are interpreted with good reason as biologically
controlled (Komar, 1964, 1975; Gebelein, 1974; Serebryakov,
1976). Distinctive microstructures in columnar and stratiform
stromatolites of the Gunflint Iron Formation contain correspondingly well-defined microbial communities (Awramik and
Semikhatov, in preparation). Preliminary data from the Gunflint, plus other observations on the spatial and temporal
distribution of distinctive microstructures (Semikhatov *et al.*,
in preparation), is consistent with an interpretation that microbiology controls stromatolite microstructure. We must warn,
however, that in such studies great care must be exercised to
discriminate between primary, probably diagenetic, and secondary microstructure.

5. We have no observable data to indicate the chemical
and physical limits on microbial existence during the geological

past. We must rely on data from Recent environments.

     6. Ancient stromatolites are common in carbonate sequences. Rare instances are known of primary mainly noncarbonate stromatolites [Ordovician (Davis, 1968), and the Lower Cambrian Puerto Blanco Formation, Sonora, Mexico (Cloud and Semikhatov, in preparation)]. It is unknown whether the silicified stromatolites from the Gunflint Iron Formation, Paradise Creek Formation and some other localities are primary or whether they were initially carbonate that was replaced by silica during diagenesis.

     7. Available evidence on fossil stromatolites indicates formation under aqueous conditions in normal marine (Playford et al., 1976), shallow, hypersaline to periodically exposed marine (Tucker, 1976), lagoonal marine (Termier et al., 1975), perhaps freshwater marsh (Hoffman, 1976), and lakes (Surdam and Wray, 1976).

     8. Stromatolites of limestone or dolomite predominate in ancient deposits, and examples have been cited to support lithification during growth of marine examples (Playford et al., 1976). Presumably the precipitation and binding of carbonate sediments by stromatolite-building blue-green algae occurred in pre-Phanerozoic marine environments and Cenozoic nonmarine environments (see Monty, 1973).

     9. Destruction of algal mats by browsing metazoans and roots of vascular plants did not apply in the pre-Phanerozoic. However, during the Phanerozoic, available paleoecological data indicate that diverse and abundant metazoans rarely coexisted with stromatolites, a relationship that holds for the Recent (see Garrett, 1970; Awramik, 1971; Monty, 1973).

     10. Horizontal zonation of algal mat communities as deduced by microstructural differences has not been confirmed in the ancient record of stromatolites, although this is not to say that such zonation does not exist. Horizontal and vertical microstructural variations have been described by Serebryakov (1976, p. 631) but their interpretation as representing ancient horizontal algal mat zonation similar to Recent models has not been substantiated.

     11. Water turbulence has been postulated to influence columnar formation in ancient stromatolites (Hoffman, 1967; Trompette, 1969). In certain instances, however, as in the Omakhta formation (Uchur Group) of the Lower Riphean of eastern Siberia, it is reported that sedimentological evidence does not support a turbulence effect on stratiform vs columnar or branching morphology (Serebryakov, 1971). Indeed, morphogenesis of macrostructure in ancient stromatolites is one of the many unresolved problems in the study of ancient stromatolites (Semikhatov et al., in press). It remains a central issue in the question of the utility of stromatolites in biostratigraphy.

     12. Ecological successions involving substrate stabilization by mat-building algae followed by halophytes and subsequent plant communities is difficult to demonstrate in the

geological record. The common Phanerozoic association of cryp-
talgalamites and evaporites suggesting sabka-like environments
(Mountjoy, 1976; Schenk, 1976) excluding most vascular plants
would limit recognition of this ecological succession.

CONCLUSIONS

Our understanding of form in Recent and ancient stromatolites progressed considerably since the pioneering efforts
of the early 1960s. We realize that we are not dealing with
the biological evolution of individual organisms through time
but with changing structures that are partly the products of
microbial (mainly procaryotic) communities that built these
laminated, mainly biosedimentary structures called stromatolites. No longer held are the views that: (1) stromatolite
morphology is entirely and exclusively the product of environmental factors, (2) stromatolites are restricted to intertidal
and supratidal zones, and (3) stromatolites are built solely
by blue-green algae. It now appears that certain stromatolites,
assemblages of stromatolites, and bioherm series are characteristic of broadly defined intervals of pre-Phanerozoic history, and these may be used with appropriate caution in inter-
continental correlation.
Microstructure is biologically controlled in Recent biogenic stromatolites and presumably also in ancient ones, but it
is important in studying ancient microstructure to distinguish
between primary, diagenetic and secondary characteristics.
Microstructure in ancient stromatolites also shows changes with
time, and, though no trends are yet discernible, this suggests
temporal variation and conceivably sequence in stromatolite-
building microbial communities.
We do not yet understand the physical and biological
factors and processes that shape stromatolite macrostructure
nor the interplay between them. We do know that current and
wave action modify columnar and domal shape (Hoffman, 1967),
but we do not understand the causes of such conspicuous features as branching in ancient columnar stromatolites.

REFERENCES

Awramik, S. M. "Precambrian Columnar Stromatolite Diversity:
Reflection of Metazoan Appearance," *Science* 174:825-827 (1971).

Awramik, S. M. "Gunflint Stromatolites: Microfossil Distribution in Relation to Stromatolite Morphology," in *Stromatolites*,
M. R. Walter, Ed. (Amsterdam: Elsevier, 1976), pp. 311-320.

Awramik, S. M. *Paleobiology of Stromatolites: Origins Life*
(in press).

Awramik, S. M., and E. S. Barghoorn. *The Gunflint Microbiota:
Precambrian Research* (in press).

Awramik, S. M., H. J. Hofmann and M. E. Raaben. In: *Stromatolites*, M. R. Walter, Ed. (Amsterdam: Elsevier, 1976), pp. 705-711.

Awramik, S. M., L. Margulis and E. S. Barghoorn. "Evolutionary Processes in the Formation of Stromatolites," in *Stromatolites*, M. R. Walter, Ed. (Amsterdam: Elsevier, 1976), pp. 149-162.

Awramik, S. M., and M. A. Semikhatov. *Microstructure of Gunflint Stromatolites* (tentative title) (in preparation).

Brock, T. D. "Relationship Between Standing Crop and Primary Productivity along a Hot Spring Thermal Gradient," *Ecology* 48:566-571 (1967).

Brock, T. D. "Environmental Microbiology of Living Stromatolites," in *Stromatolites*, M. R. Walter, Ed. (Amsterdam: Elsevier, 1976), pp. 141-148.

Cloud, P. "Major Features of Crustal Evolution," *Trans. Geol. Soc. S. Afr.*, Annex to   79:33 (1976).

Cloud, P., and M. A. Semikhatov. *Noncarbonate Stromatolites from the Lower Cambrian Puerto Blanco Formation, Sonora, Mexico* (tentative title) (in preparation).

Cohen, Y., W. E. Krumbein and M. Shilo. "The Solar Lake: Limnology and Microbiology of a Hypersaline, Monomictic Heliothermal Heated Sea-Marginal Pond (Gulf of Aqaba, Sinai)," *Rapp. Comm. Int. Mer. Medit.* 23(3):105-107 (1975).

David, R. A. "Algal Stromatolites Composed of Quartz Sandstone," *J. Sediment. Petrol.* 38:953-955 (1968).

Doemel, W. N., and T. D. Brock. "Structure, Growth, and Decomposition of Laminated Algal-Bacterial Mats in Alkaline Hot Springs," *J. Sediment. Petrol.* (in press).

Donaldson, J. A. "Aphebian Stromatolites in Canada: Implications for Stromatolite Zonation," in *Stromatolites*, M. R. Walter, Ed. (Amsterdam: Elsevier, 1976), pp. 371-380.

Eardley, A. J. "Sediments of the Great Salt Lake, Utah," *Bull. Am. Assoc. Pet. Geol.* 22:1305-1411 (1938).

Eggleston, J. R., and W. E. Dean. "Freshwater Stromatolitic Bioherms in Green Lake, New York," in *Stromatolites*, M. R. Walter, Ed. (Amsterdam: Elsevier, 1976), pp. 479-488.

Fairchild, T. R. "The Geologic Setting and Paleobiology of a Late Precambrian Stromatolitic Microflora from South Australia," *Univ. Calif. Publ. Geol. Sci.* (in press).

Garrett, P. "Phanerozoic Stromatolites: Noncompetitive Ecologic Restriction by Grazing and Burrowing Animals," *Science* 169:171-173 (1970).

Gebelein, C. D. "Distribution, Morphology, and Accretion Rate of Recent Subtidal Algal Stromatolites, Bermuda," *J. Sediment Petrol.* 39:49-69 (1969).

Gebelein, C. D. "Biologic Control of Stromatolite Microstructure: Implications for Precambrian Time Stratigraphy," *Am. J. Sci.* 274:575-598 (1974).

Gebelein, C. D. *Dynamics of Recent Carbonate Sedimentation and Ecology, Cape Sable, Florida* (Leiden: E. J. Brill, in press).

Ginsburg, R. N., L. B. Isham, S. J. Bein and J. Kuperberg. *Laminated Algal Sediments of South Florida and Their Recognition in the Fossil Record* (Unpublished Report 54-20, Coral Gables, Florida: Marine Laboratory, University of Miami, 1954).

Golubic, S. "The Relationship Between Blue-Green Algae and Carbonate Deposits," in *The Biology of Blue-Green Algae,* N. G. Carr and B. A. Whitton, Eds. (Oxford: Blackwell, 1975), pp. 434-472.

Golubic S. "Organisms that Build Stromatolites," in *Stromatolites,* M. R. Walter, Ed. (Amsterdam: Elsevier, 1976), pp. 113-126.

Golubic, S., and S. M. Awramik. "Microbial Comparison of Stromatolite Environments: Shark Bay, Persian Gulf and the Bahamas," *Geol. Soc. Am. Ann. Meet., Abstr. Prog.* 6(7): 759-760 (1974).

Golubic, S., and A. G. Fischer. "Ecology of Calcareous Nodules Forming in Little Connestoga Creek near Lancaster, Pennsylvania," *Verh. Internat. Verein. Limnol.* 19:2315-2323 (1975).

Gunatilaka, A. "Some Aspects of the Biology and Sedimentology of Laminated Algal Mats from Mannar Lagoon, Northwest Ceylon," *Sed. Geol.* 14:275-300 (1975).

Halley, R. B. "Textural Variation within Great Salt Lake Algal Mounds," in *Stromatolites,* M. R. Walter, Ed. (Amsterdam, Elsevier, 1976), pp. 435-446.

Hoffman, P. "Algal Stromatolites: Use in Stratigraphic Correlation and Paleo-Current Determination," *Science* 157:
1043-1045 (1967).

Hoffman, P. "Recent and Ancient Algal Stromatolites: Seventy
Years of Pedagogic Cross-Pollination," in *Evolving Concepts
in Sedimentology*, R. N. Ginsburg, Ed. (Baltimore: University
Press, 1975), pp. 178-191.

Hoffman, P. "Environmental Diversity of Middle Precambrian
Stromatolites," in *Stromatolites*, M. R. Walter, Ed.
(Amsterdam: Elsevier, 1976), pp. 599-612.

Hommeril, P., and M. Rioult. "Étude de la fixation des sédiments meubles par deux algues marines: *Rhodothamniella
floridula* (Dillwyn) J. Feldm. et *Microcoleus chthonoplastes*,"
Thur. Mar. Geol. 3:131-166 (1965).

Horodyski, R. J., B. Bloeser and S. P. Vonder Haar. "Laminated
Algal Mats from a Coastal Lagoon, Laguna Mormona, Baja
California, Mexico," *J. Sediment. Petrol.* (in press).

Horodyski, R. J., and S. P. Vonder Haar. "Recent Calcareous
Stromatolites from Laguna Mormona (Baja California) Mexico,"
J. Sediment. Petrol. 45:894-906 (1975).

Javor, E. J., and R. W. Castenholz. "Carbonate Precipitation
in Algal Mats in a Silicoclastic Environment: a Quantitative
Analysis," in *Abstracts Third International Symposium on
Environmental Biogeochemistry*, W. E. Krumbein, Ed. (Oldenburg:
Environmental Lab, 1977), Occasional Paper 1:68.

Kendall, C. G., St. C. and P. A. d'E Skipwith. "Recent Algal
Mats of a Persian Gulf Lagoon," *J. Sediment. Petrol.* 38:
1040-1058 (1968).

Logan, B. W. "*Cryptozoon* and Associate Stromatolites from the
Recent of Shark Bay, Western Australia," *J. Geol.* 69:
517-533 (1961).

Logan, B. W., P. Hoffman and C. D. Gebelein. "Algal Mats
Cryptalgal Fabrics and Structures, Hamelin Pool, Western
Australia," *Am. Assoc. Pet. Geol.* Mem. 22:140-194 (1974).

Monty, C. L. V. "Distribution and Structure of Recent Stromatolitic Algal Mats, Eastern Andros Island, Bahamas," *Ann.
Soc. Geol. Belg., Bull.* 90:55-100 (1967).

Monty, C. L. V. "An Autoecological Approach of Intertidal and
Deep Water Stromatolites," *Ann. Soc. Geol. Belg., Bull.*
94:265-276 (1971).

Monty, C. L. V. "Precambrian Background and Phanerozoic History of Stromatolite Communities, an Overview," *Ann. Soc. Geol. Belg., Bull.* 96:585–624 (1973).

Monty, C. L. V. "The Origin and Development of Cryptalgal Fabrics," in *Stromatolites*, M. R. Walter, Ed. (Amsterdam: Elsevier, 1976), pp. 193–250.

Mountjoy, E. W. "Intertidal and Supratidal Deposits within Isolated Upper Devonian Buildups, Alberta," in *Tidal Deposits*, R. N. Ginsburg, Ed. (New York: Springer-Verlag, 1975), pp. 387–395.

Neumann, A. C., C. D. Gebelein and T. P. Scoffin. "The Composition, Structure, and Erodability of Subtidal Mats, Abaco, Bahamas," *J. Sediment. Petrol.* 40:274–297 (1970).

Pia, J. "Die rezenten Kalksteine," *Mineralog. Petrogr. Mitt. Abt. B* 12–13:142–199 (1933).

Playford, P. E., and A. E. Cockbain. "Modern Algal Stromatolites at Hamelin Pool, a Hypersaline Barred Basin in Shark Bay, Western Australia," in *Stromatolites*, M. R. Walter, Ed. (Amsterdam: Elsevier, 1976), pp. 389–412.

Playford, P. E., A. E. Cockbain, E. C. Druce and J. L. Wray. "Devonian Stromatolites from the Canning Basin, Western Australia," in *Stromatolites*, M. R. Walter, Ed. (Amsterdam: Elsevier, 1976), pp. 543–564.

Schenk, P. E. "Carbonate-Sulfate Intertidalites of the Windsor Group (Middle Carboniferous) Maritime Provinces, Canada," in *Tidal Deposits*, R. N. Ginsburg, Ed. (New York: Springer-Verlag, 1975), pp. 373–380.

Schopf, J. W., and J. M. Blacic. "New Microorganisms from the Bitter Springs Formation (Late Precambrian) of the North-Central Amadeus Basin, Australia," *Paleontol.* 45:925–960 (1971).

Schopf, J. W., and Yu. K. Sovietov. "Microfossils in *Conophyton* from the Soviet Union and Their Bearing on Precambrian Biostratigraphy," *Science* 193:143–146 (1976).

Schwarz, H.-U., G. Einsele and D. Herm. "Quartz-Sandy, Grazing-Contoured Stromatolites from Coastal Embayments of Mauritania, West Africa," *Sedimentology* 22:539–561 (1975).

Semikhatov, M. A., C. D. Gebelein, P. E. Cloud, S. M. Awramik and W. Benmore. *Stromatolite Morphogenesis—Progress and Problems* (in preparation).

Serebryakov, S. N. "Stromatolites in the Rythmic Strata of the Riphean," *Izv. Akad. Nauk SSSR, Ser. Geol.* 10:127-134 (1971) (in Russian).

Serebryakov, S. N. "Peculiarities of Formation and Location of Riphean Siberian Stromatolites," *Akad. Nauk SSSR, Tr. Geol. Inst* 200:175 (1975) (in Russian).

Serebryakov, S. N. "Biotic and Abiotic Factors Controlling the Morphology of Riphean Stromatolites," in *Stromatolites,* M. R. Walter, Ed. (Amsterdam: Elsevier, 1976), pp. 321-336.

Sorensen, L. O., and J. T. Conover. "Algal Mat Communities of *Lyngbya conferoides* (c. Agardh) Gomont," *Publ. Inst. Mar. Sci., Austin* 8:237-249 (1962).

Surdam, R. C., and J. L. Wray. "Lacustrine Stromatolites, Eocene Green River Formation, Wyoming," in *Stromatolites,* M. R. Walter, Ed. (Amsterdam: Elsevier, 1976), pp. 535-542.

Termier, H., G. Termier, A. F. de Lapparent and F. Golshani. "Cambrian Stromatolites from Lakkarkuh, East-Central Iran," *Geol. Surv. Iran., Rept.* 32:35-47 (1975).

Trompette, R. "Les stromatolites du "Precambrien Superieur" de L'Adrar de Mauritanie (Sahara Occidental)," *Sedimentology* 13:123-154 (1969).

Tucker, M. E. "Replaced Evaporites from the Late Precambrian of Finnmark, Arctic Norway," *Sed. Geol.* 16:193-204 (1976).

von der Borch, C. C., B. Bolton and J. Warren. "Stratigraphy and Petrography of Modern Stromatolitic Limestones from Marion Lake, South Australia," *Sedimentology* (in press).

Walter, M. R., J. Bauld and T. D. Brock. "Siliceous Bacterial Stromatolites in Hot Springs and Geyser Effluents of Yellowstone National Park," *Science* 178:402-405 (1972).

Walter, M. R., J. Bauld and T. D. Brock. "Microbiology and Morphogenesis of Columnar Stromatolites (*Conophyton, Vacerrilla*) from Hot Springs in Yellowstone National Park," in *Stromatolites,* M. R. Walter, Ed. (Amsterdam: Elsevier, 1976), pp. 273-310.

Walter, M. R., S. Golubic and W. V. Preiss. "Recent Stromatolites from Hydromagnesite and Aragonite Depositing Lakes near the Coorong Lagoon, South Australia," *J. Sediment. Petrol.* 43(4): 1021-1030 (1973).

CHAPTER 15

CHEMICAL PROCESSES IN ESTUARIES: THE IMPORTANCE OF $_p$H AND ITS VARIABILITY

A. W. MORRIS

Natural Environmental Research Council
Institute for Marine Environmental Research
Citadel Road, Plymouth, UK

INTRODUCTION

Estuaries are regions of fundamental importance with respect to geochemical processes occurring on the global scale, for they represent the major route whereby weathered lithospheric material is transported to the oceanic sedimentary domain. Many global geochemical mass-balance calculations assume chemical continuity between rivers and ocean waters, neglecting the probability of rapid chemical interactions in the estuarine region brought about by the sharp change in physicochemical conditions of the aqueous environment across this interface. There are, however, a number of indications that such an assumption is not always valid.

Controlled laboratory experiments have been used in attempts to elucidate chemical interactions in estuarine systems (see Sholkovitz, 1976). Although providing an insight into the types and extent of reactions that may occur, realistic laboratory simulations of the complex and rapidly varying conditions obtained in the field are quite impractical, and are therefore limited in their predictive output.

Numerous direct attempts to obtain field descriptions of interactive processes in estuaries have been made. In reviewing the available literature, Boyle *et al.* (1974) concluded that there appears to be no generality in the reported interpretations either of the extent of nonconservative behavior or of the mechanisms involved. Furthermore, the criteria necessary for unambiguous deduction of nonconservative behavior are not always achieved. Essentially, the concentration of an individual constituent throughout the estuarine mixing regime is compared with the total salt content, which is used to deduce the

relative proportions of the fresh- and saltwater contributions
to the mixed estuarine water. Deviations from linearity of the
constituent-salinity relationship indicate nonconservative behavior only if the composition of the oceanic and riverine
components have remained constant over the time period required
to replace the water within the estuary, and if curvature of
the constituent-salinity relationship can be established. Significant subsidiary freshwater inputs are a complicating factor.
      Many of the cyclic or intermittent phenomena that poten-
tially influence chemical reactivity within the estuarine system are manifested over time intervals appreciably shorter
than required for replacement of water. For example, the rate
of input and composition of freshwater runoff, tidal velocities
and related particle suspension and deposition rates and diurnal
biological activity all vary appreciably over periods of hours
or less. It is probable, therefore, that if significant chemical reactions are occurring within an estuary, their rates,
and the instantaneous concentration of reactants and products
will also vary over correspondingly short time intervals.
      As part of the estuarine ecology program of the Natural
Environment Research Council, we have commenced fundamental
studies of interactive chemical processes in estuaries. These
studies are based on the philosophy that environmentally mean-
ingful results can be obtained only by *in situ* investigations
using an experimental procedure designed to characterize simultaneously those prevailing environmental conditions, and their
geographical and temporal variability, that influence chemical
speciation and reactivity. Determinations of the temporal and
geographical variability in pH of the Tamar Estuary (southwest
England) are described as an illustration of the applicability
of such an approach.

METHODS

      Basically, the experimental procedure involves consecu-
tive and repetitive axial traverses through the portion of the
estuarine region under investigation. During the traverses the
required chemical data are recorded continuously.
      A 37-ft long flat-bottomed Rotork Seatruck®, capable
of operating in depths as shallow as 1 m, was used for the
present work. This vessel also satisfies requirements for
speed and maneuverability in tidal streams of 5 knots or more
together with ample payload and working space for the deploy-
ment of bulky automated chemical instrumentation.
      For continuous chemical determinations, a peristaltic
pump was used to pass water (10 liter/min^{-1}) through a baffled
reservoir holding the detecting sensors. By careful design the
flushing time of this system was reduced to less than 20 sec.
For wet-chemical nutrient autoanalysis, a subsidiary stream
was passed through a filtration unit prior to reaching the
autoanalyzer system. Continuous records have been obtained for

chloride (specific ion electrode) for the determination of total salt, turbidity (Partech Electronis Ltd., Model LP-HP),
oxygen concentration (Yellow Spring Instrument Co., Model 57),
temperature, pH (glass electrode), fluorescence (Turner Model
III fluorometer) and nitrate, phosphate, silicate and nitrite
(Technicon Mark II Autoanalyser). For salinities greater than
5°/oo, where the chloride electrode response is relatively in-
sensitive, a field conductivity salinometer was used.

During each axial traverse of the estuary, the time at
which readily identifiable landmarks (bridges, piers, etc.)
were passed was recorded. The chemical data were subsequently
contoured in dimensions of time and distance along the estuary
(see Figure 1). Using this output, perturbations to a regular
distributional pattern controlled by mixing, which are brought
about by subsidiary inputs, can readily be distinguished from
perturbations arising from *in situ* interactions within the
aqueous phase.

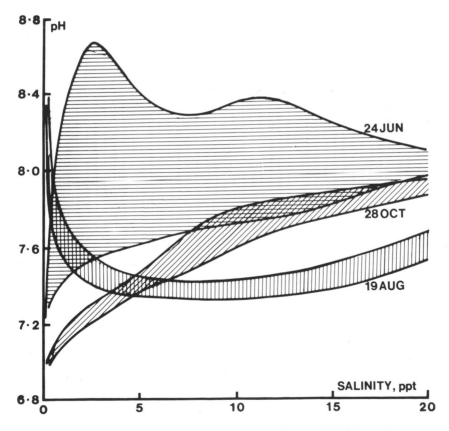

Figure 1. Envelopes illustrating the pH variability through
the estuarine mixing regime encountered in the Tamar
Estuary on three separate occasions during 1976.

    In Figure 2, the path taken by the vessel during the
investigation is shown in order to illustrate how the traverses
were adjusted to follow the tidally induced movements of the
saline intrusion.

RESULTS

    Envelopes embracing the range of pH—salinity relation-
ships encountered on three separate days during 1976 are drawn

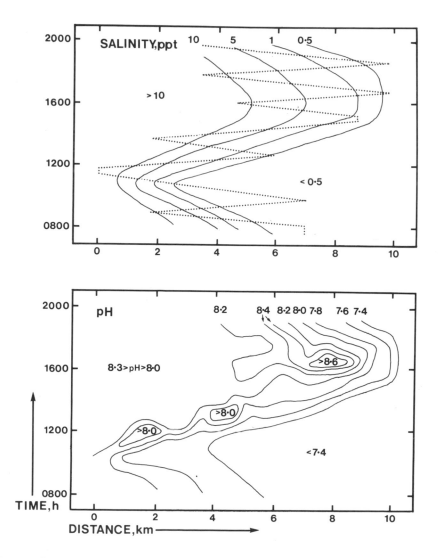

Figure 2.   Geographical and temporal distributions of salinity
    and pH in the Tamar Estuary on June 24, 1976. The dotted line
    on the salinity diagram shows the path taken by the vessel
    during the course of the investigation.

in Figure 2, with relevant details of the three investigations
listed in Table I.   Contoured on dimensions of time and distance, the results of the investigations in August and October
yielded a regular pattern in the geographical distributions of
pH, which was clearly controlled by the salinity variations
alone.   The results obtained in June yielded a more complicated
pH distribution, which is compared in Figure 1 with the simultaneous salinity values.   In all cases, there is no evidence
of geographically fixed perturbatory influences.   Therefore,
changes in pH are attributable solely to interactive behavior
within the aqueous phase.

Table I
Periods of Investigation of pH in the Tamar Estuary and the
Corresponding pH Values of the Contributory Waters

Date	Time of Investigation	Freshwater pH	Sea Water pH (salinity > 30°/oo)
June 24, 1976	0755–2215	7.0–7.2	8.0–8.3
August 19, 1976	0840–1746	>8.5	8.0–8.1
October 28, 1976	0747–1437	6.8–7.0	8.2–8.3

Clearly, a dominant factor in determining the pH distribution within the estuarine system at any time is the pH of
the freshwater source.   This remained relatively constant
throughout the course of each separate investigation, but large
seasonal differences in freshwater pH were found.   The approximately neutral freshwater conditions that occurred in June and
October are typical;   the alkaline pH values encountered in
August are attributable to a phytoplankton bloom in the freshwater.   Although markedly different pH–salinity relationships
were obtained for each investigation, those in August and
October were reproducible within narrow limits throughout the
course of each investigation.
In contrast, the pH–salinity relationships in the June
investigation were highly variable throughout the day.   For
example, the pH of water of 5°/oo salinity varied between 7.6
and 8.4.   The large overall ranges in pH at different salinities
encountered in June are the result of progressive changes in
the pH profile along the estuary.   The profiles, relative to
salinity, obtained over sequential time intervals (equal to
the time taken to complete a single traverse) are illustrated
in Figure 3.   These results indicate an overall diurnal trend
throughout the salinity range, with variable perturbations of
lesser extent superimposed.   This is seen more clearly in
Figure 4, in which the temporal variations in pH salinities of
3, 5 and 10°/oo are plotted.   In the June data there is a

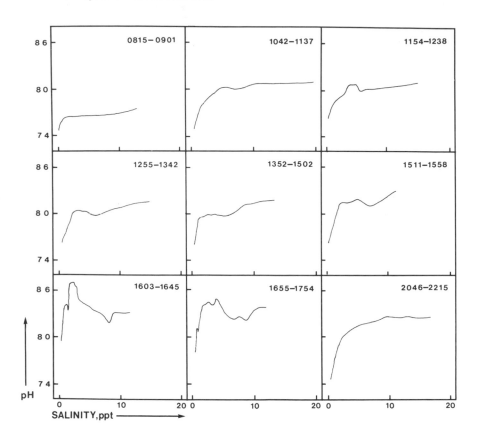

Figure 3. Progressive changes of the pH–salinity relationship
in the Tamar Estuary on June 24, 1976.

tendency for water of 2–5°/oo salinity to show subsidiary max-
ima around times of slack water; these times are indicated in
the figure. In contrast, both the August and the October data
show only a slight diurnal trend, and there are no significant
deviations at slack water. The August data are included in
Figure 4.

DISCUSSION

Short-term control of pH in natural aqueous systems is
dominated by the carbonate system. Mook and Koene (1975) have
predicted that as a result of the influence of salt content,
particularly on the activities of bicarbonate and carbonate ions,
pH in the mixing region of estuaries will not show a regular
transition between the fresh- and sea water values. Rather, for
freshwater sources of relatively low pH, there would be a minimum in the pH distribution at low salinity, whereas for freshwater sources of higher pH, a sharp decrease in pH would occur
at low salinities. The overall pH–salinity relationship is also

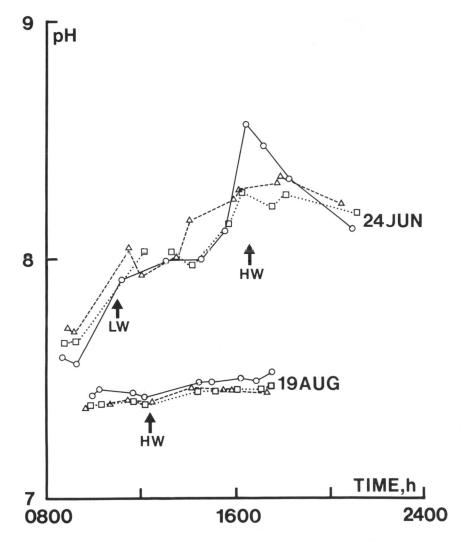

Figure 4. Diurnal variations of pH for water of 3°/oo (O——O), 5°/oo (□• •□) and 10°/oo (△---△) salinity in the Tamar Estuary on June 24 and August 19, 1976.

dependent on the total alkalinity of the fresh- and sea waters, temperature and the pH of the sea water.

None of the results obtained for the Tamar Estuary conforms with this predictive model. Individual profiles in June and October, with relatively low fresh water pH, showed a rapid increase in pH over a small salinity range (0 to *ca.* 2°/oo) followed by a less pronounced rate of increase with salinity, rather than a minimum pH at low salinity. Furthermore, the drop in pH where salt is first apparent in the August data is much sharper than predicted, and there is a shallow minimum over

an extended salinity range. The overall shapes of the pH-
salinity profiles are also incompatible with the model, particularly the transient perturbations in pH apparent throughout
the salinity range in June.

The model of Mook and Koene (1975) is, of course, a
description of stable thermodynamic equilibrium conditions.
Estuarine pH distributions will correspond to a thermodynamically stable condition only if the continuous dynamic approach to
equilibrium of the carbonate system occurring throughout the
mixing regime is rapid relative to the rate at which the component waters are mixed and if significant *in situ* perturbatory influences are absent. Apparently, the conditions per-
taining in the Tamar Estuary do not permit thermodynamic equilibrium to be attained. The consistent pH-salinity relationships
for each traverse obtained during August and October suggest
that at these times a dynamic quasiequilibrium had developed in
which consistent conditions are maintained over an extended
period by a balance of kinetic factors, in the absence of significant *in situ* perturbations. The distribution of pH in
June, however, clearly indicates the presence of significant
in situ perturbatory influences on the carbonate system and
consequently on the pH. The marked diurnal trend is undoubtedly due to the effect of diurnal photosynthetic activity on
the carbonate system. The noticeable enhanced effect confined
to the salinity range $2-5^o/oo$ indicates a concentration of
standing stock of photosynthesizing organisms, which is transported with the water mass, within this region. The more pronounced pH anomalies evident around time of slack water are
probably a consequence of reduced turbulence-induced diffusional mixing.

Changes in pH of the order illustrated here within an
estuarine system will have a profound influence on the rates
of chemical interactive reactions and therefore on any instantaneous concentrations of reactants and products. Furthermore,
pH changes that are rapid relative to the rate at which water
is replaced within an estuary will obviate the use of constituent-salinity relationships derived from single estuarine
axial traverses for qualitative and quantitative evaluations
of the effects of interactive behavior, even if the constituent
waters remain of constant composition. Therefore, it is not
surprising that interactive processes reported as occurring in
one estuary may not be demonstrable in another estuary or even,
at different times, in the same estuary. Quantitative estimates
of the results of interactive processes in estuaries will be
obtainable only when the full extent of the effects of variables
such as pH on interactive behavior has been established. Hence,
it is likely that the sum effect of interactive processes within estuaries on the global geochemical cycles of the elements
will be adequately characterized only by comprehensive field
investigations over extended time periods.

ACKNOWLEDGMENT

This work forms part of the estuarine ecology program of the Natural Environment Research Council, was partly supported by the Department of the Environment on Contract No. DGR 480/48, and is published with their permission.

REFERENCES

Boyle, E., R. Collier, A. T. Dengler, J. M. Edmond, A. C. Ng and R. F. Stallard. "On the Chemical Mass Balance in Estuaries," *Geochim. Cosmochim. Acta* 38:1719-1728 (1974).

Mook. W. G., and B. K. S. Koene. "Chemistry of Dissolved Inorganic Carbon in Estuarine and Coastal Brackish Waters," *Estuarine Coastal Mar. Sci,* 3:325-336 (1975).

Sholkovitz, E. R. "Flocculation of Dissolved Organic and Inorganic Matter During the Mixing of River Water and Sea Water," *Geochim. Cosmochim. Acta* 40:831-845 (1976).

CHAPTER 16

MICROBIAL MATS IN A HYPERSALINE SOLAR LAKE: TYPES, COMPOSITION AND DISTRIBUTION

P. HIRSCH

Institut für Allgemeine Mikrobiologie
University of Kiel, Federal Republic of Germany

INTRODUCTION

The small, hypersaline, heliothermal and monomictic "Solar Lake" south of Elat (Gulf of Aqaba) has a metalimnetic temperature maximum of 50-60°C during the winter and spring stratification and a temperature of 40-45°C at the sediment surface (4.5-5 m). The geology, limnology and annual changes of appearance of this lake have been described by various authors (Friedman *et al.*, 1973; Krumbein and Cohen, 1974, 1977). A bathymetric map (after Cohen, 1975) is given in Figure 1.

The unusual conditions of the lake have attracted attention for various reasons. The presence of cyanobacterial mats at the anoxic bottom and their high rate of photosynthetic production have stimulated investigation of anoxygenic photosynthesis (Cohen, 1975; Cohen, Padan and Shilo, 1975). Sedimentation rates and processes have been studied by Friedman *et al.* (1973) and by Krumbein and Cohen (1974, 1977). With a primary production of 5-12 g $C/m^{-2}/day^{-1}$ and an annual net sedimentation of 0.5-1 mm, evidently 95-99 percent of the primary products decayed here, pointing to a very active heterotrophic metabolism. Production of the epilimnion was considered to be very low. Unfortunately, few data are available on the presence and types of heterotrophic microorganisms (bacteria) in the mats.

The present investigation of Solar Lake mats was initiated as part of a study on distribution and properties of bioindicator bacteria in extreme environments. A first account of this work and on pure culture studies has been published (Hirsch, Müller and Schlesner, 1977; Hirsch, 1977). The observation, in these mats, of large and diverse populations of heterotrophic bacteria indicate that turnover of the primary products occurs right here.

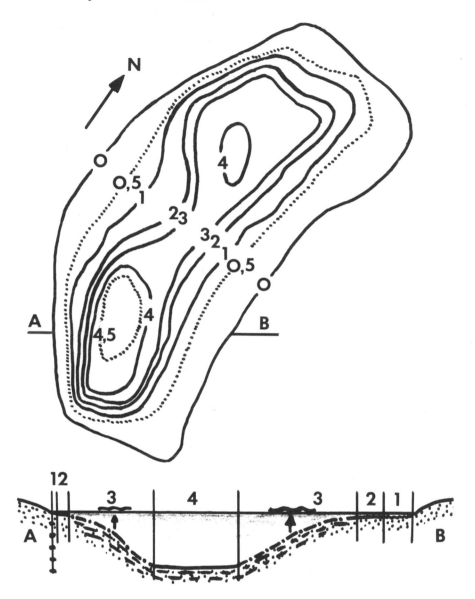

Figure 1. Bathymetric map of Solar Lake (after Cohen, 1975) and distribution of mat types along the cross section indicated in the map.

MATERIALS AND METHODS

Observation Techniques

        Water samples or mat samples were collected in sterile glass jars or plastic bags ("Whirl-Pak," USA) and transported to the laboratory of the Department of Microbiological Chemistry,

Hadassah Medical School, Hebrew University, Jerusalem. Some
samples were immediately fixed with glutaraldehyde (final conc.
2%; cacodylate buffer pH 7.0; 0.1 M). Samples with photosynthetic microorganisms were stored at the proper light intensity.
Advantage was taken of periphyton communities already
established at the sample time by collecting soda bottles and
beer cans and by further incubating these in the laboratory
(Hirsch, 1972). Precleaned glass slides were attached to rubber corks in horizontal and vertical pairs in order to achieve
in situ incubation. Incubation time was 4-5 days. After har-
vesting, some slides were immediately fixed by glutaraldehyde
vapor (30 min) and then air dried for transportation. Others
were placed directly into water samples of the same depth and
incubated.
For microscopic observation, minute droplets of water
samples were placed onto glass slides that had been coated with
2% water agar and then dried for storage. The swelling agar
absorbed most of the sample water and raised the microorganisms
against the cover slip in one convenient layer, thus creating
excellent optical conditions for life microscopy (N. Pfennig,
personal communication). Microorganisms seen were drawn, measured and recorded photographically onto Kodak Plus X or Ecta-
chrome EHB-135 color film with a Zeiss Photomicroscope.

Enrichment and Purification Techniques

Direct incubation of aseptically drawn water samples with
or without added carbon source or vitamin solution yielded enrichments in which many different microorganisms could be detected. The following filter-sterilized substrates were added:
Bacto Peptone or Yeast Extract (Difco, Detroit, Michigan)—
0.025%; vitamin solution no. 6 (Van Ert and Staley, 1971)—0.5
ml/100 ml. Incubation was dark and at 20°C or 42°C, aerobically
or anaerobically (*i.e.*, air excluded). In other enrichments,
aseptically collected glass slides were placed directly into
water samples of the same depth; incubation here was likewise
at 20°C and 42°C, respectively. Subsequently, the enrichment
cultures were streaked onto PYVG agar plates (peptone-yeast
extract-vitamin solution-glucose-agar) as suggested by Staley
(1968). The medium was prepared with either aged Solar Lake
water (salinity 73°/oo), or, later in Kiel, with 2 x concentrated artificial sea water (Lyman and Fleming, 1940). Pure cultures
were kept on agar slants or on the corresponding liquid medium.

Identification

Naming of microorganisms was only possible in some cases,
and then affiliation with a genus was attempted. Some bacteria
were named according to *Bergey's Manual* (1974), others had to
be given working names (in parentheses). Cyanobacteria were
compared to the system of Geitler (1932).

Physical and Chemical Determinations

Temperatures were measured with a telethermometer thermistor probe (Yellow Springs, Ohio, model 425C). Sulfide and chlorosity were kindly determined by Ms. Ilana Levanon (Steinitz Biological Laboratory, Elat). Sulfide was stabilized with $CdCl_2$ and titrated within a few hours (Cohen, 1975). Salinity was calculated from chlorosity according to Strickland and Parsons (1968):

$$S^o/oo = 1.8050 \; Cl^o/oo + 0.030$$

Chlorosity was determined by titration with 0.1 N $AgNO_3$ + K_2CrO_4, after treatment with H_2O_2 (30%) at pH 9.5 (Cohen, 1975).

Estimation of Frequency

The frequency of an organism in a sample was estimated after intensive microscopy had not revealed any further, additional microorganisms. The highest degree of frequency (5) indicated predominance and mass development (*i.e.*, a bloom). Occasional occurrence, but more than five individuals per sample, was marked with "+." Observation of only one to five individuals was scored with "r." In the tables the presence of an organism is indicated with an "x."

RESULTS

The Solar Lake was visited three times during March 1976. During this time the lake was maximally 4.5-m deep and highly stratified. The epilimnion had ambient temperature and low salinity (approx. $80^o/oo$ in 0.5 m). The hypolimnion had a temperature maximum in 2.5 m (52°C) and the sediment surface measured 42°C. Salinity was highest at the sediment surface ($183^o/oo$). Sulfide was found between 3.0 m and the sediment surface (max. 4.16 mg/l).

Direct observation of samples, glass slides, soda bottle inner-surface growth, mat blocks or submerged surfaces, as well as investigation of enrichments and pure cultures, resulted in recognition of 149 morphologically different microorganism forms. Seven types of distribution patterns could be differentiated among those 149 forms. Up to now 28 pure cultures were obtained. The number of eukaryotic microorganisms was low (27), and 11 of these were diatoms. There were no fungi in any of the samples.

Macroscopically and by color, four different mat-covered regions could be detected. Along the barrier that separates the lake from the Gulf, the uppermost mat (0-10 cm) was colorless to pink, only a few mm to approximately 1-cm thick, and of irregular surface structure. Semispherical, blister-like layers covered areas of up to 10 cm^2. Thirty different

microorganisms were recognized here, most of which were diatoms
(Table I). Also present in larger numbers were flexibacteria,
budding rods (*Pasteuria* ?), a *Microcyclus* sp. and some bacterial rods. Eleven of these organisms were found *only* here in
this mat type.

A yellowish-brown mat surrounded the whole lake. Along
the barrier it occurred between 10 and 35 cm depth, and on the
other shore areas this mat type covered the whole range from
0 to 35 cm. This mat was thicker and layered; the uppermost
10 cm were investigated only. There were 28 morphologically
distinct microorganisms (Table II); 8 of these occurred only
here. Most frequent were diatoms, flexibacteria and rod-shaped
bacterial forms. Since the list in Table II contains typically
aerobic bacteria (*Hyphomicrobium*, *Bdellovibrio*) and anaerobes
(*Clostridium*, *Thiospirillum*), it is evident that this mat is
highly stratified. The lower mat layers were black and contained sulfide. Toward deeper waters, but still on the shelf,
this mat type covered dark-green layers similar to the next mat
type.

Below 35 cm, a dark-green mat covered the shelf and slope
sediment. It was stratified and quite coherent; gas formation,
presumably oxygen from photosynthesis, resulted in separation
of larger patches that floated up to the lake surface. Patches
as large as 30 x 30 cm and of 4-cm thickness were wind-driven
toward the shore where they collected. The green floating
mats consisted of 22 different microorganisms, with 6 forms
specific for this mat type (Table III). Predominant were an
Oscillatoria, flexible rods, a sulfur-storing coccus (*Achroma-
tium* ?), flexible filaments and rod-shaped bacteria. There
were also three additional cyanobacteria and two ciliates. This
mat type may have corresponded to the "pinnacle mats" described
by Krumbein and Cohen (1977).

The lake center sediment was covered with a loose green
mat consisting of 24 different microorganisms (Table IV). Only
four forms were specific for this mat type, and one of these
(diatom 91) may have been dead or inactive. All predominant
microorganisms were bacteria, and most of these were photosynthetic. *Oscillatoria* 55 (presumably *O. limnetica*, Cohen, 1975)
was the major organism; it had long trichomes partially covered
with external sulfur granules. *Prosthecochloris*, a green bacterium, may have occurred as a remnant of a previous bloom
(Cohen, 1975). The majority of bacteria found were anaerobic
but not thermophilic. This was deduced when a sample of this
mat was stored in Kiel at 20°C in dim light for one year without loss of the major microorganisms.

The loose green mats contained in small numbers the new
bacterium "*Dichotomicrobium*." This often dichotomously branched
organism multiplies by bud formation at the tips of hyphae. An
extensive network formed by this bacterium in the green bottom
mat as well as on submerged slides in the upper hypolimnion
suggests that it may be indigenous, and that it is a major

Table I
Types of Microorganisms and Their Frequency of Occurrence
in the Colorless to Pink Mat Type I[a]

Organism and Number		Frequency of Appearance	Only here in Colorless Mat	Only in *Surface* Mats	Only in *Mats*, Surface or Bottom	Organisms in Mats *and* Free Water (0–0.5 m)	Organisms in Mats *and* Free Water (0–1.5 m)	Organisms in Mats and *Throughout Profile*	Organisms in mats *and* Anaerobic Bottom Layer
Diatom	4	4	.	.	.	✗	✗	.	.
Diatom	112	3	✗	✗	✗	.	.	.	.
Diatom	98	2	.	✗	.	.	.	.	.
Flexible rods	34	2	.	.	.	.	.	✗	.
Flexible rods	86	2	.	.	✗	.	.	.	.
Large, motile B.	113	1	✗	✗	.	.	.	.	.
Rods	13	1	.	.	.	✗	✗	.	.
Budding rods	111	1	✗	✗	.	.	.	.	.
Microcyclus	95	1	.	.	.	✗	✗	.	.
Sphaerotilus	110	+	✗	✗	.	.	.	.	.
Caulobacter	10	+	.	.	.	✗	.	.	.
Cyanobacterium	93	+	✗	✗	.	.	.	.	.
Oscillatoria	99	+	.	✗	.	.	.	.	.
"Prosthecocaulis"	1	+	.	.	.	.	✗	.	.
Fat rods	47	+	.	.	.	.	.	.	✗
Macromonas	50	+	.	.	.	.	.	.	✗
Leptospira	19	+	.	.	.	.	.	✗	.
Budding bacter	18	+	.	.	.	.	.	✗	.
Flagellate	77	+	✗	✗	.	.	.	.	.
Flagellate	109	+	✗	✗	.	.	.	.	.
Thiospirillum	90	r	.	.	✗	.	.	.	.
Diplococcus	62	r	.	.	✗	.	.	.	.
Bdellovibrio	105	r	.	✗	.	.	.	.	.
Clostridium	101	r	.	.	.	.	✗	.	.
Spirochaete	32	r	.	.	.	.	.	.	✗
"Thiodendron"	64	r	.	.	✗	.	.	.	.
Cyanobacterium	114	r	✗	✗	.	.	.	.	.
Spirulina	115	r	✗	✗	.	.	.	.	.
Saprospira	66	r	✗	✗	.	.	.	.	.
Hyphomicrobium	9	r	✗	✗	.	.	.	.	.

[a]For explanation of symbols, see Methods section.

mat-forming organism in this lake.   Preliminary data on eight
pure cultures of "*Dichotomicrobium*" have been published elsewhere (Hirsch, 1977; Hirsch, Müller and Schlesner, 1977).   A
detailed description and formal naming are in preparation.

A comparison of the distribution and frequency of the
main mat microorganisms in mats and free lake water indicates
that most of the mat organisms also occur in the free water
(Table V).   Conversely, of 149 different lake microorganisms,

Table II
Types of Microorganisms and Their Frequency of Appearance
in the Yellowish-Brown Mat Type II

Organism and Number		Frequency of Appearance	Only *here* in Yellow-Brown Mat	Only in *Surface* Mats	Only in *Mats*, Surface or Bottom	Organisms in Mats *and* Free Water (0-0.5 m)	Organisms in Mats *and* Free Water (0-1.5 m)	Organisms in Mats and *Throughout Profile*	Organisms in Mats *and* Anaerobic Bottom Layer
Diatom	98	4	.	X	.	.	.	.	.
Diatom	4	3	.	.	.	X	X	.	.
Flexible rods	86	2/3	.	.	X	.	.	.	.
Thick filaments	35	2	.	.	.	.	.	.	X
Diatom	2	2	.	.	.	X	X	.	.
Rod-shaped bact.	13	1	.	.	.	X	X	.	.
Oscillatoria	99	+	.	X	.	.	.	.	.
Oscillatoria	55	+	.	.	X	.	.	.	.
Microcyclus	95	+	.	.	.	X	X	.	.
"Prosthecocaulis"	1	+	.	.	.	.	X	.	.
Rods w.gasvesic.	94	+	.	X	.	.	.	.	.
Coccus w.sulfur	89	+	.	.	.	.	.	.	X
Cyanobacterium	107	+	X	X	.	.	.	.	.
Hyphomocrobium	106	+	X	X	.	.	.	.	.
Leptospira	19	r	.	.	.	.	.	X	.
Diplococcus	62	r	.	.	X	.	.	.	.
Bdellovibrio	105	r	.	X	.	.	.	.	.
Clostridium	101	r	.	.	.	.	X	.	.
Spriochaete	87	r	.	.	X	.	.	.	.
Thiospirillum	100	r	X	X	.	.	.	.	.
Cocci, small	71	r	.	.	.	.	X	.	.
Diatom	102	r	X	X	.	.	.	.	.
Rods, attached	103	r	X	X	.	.	.	.	.
Pedomicrobium	27	r	.	.	.	.	X	.	.
Polyspheroid	104	r	X	X	.	.	.	.	.
Rods in slime	20	r	X	X	.	.	.	.	.
Chromatium	40	r	.	.	.	.	.	.	X
Chrysophyte	108	r	X	X	.	.	.	.	.

the mats contained a total of 64, *i.e.*, 43 percent. Three
forms—a diatom, a budding bacterium (*Pasteuria* ?), and a large,
motile bacterium—were found only in mats, and only in one mat
type. These latter microorganisms may be an indication that
the mats differentiated here are indeed ecologically definable
habitats.

DISCUSSION

The key question in this investigation is whether a microorganism can be identified by its morphological properties. Normally, we would have to understand the full range of its morphological diversity, and in most cases we do not know this range. Laboratory conditions may reveal certain morphological types among members of a population or in a pure culture, especially if this organism is "pleomorphic." Such pleomorphy results from a naturally weak or defective cell envelope, from differentiation during the life cycle, or from the adjustment, of an "ecotype," to a very specific and sometimes extreme

Table III

Types of Microorganisms and Their Frequency of Appearance in the Green Floating Mat Patches (Mat Type III)

Organism and Number		Frequency of Appearance	Only *here* in Green, Floating Mats	Only in *Surface* Mats	Only in *Mats*, Surface or Bottom	Organisms in Mats *and* Free Water (0–0.5 m)	Organisms in Mats *and* Free Water (0–1.5 m)	Organisms in Mats and *Throughout Profile*	Organisms in Mats *and* Anaerobic Bottom Layer
Oscillatoria	55	3	.	.	ж	.	.	.	.
Flexible rods	86	1	.	.	ж	.	.	.	.
Coccus w.sulfur	89	1	.	.	.	.	.	.	ж
Thin, flex. filam.	11	1	.	.	.	.	ж	.	.
Rod–shaped bact.	13	1	.	.	.	ж	ж	.	.
Diatom	98	+	.	ж	.	.	.	.	.
Leptospira	19	+	.	.	.	.	.	ж	.
Budding bacter.	18	+	.	.	.	.	.	ж	.
Spirillum thin	90	+	.	.	ж	.	.	.	.
Diatom	2	+	.	.	.	ж	ж	.	.
Rod w.gasvesicl.	94	+	.	ж	.	.	.	.	.
Beggiatoa	75	+	ж	ж	.	.	.	.	.
Cyanobacterium	93	+	ж	ж	.	.	.	.	.
Cyanobacterium	36	+	.	.	.	.	.	.	ж
Rods, thin, col.	16	+	.	.	.	.	ж	.	.
Microcyclus	95	r	.	.	.	ж	ж	.	.
"Prosthecocaulis"	1	r	.	.	.	.	ж	.	.
Macromonas	50	r	.	.	.	.	.	.	ж
Spirillum w.S°	54	r	ж	ж	.	.	.	.	.
Ciliate	96	r	ж	ж	.	.	.	.	.
Ciliate	63	r	ж	ж	.	.	.	.	.
Oscillatoria	97	r	ж	ж	.	.	.	.	.

Table IV
Types of Microorganisms and Their Frequency of Appearance
in the Green Loose Bottom Mats Type IV

Organism and Number		Frequency of Appearance	Only here in Green Bottom Mats	Only in *Mats*, Surface of Bottom	Organisms in Mats *and* Free Water (0-0.5 m)	Organisms in Mats *and* Free Water (0-1.5 m)	Organisms in Mats and *Throughout Profile*	Organisms in Mats *and* Anaerobic Bottom Layer
Oscillatoria	55	5	.	X	.	.	.	.
Flexible rods	34	2	.	.	.	.	X	.
Flexible rods	86	2	.	X	.	.	.	.
Prosthecochloris	38	2	.	.	.	.	.	X
Chromatium	40	1	.	.	.	.	.	X
Rods, red, small	85	1	.	.	.	.	.	X
Macromonas	50	+	.	.	.	.	.	X
Leptospira	19	+	.	.	.	.	X	.
Spirillum thin	90	+	.	X	.	.	.	.
Spirochaete	87	+	.	X	.	.	.	.
"Dichotomicrobium"	12	+	.	.	.	.	X	.
Vibrio thick	42	+	.	.	.	.	.	X
Cyanobacterium	83	+	.	.	.	.	.	X
Rod-shaped bact.	13	r	.	.	X	X	.	.
Rods, thick	47	r	.	.	.	.	.	X
Budding bacter.	18	r	.	.	.	.	X	.
Diplococci	62	r	.	X	.	.	.	.
Spirochete large	32	r	.	.	.	.	.	X
Thiodendron	64	r	.	X	.	.	.	.
Coccus w.sulfur	89	r	.	.	.	.	.	X
Thiospirillum	84	r	X	.	.	.	.	.
Rods, thin	88	r	X	.	.	.	.	.
Diatom	91	r	X	.	.	.	.	.
Flexible filamt.	92	r	X	.	.	.	.	.

environmental condition. Morphological variation in the natural habitat is difficult to assess because of identification
problems.

The degree of morphological change may vary. Many rod-
shaped bacteria can attain different lengths, but their cell
diameter varies only slightly (*E. coli*). Others, such as
Bdellovibrio sp. vary greatly with respect to diameter and
length. Again others, such as "*Dichotomicrobium*," may show a

Table V
Frequency and Distribution of Main Mat Organisms in the
Four Mat Types and in the Free Solar Lake Water

Organism and Number	Frequency of Appearance				Present in Free Water			
	Colorless to Pink Mat Type	Yellow-Brown Mat Type	Green Floating Mats	Green Mat Type on Bottom	Throughout Profile	Upper 0.5 m	Upper 1.5 m	Bottom Only
Diatom 4	4	3	.	.	.	+	+	.
Diatom 112	3	.	.	.	.	.	.	.
Diatom 98	2	4	.	.	.	.	.	.
Flexible rods 34	2	.	.	2	+	.	.	.
Flexible rods 86	2	3	1	2	.	.	.	.
Large, motile B. 113	1	.	.	.	.	.	.	.
Rod-shaped B. 13	1	1	1	.	.	+	+	.
Budding rods 111	1	.	.	.	.	.	.	.
Microcyclus 95	1	.	.	.	.	+	+	.
Filaments, thick 35	.	2	.	.	.	.	.	+
Diatom 2	.	2	.	.	.	+	+	.
Oscillatoria 55	.	.	3	5	.	.	.	.
Coccus w.S° 89	.	.	1	.	.	.	.	+
Flexible filam. 11	.	.	1	.	.	.	+	.
Prosthecochloris 38	.	.	.	2	.	.	.	+
Chromatium 40	.	.	.	1	.	.	.	+
Rods, red, small 85	.	.	.	1	.	.	.	+
Total number of microorganisms	30	28	22	24				
Total number of microorganisms specific for mats	18	16	11	10				

whole range of cell diameters, lengths and shapes in a normal fast-growing young culture due to their special differentiation processes.

"*Dichotomicrobium*" with tetrahedral cells, with hyphae and buds, occurred in the lake between 0 and 3 m as well as between 3.5 and 4.5 m. The cells were easily recognizable. Yet, the conditions were quite different, *i.e.*, aerobiosis, 20°C and low salinity was one extreme, and anaerobiosis, 52°C and 152°/oo salinity was the other extreme. Laboratory-pure cultures showed only little morphological variation. Strain 958 was tested for growth between 16 and 65°C. At 52°C, which had been the extreme temperature in the lake during observation time, growth occurred, and the cells resembled those seen in the lake. The basic morphological features (tetrahedral shape, hyphae, buds) were observed with cells grown in the whole temperature range. There were, however, differences in the average hyphal length, in the cell size, and in the number of buds or side-branches of hyphae. Thus, some morphological characters vary and others are stable. It is with the aid of those stable characters that one may be able to identify microbial assemblages morphologically.

In the special case of the Solar Lake, with its drastic changes of salinity with depth, one could expect morphological changes due to salinity effects. But, what is the stability of salinity stratification? During most of the year, at least, salinity changes in the microhabitat of Solar Lake microorganisms seem to be minor.

The application of several different observation methods for recognition of lake microorganisms makes it likely that most forms present were actually seen. However, since only a short period during one season was investigated, it must be assumed that other seasonal aspects vary greatly from this chapter's descriptions. Also, more cultural work, perhaps with different media, is needed. Because one cannot rely only on cultural work (Brisou *et al.*, 1974), direct observation techniques should not be overstressed and should be supported by physiological data.

The question of activity has to be solved as well. The mere presence of an organism in a habitat is not necessarily an indication of its activity. *In situ* activity measurements and turnover rate experiments with specific substrates, such as described for sulfate-reducing bacteria (Jørgensen, 1977), have to be carried out. Furthermore, the fate of marginal mats during turnover time have to be investigated with respect to heterotrophic microbial diversity. Decomposition of cyanobacteria by myxobacteria has been observed (Shilo, 1970). The most intriguing question, however, is that of stability of mat composition over a several years' period. Where and how do mat organisms survive during adverse times? Where do they come from? Answers to this will certainly be needed to solve many geomicrobiological problems related to mat formation in this lake.

ACKNOWLEDGMENTS

I would like to thank Prof. M. Shilo and Drs. M. Varon and M. Kessel for their kind hospitality shown me at the Department of Microbiological Chemistry, Hebrew University, Jerusalem. Skillful technical help of B. Doose and A. Gräter (Kiel), as well as of I. Levanon (Elat), is gratefully acknowledged. The Steinitz Biological Laboratory (Elat) has been helpful during the course of this work. The investigations were supported by the Deutsche Forschungsgemeinschaft.

REFERENCES

Bergey's Manual of Determinative Bacteriology, 8th ed., R. E. Buchanan and N. E. Gibbons, Eds. (Baltimore: Williams and Wilkins Publishing Company, 1974).

Brisou, J., D. Courtois and F. Denis. "Microbiological Study of a Hypersaline Lake in French Somaliland," *Appl. Microbiol.* 27:819-822 (1974).

Cohen, Y. "Dynamics of Prokaryotic Photosynthetic Communities of the Solar Lake," Ph.D. Thesis, Jerusalem (1975).

Cohen, Y., E. Padan and M. Shilo. "Facultative Anoxigenic Photosynthesis in the Cyanobacterium *Oscillatoria limnetica*," *J. Bacteriol.* 123:855-861 (1975).

Friedman, G. M., A. G. Amiel, M. Brown and D. S. Miller. "Generation of Carbonate Particles and Laminites in Algal Mats— Example from Sea-Marginal Hypersaline Pool, Gulf of Aqaba, Red Sea," *Bull. Am. Assoc. Petrol. Geol.* 57:541-557 (1973).

Geitler, L. "Cyanophyceae," *Rabenhorsts Kryptogamenflora* 14: 1-1196 (1932).

Hirsch, P. "Neue Methoden zur Beobachtung und Isolierung ungewöhnlicher oder wenig bekannter Wasserbakterien," *Zeit. Allg. Mikrobiol.* 12:203-218 (1972).

Hirsch, P. "Unusual Bacteria of a Solar Lake: Distribution and Pure Culture Studies," *Abst. Annual Meeting Am. Soc. Microbiol.* 33 (1977).

Hirsch, P., M. Müller and H. Schlesner. "New Aquatic Budding and Prostecate Bacteria and Their Taxonomic Position," *Proc. Symp. Aquatic Microbiol., Soc. Applied Bacteriol, Lancaster 1976* (in press).

Jørgensen, B. B. "Sulfate Reduction in Solar Lake Algal Mats (Sinai)," *Third Int. Symp. Environmental Biogeochem., Wolfenbüttel, Proceedings* (1977).

Krumbein, W. E., and Y. Cohen. "Biogene, klastische und evaporitische Sedimentation in einem mesothermen, monomiktischen, ufernahen See (Golf von Aqaba, Sinai)," *Geol. Rundschau* 63: 1035-1065 (1974).

Krumbein, W. E., and Y. Cohen. "Primary Production, Mat Formation and Lithification: Contribution of Oxygenic and Facultative Anoxygenic Cyanobacteria," in *Fossile Algae*, E. Flügel, Ed. (Berlin, Heidelberg: Springer-Verlag, 1977), pp. 37-56.

Lyman, J., and R. H. Fleming. "Composition of Sea Water," *J. Marine Res.* 3:134-146 (1940).

Shilo, M. "Lysis of Blue-Green Algae by Myxobacter," *J. Bacteriol.* 104:453-461 (1970).

Staley, J. T. "*Prosthecomicrobium* and *Ancalomicrobium*, New Prosthecate Freshwater Bacteria," *J. Bacteriol.* 95:1921-1942 (1968).

Van Ert, M., and J. T. Staley. "Gas Vacuolated Strains of *Microcyclus aquaticus*," *J. Bacteriol.* 108:236-240 (1971).

SULFATE REDUCTION IN CYANOBACTERIAL MATS OF SOLAR LAKE (SINAI)

B. BARKER JØRGENSEN

Institute of Ecology and Genetics
University of Aarhus
Aarhus C, Denmark

Y. COHEN

H. Steinitz Marine Biological Laboratory
P.O. Box 469
Elat, Israel

INTRODUCTION

Dense cyanobacterial mats are known from a number of tropical coasts where high salinity, temperature, and light intensity favor this growth form. In the hypersaline Solar Lake on the Sinai coast of the Gulf of Elat, 1-m-thick cyanobacterial mats form the littoral sediments. A regular lamination reflects seasonal variations in the types of microorganisms growing on the mat surface. Thus, diatoms and coccoid cyanobacteria dominate in summer while filamentous cyanobacteria dominate in winter. Also, photosynthetic and colorless sulfur bacteria form a conspicuous component of the mat. The annual layer thickness of 1.2 mm can be used to date the various layers. A progressing mineralization with depth in the mat is demonstrated by an increasing concentration of biogenic carbonate. A more detailed description of the structure and development of the mats is given by Friedman (1973) and Krumbein and Cohen (1974).

Due to the extreme hydrographical conditions of Solar Lake (temperatures up to 62°C, salinity up to 180°/oo), hardly any benthic fauna is present which could burrow into the cyanobacterial mats and disturb the lamination. The mats therefore constitute an ideal system for investigating the dynamics of mineralization with depth and thus with time after deposition. From measurements of the vertical gradients in the chemical composition and in the turnover of inorganic sulfur compounds it has been possible to set up a budget of the sulfur cycle and to estimate the importance of anaerobic respiration for the

mineralization of the mat (Jørgensen and Cohen, 1977). This
chapter will discuss some of the results of bacterial sulfate
reduction in the mats.

METHODS

Sediment cores up to 80-cm long, which retained an undisturbed stratification, were collected in PVC tubes from a
small area of the littoral mats. They were brought to the laboratory at the *in situ* temperature, and further treatment was
initiated within a few hours after sampling.

The rate of sulfate reduction was measured with a radiotracer technique described by Jørgensen and Fenchel (1974).
Labeled sulfate dissolved in Solar Lake water was injected in
5-μl portions into whole cores through the wall of the coring
tubes. After a few hours incubation at the *in situ* temperature,
the bacterial activity was stopped, and the rate of sulfate reduction could be calculated from the amount of radioactive sulfide formed.

RESULTS AND DISCUSSION

Measurements of sulfate reduction were made with short
depth intervals from the surface of the cyanobacterial mat to
80-cm depth. Repeated measurements in September and December
at 35° and 29°C, respectively, showed little seasonal variation
in the bacterial activity. With depth, however, the rate of
sulfate reduction decreased steeply from extremely high values
at the surface to low values in the deeper parts (Figure 1).
Thus, the heterotrophic activity is mainly concentrated within
the uppermost few mm of the mat where the photosynthetic production also takes place. It can be calculated from Figure 1
that 50 percent of the sulfate reduction in the mat takes place
within the uppermost 5 mm and 90 percent within the uppermost
3 cm.

As seen in Figure 1 the activity of the sulfate reducers
decreases extremely regularly with depth. This is in contrast
to normal shallow water sediments where the bacterial distribution is much more heterogeneous, partly due to the presence of
burrowing macrofauna (Jørgensen, 1977). In Figure 1 the approximate age of the sediment is also indicated. Even in 600-year-
old layers anaerobic decomposition progresses at measurable
rates.

The depth variation in the rate of sulfate reduction is
seen in Figure 1 to be rather closely described by the power
function: rate = 2040 $:$ $x^{-2.00}$ nmol SO_4^{2-} cm^{-3} day^{-1}, where x
is the depth below the surface in cm (x $\geqslant$ 0.5 cm). Thus, there
is a 100-fold decrease in activity from 0.5- to 5-cm depth and
a 10,000-fold decrease from 0.5 to 50 cm. The organic content
of the mat measured per unit volume decreases only by a factor
of 2 from the surface to 75-cm depth. The turnover rate of the

total organic pool must therefore decrease almost as rapidly as the sulfate reduction rate. Calculations show that the surface layers must be very open to organic influx from the photosynthetic zone in order to balance the mineralization rate. With depth the sediment constitutes an increasingly closed system.

This is also the case with respect to dissolved sulfate and sulfide which, at the surface, have short turnover times of 4 hours and 3 weeks, respectively. Half a meter down in the mat the corresponding figures are 0.5 years and 160 years.

Although the rate of anaerobic mineralization 5 mm below the mat surface is the highest yet recorded, the total rate of decomposition per unit area is less extreme due to the steep activity gradient. Thus, 65 mmol SO_4^{2-} m^{-2} day^{-1} are being

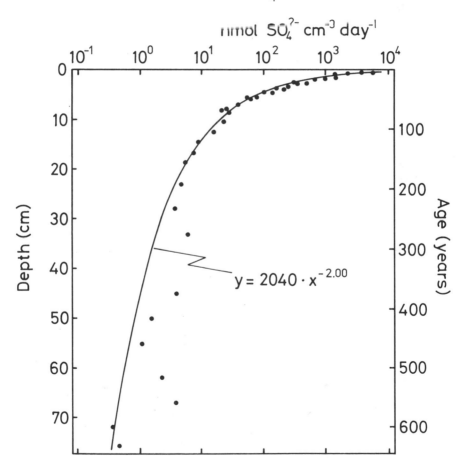

Figure 1. Rates of bacterial sulfate reduction in cyanobacterial mats of Solar Lake (Sinai). The approximate age of the mat layers is indicated. The depth variation of the metabolic rates is described by the indicated function (curve).

reduced corresponding to the mineralization of 1.6 g org. C m^{-2} day^{-1} assuming a stoichiometry of 2 mol org. C oxidized to CO_2 per 1 mol of sulfate reduced. Krumbein *et al.* (1977) measured the rate of photosynthesis in isolated fragments of the mat and found extremely high values of about 10 g C m^{-2} day^{-1}. Although these measurements show potential rates rather than *in situ* rates, they do indicate that the cyanobacterial mats are extremely productive systems. The accretion of 1.2-mm-thick annual layers represents only about 1 percent of the total biomass produced. The rest is rapidly being mineralized either aerobically or anaerobically via the sulfate-reducing bacteria.

A crude control of the accuracy of the high rates of sulfate reduction measured with the radiotracer technique was obtained in the following way. During winter a strong halocline develops in the lake water and the hypolimnion rapidly becomes anoxic and enriched in H_2S. This is produced mainly by cyanobacterial mats covering the slopes of the lake. The central bottom consists of precipitated gypsum and carbonate with a low organic content. It has an almost 100-fold lower rate of sulfate reduction than the cyanobacterial mats. Thus, the average release of H_2S from the sediments into the hypolimnion must be considerably less than the 65 mmol m^{-2} day^{-1} that are produced in the mats. The maximum rate of H_2S accumulation in the hypolimnion calculated from the figures of Cohen *et al.* (1977) is 22 mmol m^{-2} day^{-1}. This indicates that the measured rates of H_2S production cannot be highly overestimated.

ACKNOWLEDGMENTS

We wish to thank Ilana Levanon for her invaluable help during this study.

REFERENCES

Cohen, Y., W. E. Krumbein, M. Goldberg and M. Shilo. "Solar Lake (Sinai); 1. Physical and Chemical Limnology," *Limnol. Oceanog.* 22:597-608 (1977).

Friedman, G. M. "Generation of Carbonate Particles and Laminates in Algal Mats. Example from Sea-Marginal Hypersaline Pool, Gulf of Aqaba, Red Sea," *Am. Assoc. Petrol. Geol. Bull.* 57:541-557 (1973).

Jørgensen, B. B. "The Sulfur Cycle of a Coastal Marine Sediment (Limfjorden, Denmark)," *Limnol. Oceanog.* (in press).

Jørgensen, B. B., and Y. Cohen. "Solar Lake (Sinai). 5. The Sulfur Cycle of the Benthic Cyanobacterial Mats," *Limnol. Oceanog.* 22:657-666.

Jørgensen, B. B., and T. Fenchel. "The Sulfur Cycle of a Marine Sediment Model System," *Mar. Biol.* 24:189-201 (1974).

Krumbein, W. E., and Y. Cohen. "Biogene, klastische und evaporitische Sedimentation in einem mesothermen monomiktischen ufernahen See (Golf von Aqaba)," *Geol. Rundschau.* 63:1035-1065 (1974).

Krumbein, W. E., Y. Cohen and M. Shilo. "Solar Lake Sinai). 4. Stromatolitic Cyanobacterial Mats," *Limnol. Oceanog.* 22:635-656 (1977).

CHAPTER 18

ALGAL MATS AND THEIR LITHIFICATION

W. E. KRUMBEIN

University of Oldenburg
P.O. Box 25 03
D-2900 Oldenburg, Federal Republic of Germany

INTRODUCTION

Lithification and cementation in natural sedimentary environments have been studied frequently and the summaries of such studies are increasing in literature. A textbook on stromatolites and lithification processes in stromatolites has been published recently (Walter, 1976). Sedimentation and lithification of carbonates in general (Bathurst, 1975) and in special areas (Purser, 1972) can be cited, as well as special textbooks on cementation of loose material (Bricker, 1971). Carbonate precipitation and lithification processes in recent marine environments caused by photosynthetic microorganisms attracted attention very early (Darwin, 1841). In recent years many authors have stressed the importance of photosynthesis and photosynthetic CO_2 uptake and subsequent carbonate precipitation in marine and terrestrial environments (Krumbein, in press).

This chapter will emphasize the environments in which photosynthetic activity serves almost exclusively as an initiation of carbonate precipitation and lithification inasmuch as it produces reduced organic compounds, which in turn are degraded by an associated bacterial flora. This flora then alters the environment and produces conditions favorable for lithification and cementation by carbonates forming in the deeper layers of the sedimentary column.

Lithification processes in algal or cyanobacterial mats have been studied recently by Krumbein and Cohen (1974, 1977), Krumbein *et al.* (1977), Friedman *et al.* (1973), Monty (1976),

Golubić (1976), and Halley (1976). Freshwater mat lithification has been described by Monty and Hardie (1976), Hardie
(1975), and Eggleston and Dean (1976). In many cases photosynthetic activity of the associated algae have been mentioned
with or without the combined activity of bacteria associated
with the algal mat. Lithification in thermal environments has
been analyzed with or without consideration of the microbial
mediated processes by Walter (1976) and Walter *et al.* (1976).
Initiation of stromatolite growth and lithification processes
in mesothermal environments have been studied by Krumbein *et
al.* (1977). Studies on the Baja California sites are presented in this book (Philp *et al.*, 1978; Tibbetts and Maxwell,
1978) and by von der Haar (1976), Horodyski and von der Haar
(1975), and Horodyski *et al.* (in press).

This literature indicates that consideration must be
given to four different processes of carbonate deposition and/
or silica or iron oxide deposition in contact with algal mats.

1. *Inorganic or biological precipitation* that is not
controlled or influenced by the biota forming the living mat
structure takes place elsewhere and the products of these precipitation or mineralization processes are imported to the mat
environment *sensu strictu*. Here they are   sorbed to the mat
or laminated structures and initiate or enhance the lithification process of laminated mats.

2. *Precipitation of minerals* takes place within the mat
environment on or in the microorganisms forming the mat or parts
of the laminated structures. The precipitation is species-de-
pendent and morphologically discernible as a part of the general structure and skeleton of the organisms (*e.g.*, *Schizothrix*,
Rivularia), described by Schneider (1977). Another example
from nonmarine stromatolitic environments is described by
Krumbein and Potts (in preparation).

3. *The activity of photosynthetic bacteria* and/or algae
changes the environmental conditions by reducing CO_2 to organic
carbon compounds, thus shifting the solubility equilibrium
toward inorganic precipitation of carbonates. In some cases
these are deposited irregularly on the algal or microorganism
surfaces or they are precipitated elsewhere and then absorbed
to the sticky slime surfaces of the algae or bacteria within
the environment. Examples are given by Golubić (1976),
Schneider (1977), Krumbein and Cohen (1977), and Krumbein (in
preparation).

4. *Microbial mediated transformations* of reduced organic carbon compounds and other sources of energy, carbon and
nitrogen for bacteria yield many new compounds. Organic compounds are oxidized aerobically or by fermentative pathways.
Ammonia, bicarbonate, CO_2, oxygen losses, pH shifts, stable organic acids, chelating compounds, and surface-active substances
are intermediate or end products. Microbially produced organic
substances that are excreted immediately to the cell environment (*e.g.*, glycolate, succinate), thereby denitrifying activity

and sulfate reduction in the anaerobic layers of the mats, will lead to various conditions under which carbonate is precipitated (Krumbein, in press).

On the basis of these considerations investigations have been made in several environments to study early stages in the lithification process of algal mats.

METHODS

Recent algal and cyanobacterial mats have been studied in the field, by carbonate analyses, Scanning Electron Microscopy, EDX analyses, X-ray analyses, total organic carbon compounds by productivity methods, and bacteriological analyses of the decay processes involved in the transformation of reduced organic carbon compounds into the mineral form (Brock and Brock, 1967; Krumbein and Cohen, 1974, 1977; Krumbein ot al., 1977). The methodology also includes isotopic methods such as the estimation of quantitative sulfate reduction within an algal core (Jørgensen and Cohen, 1977). Field and laboratory methods are described also by Preiss (1976).

Laboratory experiments on bacterial carbonate production and the analysis of the carbonates have shown the importance not only of heterotrophic bacteria but also of sulfate-reducing anaerobic bacteria (Krumbein, 1973, 1974). Literature on bacteriological experiments, on carbonate precipitation, and lithification in recent sedimentary environments has been reviewed by Krumbein (in press).

RESULTS AND DISCUSSION

Elsewhere in this book carbonate generation in recent cyanobacterial mats is described morphologically. We have worked in the same environment and in several other environments containing high amounts of carbonates generated *in situ*.

The results of a detailed analysis of photosynthetic activity in the algal mat combined with the study of the decay environment demonstrate clearly that in the case of the Solar Lake mats (Gulf of Aqaba or Elat, Sinai) primary production within a laminated environment (recent stromatolite) is extremely high. Recently we have measured oxygen consumption values on Solar Lake mats which reached productivities of 8 to 10 g C m^{-2} day^{-1}. In laboratory experiments, mats of Laguna Mormona (Baja California, Mexico) were almost as active as Solar Lake mats. The productivity measured by the oxygen method reached values between 5 and 7 g C m^{-2} day^{-1}. The apparent differences in productivity can be explained by different salinities (see Cohen *et al.*, 1977; von der Haar, 1976) and by different cyanobacterial populations responsible for primary production within the mats.

The mat type investigated in Baja California was made up by the following organisms:

Microcoleus sp., *Lyngbya* sp., *Entophysalis* sp., *Pleurocapsa* sp., and several *Chromatium* sp. (see also Horodyski *et al.*, in press). Solar Lake mats are made up almost exclusively of two species of *Oscillatoria, Microcoleus chtonoplastes*, one *Lyngbya* sp., *Aphanothece* sp. and *Aphanocapsa* sp., and the diatoms of *Nitzschia* sp., *Amphora* sp. and *Navicula* sp.

Primary production is restricted to the uppermost 4 mm of the algal and bacterial laminated mats, with photosynthetic potential still present to a depth of 4 to 5 cm. Homogenized parts of the lower mat environment, representing ages between 40 and 80 years, still exhibit active photosynthesis when exposed to light. When the whole mat is exposed to light (exposure of cores 4-cm diameter and 6-cm thickness and subsequent sectioning of the central parts), CO_2 incorporation in deeper parts of the mat occurs only by dark fixation processes in bacteria, cyanobacteria and algae. In several cases, CO_2 fixation in the dark was even higher than in the parallel light experiments.

These experiments clearly demonstrate that CO_2 fixation by photosynthetic activity is restricted to the uppermost 4 mm of the mats, while dark fixation occurs also in deeper parts. Carbonate particles occur only in the mat environment and increase considerably with depth in Baja California mats (Javor, 1977). In the case of Solar Lake mats, precipitates occur only from 3 cm downwards in noteworthy amounts. Therefore, the lithification and calcification processes are related strictly to processes other than photosynthetic CO_2 incorporation. Of several different approaches for solving this problem, the SEM and EDX methods to analyze the algae mats will be described here. In other experiments (Krumbein *et al.*, 1977; Krumbein and Cohen, 1977; Krumbein 1973, 1974, in preparation) we have positive laboratory evidence of carbonate precipitation initiated in pure cultures of *Desulfovibrio*, several other anaerobic bacteria and aerobic heterotrophic bacteria isolated from mat environments. The results of the SEM and EDX analyses are shown in Figures 1 through 11.

The initial steps of carbonate precipitation and lithification in this environment, then, are caused by the metabolic activities of bacteria dwelling within this environment. These activities bring about carbonate precipitation, liberation of nitrogen and phosphorus, and the dissolution of diatoms.

It is fascinating to see that within an environment in which the pH value never exceeds pH 7, carbonates are deposited and the silica frustules of diatoms are completely dissolved. Figures 9 and 10 show that bacteria settling on diatoms are gradually enriched with Ca and Mg. They are then coated by crystals of different sizes and forms, and at the same time the diatoms dissolve completely. Ehrlich (in press) has also stated that the numerous diatoms occurring mainly in the summer mat (Krumbein and Cohen, 1974, 1977) disappear in deeper parts of the algal mats, which in the case of Solar Lake make up more

than 100 cm of organic sediment with perfectly preserved lamination. Since silica usually is mobilized only within environments of pH values above 9, this has to be attributed to
special microbial mediated reactions. They may be explained
by exchange of phosphorus and silica in organic compounds and
by polysaccharides in which carbon is replaced by silica
(Heinen, 1965; Lauwers and Heinen, 1974). From our analysis
of photosynthetic activity, bacterial decay processes, and
lithification of bacteria within algal laminated sediments, we
conclude that bacterial decay processes within stromatolitic
mats are mainly responsible for calcification, desilification,
and the transfer of reduced organic carbon compounds into inorganic carbonates. A relatively high percentage of approximately 2 to 4 percent organic carbon of the initial concentration of 16 to 18 percent organic carbon is preserved within
the final rock generated from the lithifying mat.

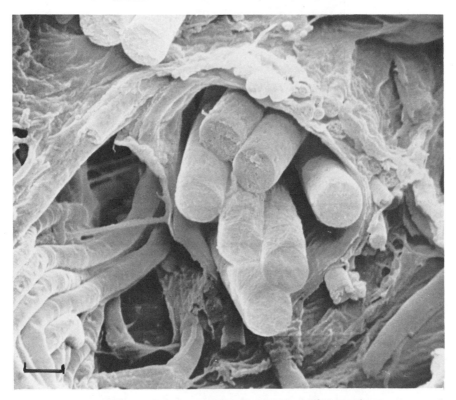

Figure 1. Cyanobacterial mat built up by *Microcoleus* sp. and
filamentous bacteria frequent in this mat type. Mat was
fixed *in situ* with glutaraldehyde and dried in alcohol. After this, critical point drying was used. The mat is held
together mainly by the common mucous sheaths of *Microcoleus*
bundles. Filamentous bacteria, rods, and cocci are kept outside the active living *Microcoleus* bundle. Scale: 2 μm
(Cambridge Instruments).

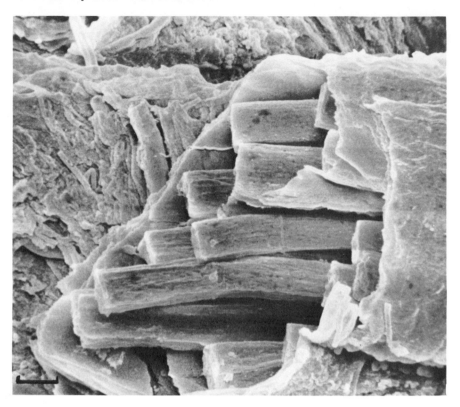

Figure 2. Mat from 2-cm depth. The *Microcoleus* filaments are
   deflated, corroded. First indications of crystallization
   are visible. Scale: 2 μm.

CONCLUSIONS

From 1970 to 1976, we studied several cyanobacterial
mat environments. These included the Solar Lake, the beachrock of El Hamira, the lagoon at Ras Muhammed, mangrove environments, and several other places along the shores of the Gulf
of Aqaba. In the United States and Mexico we studied mats of
the thermal environment of Lake View (Oregon), Lassens National
Park (California), the Olympic Mountains National Park hot
springs environment (Puget Sound), desert mats of the Mohave
Desert (California), and several mat environments along the
shores of Baja California (namely, Guerrero Negro and Mormona
Bay).

From studies of primary productivity, degradation of
organic matter, morphological studies in the field, ultramor-
phological studies with SEM and from chemical and X-ray analyses of the sediments of the bacterially influenced environments,
the following conclusions were drawn.
1. Primary productivity in many of these areas is increasing
    considerably with increasing water temperature up to maxi-
    mum productivities at temperatures around 50°C.

2. Primary productivity is largely enhanced in the presence
    of
    a. hydrogen sulfides produced by sulfate reduction or de-
        sulfurication, in the case of the mat and beachrock
        environments along the coast of the Gulf of Aqaba and
        the Baja California coast; or
    b. in the presence of naturally produced hydrogen sulfide
        from volcanic sources (Olympic Mountains National Park,
        Lassens National Park). Of the several possible causes
        we mention the established evidence of high anoxygenic
        productivity of cyanobacteria in the Solar Lake and

Figure 3. Section of mat from Solar Lake (Sinai). *Oscillatoria* sp. exposes partially stripped-off sheath covered with
filamentous bacteria. Thin noncombined trichomes of *Microcoleus* and many filamentous bacteria are combined with big
Chromatium violescens, several of which are covered by micritic carbonate crystals. To the lowermost left *Nitzschia*
sp. is in complete decomposition. Aragonite crystals are
growing in the center. Scale: 3 μm (Kontron, München).

Figure 4. *Spirulina* sp. embedded in crystal aggregates formed
in part by encrusted filamentous bacteria. Above the middle
filament the end of a crystallized filament of a thin organism is detectable. Carbonate crystallization is relatively
high in this depth. Note that *Spirulina* sp. is almost completely free of any deposit. Neither precipitation nor the
settlement of carbonate particles takes place on this organism, making it unsuitable for lithification.

      the high productivity of photosynthetic sulfur-depen-
dent bacteria such as *Chromatium*, *Prostecochloris*,
Chloroflexus, and others (Walter *et al.*, 1976).
3. In most of the cases where lithification was observed, it
    was carbonate lithification, which was not related to photo-
    synthetic depletion of CO_2.
4. Lithification processes started within the decay en-
    vironment below the active photosynthetic zone. They were
    morphologically related to bacterial filaments and uni-
    cellular bacteria and algae.
5. Lithification stages of bacteria cells can be demonstrated
    within field samples by combining SEM with electron disper-
    sive X-ray analyses by using spot analyses, line-scan or
    distribution maps.
6. At the same time some of the environments show generation
    of framboidal pyrite nodules (Figure 6). These may be

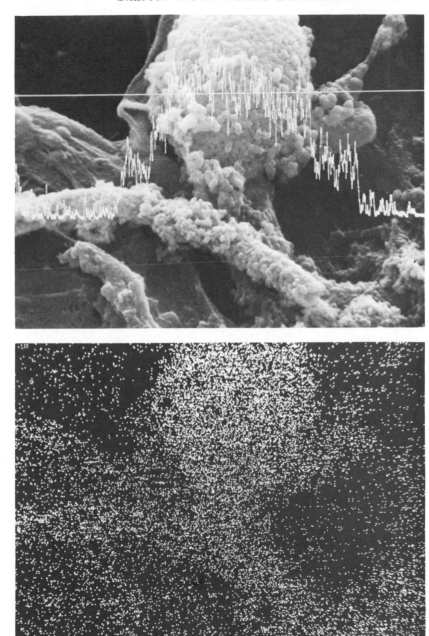

(a)

(b)

Figure 5a,b. Aphanocapsa sphere and trichome of *Oscillatoria* sp.
Both are coated by granular round particles, which on first
view within this sulfur-rich environment were taken for pyrite granules (see Figure 6). EDX-line scan and distribution map demonstrate no sulfur but high concentration of
phosphorus and calcium. The trichome is empty as can be
seen at the lower right end (see also Krumbein, 1975).

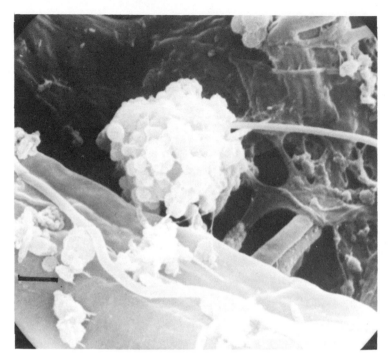

Figure 6.   Slime-coated bundle of trichomes on which a filamentous bacterium has settled.   The granule ball in this
case had high concentrations of sulfur, indicating sulfur
droplet formation outside the frequently occurring *Achrom-
atium* sp. which may calcify or be transformed into pyritic
structures (Kontron, München).

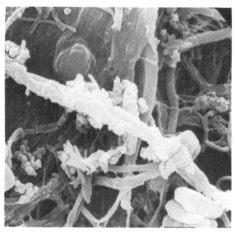

        (a)   (b)

Figure 7a,b.   Crystallizing bacteria from algal mat (a) and
from laboratory precipitation experiment (b).   (Cell size in
both cases 2 µm.   In Figure 7a (top region) remainders of a
dissolving *Nitzschia* sp. can be seen.

Figure 8. Diatom in dissolution from deeper parts of mat (6 cm). The *Microcoleus* trichomes now are completely calcified. The combined carbonate deposition and dissolution of silica can clearly be seen. Scale: 4 µm (Kontron, München).

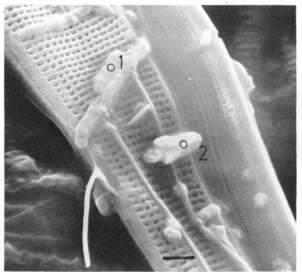

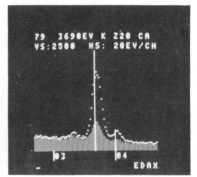

(a)   (b)

Figure 9a,b. Bacteria in different stages of calcification settling on *Nitzschia* sp. Spot 1: The smooth surface of the rod shows no sign of crystallization, while the crystal in spot 2 represents a completely calcified bacterial cell, which can be demonstrated by still present phosphorus concentrations. The EDS spot analyses are of the two spots. Spot 1 is represented by the hatched line, spot 2 by the dotted line. On the second spot the high degree of calcification is expressed by the much higher Ca peak, which is combined with lower silica concentration (not shown). The EDX spot analysis was taken under the same conditions for both spots. Scale: 1 µm (Cambridge Instruments and EDAX, Dortmund).

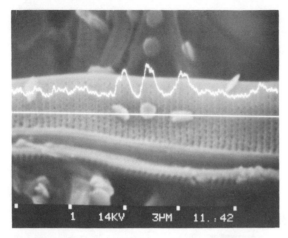

Figure 10. Line-scan of
    calcium over lithifying
    bacteria settling on
    Nitzschia thermalis.
    Line-scan taken on our
    SEM 180 EDX combination.
    Distance between bars 3 μm.

(a)   (b)

Figure 11a,b. Development of pseudo-ooidal structure and
    lithification in mats; 11a shows development of carbonate
    spherulites from bacterial culture in sea water and algal
    material (see also Krumbein, 1973). Bacteria have been iso-
    lated from beach rock environment in which mats are forming
    and agglutinating the sand grains. 11b: Spherulitic and
    elongated crystallized structures from Solar Lake mats,
    which are clearly connected to bacterial crystallizations
    and the encrustation of *Microcoleus* bundles. Scale: 11a =
    2 μm, 11b = 200 μm.

    caused by fossilized bacteria and by physical-chemical
    precipitation from bacterial sulfide.
7. Laboratory experiments prove that bacteria, while degrading
    algal and photosynthetic bacterial material, precipitate
    several different carbonates in various forms and morpho-
    logical shapes (Figures, 3, 4, 5, 7 and 11).
8. Within the decay environment at pH values below 7 and at

simultaneous carbonate precipitation, silica frustules of
associated diatom populations are completely dissolved
(Figures 3, 7a and 7). This may evoke the impression that
diatoms are recent newcomers in such environments, which
is not true.

9. Different filamentous and coccoid cyanobacteria are lithified partially or not, depending on slime production, capa-
bility of movement, outer morphology and microenvironments.
For example, *Spirulina* sp. does not lithify because its
spiral shape opposes settlement of particles and organisms
(Figures 1, 2, 4 and 8).

10. The resulting carbonate sediments are extremely rich in
different particle forms such as onkoids, spherulites,
flakes, filaments, tubes, chips, sandwiched structures and
pseudo-ooids (see also Krumbein, 1975). The final carbonate
structures rarely resemble the organism initiating the
carbonate deposition. On the contrary, most of the organisms causing lithification are destroyed by the process
they have declenched.

ACKNOWLEDGMENTS

Parts of this work have been made possible by grants
Kr. 333/8 and Kr. 333/12 of the Deutsche Forschungsgemeinschaft.
I am indebted to Cambridge Instruments, Dortmund; Philips, Eind-
hoven, Kontron, München; Ortec, München, and EDAX, Dortmund for
some of the material. Several of the micrographs and EDX
analyses have been done also at the Cambridge SEM 180/Ortec
combination in our laboratory. I wish to express my gratitude
to the numerous colleagues who have helped me in reaching places,
receiving information, and processing the data: C. Lange,
I. Raether, and G. Koch of the University of Oldenburg. The
staff of the H. Steinitz Marine Biology Laboratory, Elat, has
helped in field and laboratory work on the Solar Lake. Without
the aid of K. Nealson and F. Vidal of the Scripps Oceanographic
Institution, I would not have been able to do the field work in
Mexico. I am also indebted to B. Javor and B. Bloeser for valuable information on their work in progress at Baja California.
I am indebted to Yehida Cohen for sharing fieldwork in all
environments.

REFERENCES

Bathurst, R. G. C. *Carbonate Sediments and Their Diagenesis*,
2nd ed. (Amsterdam: Elsevier, 1975).

Bricker, O. P. *Carbonate Cements* (Baltimore: J. Hopkins University Press, 1971).

Brock, T. D., and M. L. Brock. "The Measurement of Chlorophyll,
Primary Productivity, Photophosphorylation, and Macromolecules
in Benthic Algae Mats," *Limnol. Oceanog.* 12:600-605 (1967).

Cohen, Y., W. E. Krumbein, M. Goldberg and M. Shilo. "Solar Lake (Sinai). 1. Physical and Chemical Limnology," *Limnol. Oceanog.* 22:597-608 (1977).

Cohen, Y., W. E. Krumbein and M. Shilo. "Solar Lake (Sinai). 2. Distribution of Photosynthetic Microorganisms and Primary Production," *Limnol. Oceanog.* 22:609-620 (1977).

Cohen, Y., W. E. Krumbein and M. Shilo. "Solar Lake (Sinai) 3. Heterotroph Bacterial Distribution and Production," *Limnol. Oceanog.* 22:621-634 (1977).

Darwin, C. "On a Remarkable Bar of Sandstone off Pernambuco on the Coast of Brazil," *The London Edinburgh and Dublin Phil. Mag. and J. o. Sci.* 19:257-261 (1841).

Eggleston, J. R., and W. E. Dean. "Freshwater Stromatolitic Bioherms in Green Lake, New York," in *Stromatolites, Developments in Sedimentology 20,* M. R. Walter, Ed. (Amsterdam/Oxford/New York: Elsevier, 1976), pp. 479-488.

Ehrlich, A. "Living and Subfossil Diatoms of a Hyperhaline Heliothermic Pond on the Western Shore of the Gulf of Elat (N. E. Sinai)" (in preparation).

Friedman, G. M. "Algal Mats as Agents of Calcium Carbonate Precipitation," *infra,* pp. 227-235.

Friedman, G. M., A. J. Amiel, M. Braun and D. S. Miller. "Generation of Carbonate Particles and Laminites in Algal Mats, Example from Sea-Marginal Pool, Gulf of Aqaba, Red Sea," *Am. Assoc. Petrol. Geol. Bull.* 57:541-557 (1973).

Golubić, S. "Organisms that Build Stromatolites," in *Stromatolites, Developments in Sedimentology 20,* M. R. Walter, Ed. (Amsterdam/Oxford/New York: Elsevier, 1976), pp. 113-126.

Golubić, S. "Taxonomy of Extant Stromatolite-Building Cyanophytes," in *Stromatolites, Developments in Sedimentology 20,* M. R. Walter, Ed. (Amsterdam/Oxford/New York: Elsevier, 1976), pp. 127-140.

Haar, S. P. Vonder. "Evaporites and Algal Mats at Laguna Mormona, Pacific Coast, Baja California, Mexico," Ph.D. thesis, University of Southern California, Los Angeles (1976).

Halley, R. B. "Textural Variation within Great Salt Lake Algal Mounds," in *Stromatolites, Developments in Sedimentology 20,* M. R. Walter, Ed. (Amsterdam/Oxford/New York: Elsevier, 1976), pp. 435-446.

Hardie, L. A. "Algal Crusts and Their Environmental Significance," in *Sedimentation on the Modern Carbonate Tidal Flats of Northwest Andros Island, Bahamas*, Studies in Geology Series, L. A. Hardie, Ed. (Baltimore, Maryland: Johns Hopkins Press, 1975).

Heinen, W. "Siliciumstoffwechsel bei Mikroorganismen VII. Mitt. Verteilung der Kieselsäure in Zellfraktionen von *Proteus mirabilis* und der Nachweis von Kohlenhydrat-Kieselsäureestern," *Arch. Mikrobiol.* 52:69–79 (1965).

Horodyski, R. J., and S. P. Vonder Haar. "Recent Calcareous Stromatolites from Laguna Mormona (Baja California) Mexico," *J. Sediment. Petrol.* 45:894–906 (1975).

Horodyski, R. J., B. Bloeser and S. P. Vonder Haar. "Laminated Algal Mats from a Coastal Lagoon, Laguna Mormona, Baja California, Mexico," *J. Sediment. Petrol.* (in press).

Javor, B. J., and R. W. Castenholz. "Carbonate Precipitation in Algal Mats in a Silicoclastic Environment: a Quantitative Analysis," in *Abstracts of the III. International Symposium on Environmental Biogeochemistry, Wolfenbüttel 1977*, W. E. Krumbein, Ed. (University of Oldenburg, Environmental Laboratory, Occasional Publication No. 1, March 1977), p. 68.

Jørgensen, B. B., and Y. Cohen. "Solar Lake (Sinai). 5. The Sulfur Cycle of the Benthic Cyanobacterial Mats," *Limnol. Oceanog.* 22 (in press).

Krumbein, W. E. "Mikrobiologische Untersuchungen zur Fällung von Kalziumkarbonat aus Meerwasser," in *Biologische Anstalt Helgoland* (Hamburg: Jahresberichte, 1973), pp. 50–54.

Krumbein, W. E. "On the Precipitation of Aragonite on the Surface of Marine Bacteria," *Naturwissenschaften* 61:167 (1974).

Krumbein, W. E. "Biogenic Monohydrocalcite Spherules in Lake Sediments of Lake Kivu (Africa) and the Solar Lake (Sinai)," *Sediment.* 22:631–634 (1975).

Krumbein, W. E. "Precipitation of Carbonates by Bacteria and Algae," in *Biological Cycling of Minerals*, D. J. Swain and P. A. Trudinger, Eds. (Amsterdam: Elsevier, in press).

Krumbein, W. E. "Photolithotrophic and Demolithotrophic Activity of Bacteria and Algae as Related to Beachrock Formation and Degradation (Gulf of Aqaba, Sinai)" (submitted to *Geomicrobiology J.*).

Krumbein, W. E., and Y. Cohen. "Biogene, klastische und evaporitische Sedimentation in einem mesothermen monomiktischen
ufernahen See (Golf von Aqaba)," *Geol. Rdsch.* 63:1035-1064
(1974).

Krumbein, W. E., and Y. Cohen. "Primary Production, Mat Forma-
tion and Lithification Changes of Oxygenic and Facultative
Anoxygenic Cyanophytes (Cyanobacteria)," in *Fossil Algae,
Recent Results and Developments,* E. Flügel, Ed. (Berlin/
Heidelberg/New York: Springer-Verlag, 1977), pp. 37-56.

Krumbein, W. E., Y. Cohen and M. Shilo. "Solar Lake (Sinai).
4. Stromatolitic Cyanobacterial Mats," *Limnol. Oceanog.* 22:
635-656 (1977).

Lauwers, A. M., and W. Heinen. "Biodegradation and Utilization
of Silica and Quartz," *Arch. Mikrobiol.* 95:67-78 (1974).

Maxwell, J. R., P. J. C. Tibbetts, C. D. Watts and S. Golubić.
"Carotenoids in Algal Mat Cores from Baja California (Mexico)
and Shark Bay (W. Australia)," *infra.*

Monty, C. L. V. "The Origin and Development of Cryptalgal Fabrics," in *Stromatolites, Developments in Sedimentology 20,*
M. R. Walter, Ed. (Amsterdam/Oxford/New York: Elsevier, 1976),
pp. 193-250.

Monty, C. L. V., and L. A. Hardie. "The Geological Significance
of the Freshwater Blue-Green Algal Calcareous Marsh, in
Stromatolites, Developments in Sedimentology 20, M. R. Walter,
Ed. (Amsterdam/Oxford/New York: Elsevier, 1976), pp. 447-478.

Philp, R. P., M. Calvin, S. C. Brassell, G. Eglinton and S. P.
Lomas. "Hydrocarbon and Fatty Acid Distributions in Recently
Deposited Algal Mats at Laguna Guerrero, Baja California
(Mexico)," *infra,* **pp. 22.**

Preiss, W. V. "Basic Field and Laboratory Methods for the Study
of Stromatolites," in *Stromatolites, Developments in Sedimentology 20,* M. R. Walter, Ed. (Amsterdam/Oxford/New York:
Elsevier, 1976), pp. 5-14.

Purser, B. H., Ed. *The Persian Gulf. Holocene Carbonate Sedimentation and Diagenesis in a Shallow Epicontinental Sea*
(Berlin/Heidelberg/New York: Springer-Verlag, 1973).

Schneider, J. "Carbonate Construction and Decomposition by
Epilithic and Endolithic Microorganisms in Salt and Freshwater," in *Fossil Algae, Recent Results and Developments,*
E. Flügel, Ed. (Berlin/Heidelberg/New York: Springer-Verlag,
1977), pp. 248-261.

Walter, M. R. Ed. *Stromatolites, Developments in Sedimentology 20* (Amsterdam/Oxford/New York: Elsevier, 1976).

Walter, M. R., J. Bauld and T. D. Brock.   "Microbiology and Morphogenesis of Columnar Stromatolites (Conophyton, Vacerrilla) from Hot Springs in Yellowstone National Park," in *Stromatolites, Developments in Sedimentology 20,* M. R. Walter, Ed. (Amsterdam/Oxford/New York: Elsevier, 1976), pp. 273–310.

CHAPTER 19

"SOLAR LAKE": A SEA-MARGINAL POND OF THE RED SEA
(GULF OF AQABA OR ELAT) IN WHICH ALGAL MATS
GENERATE CARBONATE PARTICLES AND LAMINITES

GERALD M. FRIEDMAN

Department of Geology
Rensselaer Polytechnic Institute
Troy, New York 12181 USA

GENERAL SETTING OF POOL

Small hypersaline pools are present locally along the
Red Sea Coast. The sea-marginal hypersaline pool under study
is along the west shore of the Gulf of Aqaba (or Elat; the
terms are synonymous), a northern segment of the Red Sea, about
18 km south of the town of Elat (Figure 1). The pool is between a bay on the north, which follows an old fault or frac-
ture zone and is locally known as a "fjord," and a big fan on
the south, which is part of a wadi known as Wadi Murah (Figure
2). The rocks of the surrounding terrain are part of the rugged
mountains of the Sinai Peninsula and form the northernmost segment of the Arabo-Nubian Precambrian shield. The pool, which
is about 140 m long and about 65 m wide, is in a semicircular
depression within the complex of igneous and metamorphic rocks
and is separated from the ocean by a gravel bar, 45-60 m wide
and up to 3 m high.

In the Gulf of Aqaba beyond this gravel bar, reefs and
carbonate skeletal sediments floor a narrow shelf, 100-150 m
wide, which is bounded by submarine fault planes that are vir-
tual precipices. The shores continuous to the pool are equally
precipitous. The surface of the bar that separates the pool
from the ocean consists of loose igneous and metamorphic rock
gravel with abundant molluscan shell fragments. Below this
veneer of loose gravel the bar must be cemented tightly to
isolate the pool from the ocean.

The bathymetry of the pool shows three distinct zones:
shelf, slope and bottom. The shallow shelf is carpeted by
blue-green algal mats; at the shelf edge the algal mats abruptly tear and their edges hang down loosely. The slope and

Figure 1.   Sea-marginal pool, Gulf of Aqaba or Elat, Red Sea.
Gravel bar (on left) separates pool from Red Sea.   Algal mats
grow on bottom in shallow water around the periphery of the
pool.   Vehicle and person on gravel at upper left indicate
scale.

Figure 2.   Vertical aerial
photograph of sea-marg-
inal pool and vicinity
on west coast of Gulf.
Pool is appoximately
140 m long and 65 m
wide.

bottom are floored by white gypsum. Water depth of the flat bottom is about 5-m below mean sea level.

Of interest in this study are the carbonate sediments that are interlaminated with the algal mats or are particles within these mats.

VERTICAL SEQUENCE

Cores through the shallow shelf show that the dense mass of algal mats overlies a carbonate mud in which the gastropod *Cerithium* is abundant. This close relation between algal mats and sediments rich in *Cerithium* is common. The origin of the hypersaline pool can best be explained in terms of the relation between *Cerithium* and algal mats.

In a vertical sequence the presence of *Cerithium* in the sediments signifies salinity close to that of sea water, whereas the presence of algal mats signifies hypersaline conditions. Three cores penetrated 35-52 cm of algal mats before reaching the underlying *Cerithium* carbonate mud. A radiocarbon date on organic matter in the *Cerithium* carbonate mud below the algal mats gave an age of 4655 ± 555 years. This age dates open-marine conditions and implies that the pool was open to the ocean at that time. The dated carbonate mud was sampled 7-cm below the contact with the algal mats. Organic matter from algal mats 7-cm above the contact with the *Cerithium* carbonate mud gave an age of 1918 ± 370 years. The presence of algal mats indicates hypersaline conditions and, hence, that the separation of the pool and its isolation from the ocean had occurred before this date. The change from *Cerithium* carbonate mud to algal-mat sedimentation, and hence the separation of the pool from the ocean, occurred between 4655 ± 555 and 1918 ± 370 years B.P. If 7 cm of sediment accumulated for each of the two different facies above and below the contact, the pool must have separated from the ocean by approximately 2500-4000 years B.P. Therefore, the bar that isolates the pool from the ocean came into existence in the interval between these two dates.

ALGAL MATS

The algal mats break up into discrete polygons that are usually 0.3-1.0-m across. Margins of the polygons curl up around the edges and grow upward. Closer to the edge of the shelf—that is, in deeper water—the mats form much larger polygons, about 0.5-1.0-m across, and are devoid of raised or curled-up edges. These are the lily-pad type algal mats similar to those known from the Persian Gulf (Kendall and Skipwith, 1968). Near the shelf edge the mats hang together without any apparent separation into polygons, but at the shelf edge the mats tear off and hang down like loose blankets. At the shore of the pond the color of the mats is black, but the color of

the raised curled-up edges is brown. As the water deepens, the
black color of the mats gives way sharply to brown. Despite
the sharp change in color, the cracks of the polygons persist
undisturbed across the color of boundary. At the shelf edge,
where the profile of the pool abruptly steepens and mats tear
off, they take on green coloration.

    In cores the algal mats consist of alternating black
and gray laminites that resemble varves. Organic matter com-
poses each of these laminites, which are flat or gently undul-
ating. Interlaminated between the algal mats are grayish-white
laminites of aragonite and high-magnesian calcite. Embedded
in the algal mats are abundant sedimentary particles: oncolites,
ooids, peloids, and grapestones.

Carbonate Sediments

    In addition to the above-mentioned sand-size sediment-
ary particles embedded in the algal mats are other nondescript
particles. Thin carbonate laminites are present between the
algal mats.

Peloids

    Many particles consist of cryptocrystalline to micron-
size carbonate devoid of internal structure. Their outlines
may be that of a peloid, of rounded to elliptical, irregular,
elongate, or even wedge shape. Peloids may be cemented together to form grapestones.

Ooids

    Ooids commonly consist of a cryptocrystalline nucleus
and a radial rim. Some ooids appear to be devoid of a nucleus,
and hence are technically spherulites and not true ooids. Yet
they are identical in morphology to the true ooids except for
the absence of a nucleus. The radial fibers that normally make
up the rim project into the very center of the particle. Spherulites are present in ancient algal limestones (Meijer, 1971),
and their origin is related closely to ooids, as shown by transitions between them. Ooids are commonly semiopaque because of
the high content of organic matter; some have concentric in
addition to the radial lines.

Oncolites

    Particles that are commonly rounded but also variably
shaped, with semiopaque to opaque algal organic matter lines,
are termed *oncolites*, following Heim (1916) and Flügel and
Kirchmayer (1962). The particles are cryptocrystalline or fibrous or have alternating fibrous, transparent, cryptocrystalline and semiopaque layers. Some cryptocrystalline particles

enclose one or more rings of semiopaque algal matter. Some oncolites are of extremely irregular shape and defy simple description.

This study shows that oncolites and radial ooids are not mutually exclusive; in fact, not only do they coexist, but they show transitional stages indicating that their origins are related closely and are a product of algal precipitation. Some ooids and spherulites show incipient opaque algal coatings; as these coatings become more developed and accentuated the particles are oncolites rather than ooids or spherulites.

Grapestones and Flakes

Peloids, ooids and oncolites commonly are cemented together to form grapestones. Grapestones may consist of any one of these three particles or of a mixture of any or all of them. The cement between them may be fibrous or cryptocrystalline. Where many particles are cemented together and the compound particles become larger than sand size, the term *flake* applies. Flakes consist of flat, compound, allochemical particles that have become cemented together. They may be several centimeters long. These flakes resemble those in the grapestone facies of the Bahamas (Purdy, 1963a,b).

Carbonate Laminites

Grayish-white carbonate laminites, about 0.5-mm thick, are present between the gray and black algal mats (Figure 3). These laminites are cryptocrystalline and semiopaque or fibrous and transparent. Cryptocrystalline and fibrous laminites may alternate (Figure 4).

Because carbonate mud is absent from the pool and from the contiguous Red Sea, the laminites of the pool must have been precipitated in the algal mats. The laminites have the typical cryptocrystalline or fibrous fabric that characterizes particles embedded in the algal mats.

MINERALOGY

The blue-green algae precipitate particles and laminites which consist of cryptocrystalline, semiopaque, high-magnesian calcite and fibrous transparent aragonite. Microprobe data show that cryptocrystalline cement, particles or laminites have overall concentrations of 3-8 percent magnesium with spots ("hot spots") between 8 and 16 percent. About a third of this magnesium concentration is in the organic matter, as will be explained later. The strontium concentration in the cryptocrystalline carbonate ranges between 3000 and 9000 ppm as determined by microprobe; the lowest values are in the "hot spots" where the magnesium concentration is highest.

The scanning electron microscope shows fibrous aragonite

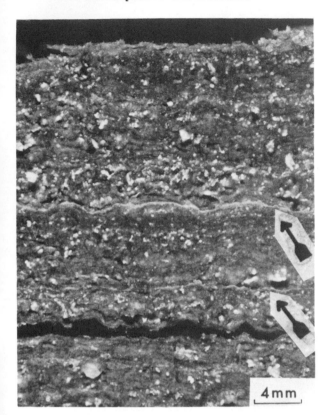

4mm

Figure 3. Laminites of
   calcium carbonate be-
   tween algal mats (see,
   for instance, arrows).
   Abundant carbonate particles (peloids, ooids and
   oncolites) are embedded
   in algal mats. Core
   from shelf of pool.

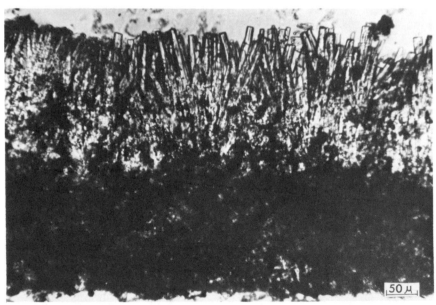

50 μ

Figure 4. View in thin section of carbonate laminites consisting of cryptocrystalline high-magnesian calcite (below) and
   fibrous aragonite (above).

consisting of prismatic crystals, and cryptocrystalline high-
magnesian calcite composing a mosaic of micron–size rhombohe-
drons.   The observation that algally precipitated particles
and laminites as well as cement between particles consist of
micron–size polyhedral blocks of calcite in the depositional
environment vitiates much current thinking that claims that all
micritic limestones have formed neomorphically from aragonite
needles (Folk, 1965).   The evidence suggests that cryptocrystalline carbonate analogous to the micrite of ancient limestones
may consist initially of metastable high–magnesian calcite,
which during diagenesis stabilizes to low–magnesian calcite
(Friedman, 1964).   Thus, many ancient micrites, especially
those present with stromatolites, may have originated as algally precipitated carbonate.   This carbonate, when present
between particles, is therefore matrix and cement combined.

The ooids are low in magnesium and high in strontium.
The magnesium concentration is too low to be detected with the
microprobe, whereas the strontium concentration ranges between
8 and 12°/oo.   Hence, the ooids consist of aragonite.

ORGANIC MATTER, MAGNESIUM CONCENTRATION

In cryptocrystalline cement or laminites, the molecular
percentage of $MgCO_3$ in the "hot spots" is between 30 and 60.
Organic matter holds a third of this magnesium.   In a sample
consisting of ooids bound together with a cryptocrystalline
cement, the total magnesium concentration was 2.4 percent.   Although pure cement could not be isolated in this sample,
the magnesium must be mostly in the cement because ooids are
low in magnesium.   Removal of the organic matter with buffered
H_2O_2 and analysis by atomic absorption spectrometry showed
about 0.8 percent magnesium in this sample to be in the effluent
and 1.6 percent in the carbonate sediment, from which organic
matter had been removed.   Hence, a third of the magnesium is
present as a magnesium–organic complex and the remainder as
high–magnesian calcite.

X–Ray analysis, using the graphs of Goldsmith and Graf
(1958), shows that the molecular percentage of $MgCO_3$ in the
high–magnesian calcite is approximately 37.   If we assign a
third of the magnesium of the "hot spots" (molecular percentage
of $MgCO_3$: 30–60) to organic matter, then the molecular percentage of $MgCO_3$ in the carbonate phase ranges between 20 and 40.
Similar experiments showed 1.9 percent magnesium to be in the
organic matter of algal mats as a magnesium–organic complex;
the lithified sediment below the algal mats contained 0.7 percent magnesium in the organic matter.   Thus the organic matter
of the algal mats is magnesium–rich.   In fact, the total magnesium concentration in organic matter plus carbonate phase
may be as high as that of dolomite.   The microenvironment of
the algae is one in which magnesium is enriched in both the

organic matter and in the calcium carbonate phase, which the
algae precipitate.
    For more details on the carbonate particles and lamin-
ites in algal mats of this pool see Friedman *et al.* (1973),
Krumbein and Cohen (1974), and Krumbein *et al.* (1977).

REFERENCES

Flügel, E., and M. Kirchmayer. "Zur Terminologie der Ooide,
    Onkoide und Pseudooide," *Neues Jahrb. Geologie u. Paläon-
    tologie Monatsh* 3:113-123 (1962).

Folk, R. L. "Some Aspects of Recrystallization in Ancient Lime-
    stones," in *Dolomitization and Limestone Diagenesis: Soc.
    Econ. Paleontologists Mineralogists,* Spec. Pub. 13:14-48
    (1965).

Friedman, G. M. "Early Diagenesis and Lithification in Carbon-
    ate Sediments," *J. Sed. Petrol.*   34(4):777-813 (1964).

Friedman, G. M., A. J. Amiel, Moshe Braun and D. S. Miller.
    "Generation of Carbonate Particles and Laminites in Algal
    Mats--Example from Sea-Marginal Hypersaline Pool, Gulf of
    Aqaba, Red Sea," *Am. Assoc. Petrol. Geol. Bull.* 57(3):
    541-557 (1973).

Goldsmith, J. R., and D. L. Graf. "Structural and Compositional
    Variations in Some Natural Dolomites," *J. Geol.* 66(6):
    678-693 (1958).

Heim, A. "Monographie der Churfürsten-Mattstock-Gruppe, III.
    Stratigraphie der Unteren Kreide und des Jura. Zur Litho-
    genesis," *Beitr. Geol. Karte Schweiz., N.F.* 20(50):369-662
    (1916).

Kendall, C. G. St. C., and P. A. d'e. Skipwith. "Recent Algal
    Mats of a Persian Gulf Lagoon," *J. Sed. Petrol.*   38(4):
    1040-1058 (1968).

Krumbein, W. E., and Y. Cohen. "Biogene, klastische und evapor-
    itische Sedimentation in einem mesothermen, monomiktischen
    ufernahen See (Golf von Aqaba, Sinai)," *Geol. Rundschau*
    63:1035-1065 (1974).

Krumbein, W. E., Y. Cohen and M. Shilo. "Solar Lake (Sinai).
    4. Stromatolitic Cyanobacterial Mats."

Meijer, J. J., de. "Carbonate Petrology of Algal Limestones
    "Lois-Ciguera Formation, Upper Carboniferous, Leon, Spain,"
    Leidse Geol. Mededelingen 47:1-53 (1971).

Purdy, E. "Recent Calcium Carbonate Facies of the Great Bahama Bank: Petrography and Reaction Groups," *J. Geol.* 71(3): 334-355 (1963a).

Purdy, E. "Recent Calcium Carbonate Facies of the Great Bahama Bank: Sedimentary Facies," *J. Geol.* 71(4):472-497 (1963b).

CHAPTER 20

NUTRIENT PRODUCTION IN NEARSHORE TIDAL FLAT PORE WATERS: A KINETIC STUDY

W. BERRY LYONS

   Department of Earth Sciences
   University of New Hampshire
   Durham, New Hampshire 03824   USA

W. F. FITZGERALD

   Marine Sciences Institute
   University of Connecticut, Avery Point
   Groton, Connecticut   06340   USA

INTRODUCTION

The pore fluids of sediments are a sensitive indicator of diagenetic reactions taking place in the sedimentary environment (Siever *et al.*, 1965; Sholkovitz, 1973).   In recent anoxic marine sediments, the major diagenetic reaction taking place was the bacterially mediated reduction of sulfate (Goldhaber and Kaplan, 1974).   This process results in the production of various reaction by-products and flux of chemical constituents from the sediments into the overlying water (Berner, 1976). The rate of sulfate reduction is directly related to the amount of metabolizable organic carbon in the sediment (Berner, 1964; Berner, 1970; Lyons *et al.*, in press), and the sedimentation rate (Goldhaber and Kaplan, 1975).   Recently Berner (1974) has applied a steady-state kinetic model to the anoxic diagenesis of recent marine sediments, with particular reference to the reduction of sulfate and the production of ammonia and phosphate. Murray and Grundmanis (in press) have used this model to determine the rate constants of anoxic decomposition in sediments of Saanich Inlet, B.C., Canada, an anoxic basin.   We have applied Berner's model to three sets of data from a tidal flat in Branford Harbor, Connecticut, USA.

METHODS

          Cores were taken by hand at low tide with acid pre-
cleaned polyvinyl chloride (PVC) core barrels (4-cm o.d.). The
cores were immediately placed in larger diameter (6-cm i.d.)
PVC core carriers, purged with N_2 gas, sealed with PVC caps and
returned to the laboratory. Upon the return to the laboratory
the core barrels were placed in a 6 ft x 3 ft x 2 ft glove box,
which had been purged with N_2. The cores were then extruded, sec-
tioned, centrifuged and filtered through precleaned (Patterson
and Settle, 1974) 0.45-µ Nucleopore T.M. filters at approximately
in situ temperatures. The inert atmosphere was maintained to
avoid the possible oxidation of reduced chemical species present in the pore waters. Bray *et al.* (1973) and Troup *et al.*
(1974) have shown that this is necessary if accurate phosphate
and trace metal data are to be obtained from anoxic pore water
samples. Cores were taken at three different times of the year:
late summer (August 1975), winter (February 1976) and spring
(May 1976) at approximately the same general location on the
tidal flat. This was done to ascertain if the seasonal temperature change (20°C to 1°C) of the estuarine water had any
effect on the pore water chemistry.
          After filtration, a 10.00-ml sample of pore water from
each section of sediment core was pipetted into a 19-ml poly-
ethylene vial, removed from the glove box and, within 24 hr
titrated for alkalinity using the method of Gieskes and Rogers
(1973). The titration was followed potentiometrically and the
end point was determined using a Gran calculation. The precision of this method was ±0.5%. The final pH of the samples
was ~3. The titrated samples were then frozen and analyzed
within six weeks for phosphate and ammonia. Phosphate was
determined colorimetrically using the method of Murphy and
Riley (1962) modified for higher concentrations by Bray (1973).
The precision of the measurement was found to be ±4% at the
various concentrations encountered in this study. Ammonia was
determined by the ion-specific electrode method of Gilbert and
Clay (1973) with modifications for smaller sample volumes. The
precision of the measurement was ±7% at the concentrations
encountered.

RESULTS

          The data are tabulated in Table I. In general the ti-
tration alkalinity, ammonia and phosphate increase with depth,
similar to data from other estuarine and continental margin
sediments (Matisoff *et al.* 1975, Sholkovitz, 1973). The decrease in pore water phosphate in the lower sections of the
sediment may be due to vivianite $(Fe_3(PO_4)_2 \cdot 8 H_2O)$ formation
(Lyons and Fitzgerald, 1976). We have applied Berner's (1974)
steady-state diagenesis equations to our ammonia and phosphate
data and Murray and Grundmanis' (in press) adaption of Berner's

Table I
Pore Water Data from Branford Harbor, Connecticut, USA

Depth of Sediment Section (sm)	pH	Titration Alkalinity $(megl^{-1})$	NH_4^+ (mMl^{-1})	PO_4^{3-} (mMl^{-1})
August 28, 1975				
0-8	-	-	0.43	0.52
8-16	8.25	7.06	0.51	0.43
16-26	8.30	9.98	0.79	0.57
26-39	8.34	14.01	0.99	0.58
39-52	8.32	15.79	1.09	0.65
52-75	8.27	18.18	1.21	0.75
February 23, 1976				
0-8	7.91	4.80	0.19	0.21
8-16	8.20	8.86	0.45	0.44
16-26	8.28	14.82	0.44	0.63
26-39	8.28	17.01	0.41	0.64
39-52	8.28	19.82	0.51	0.60
52-75	8.38	19.88	0.68	0.65
May 10, 1976				
0-8	8.08	7.39	0.10	0.57
8-16	8.32	11.05	0.27	0.73
16-26	8.45	15.49	0.25	0.93
26-39	8.38	18.31	0.59	0.82
39-52	8.42	22.01	1.01	0.85
52-75	8.45	16.27	1.15	0.71

equations to our alkalinity data, which have been corrected for sulfide, ammonia and phosphate contributions. K_A, K_N and K_P values have been determined for each core, where K_A, K_N and K_P are the first-order rate constants for the production of carbonate alkalinity, nitrogen (ammonia) and phosphorus (phosphate) respectively by the decomposition of organic matter during anoxic microbial metabolism.

The reader should consult Berner (1974) for a thorough discussion of the derivation, assumptions and limits of the equations and the ensuing models. In calculating the k values from the model, we have used the sedimentation rate of 0.45 cm yr^{-1} determined for the central nearshore area of Long Island Sound by Thomson *et al.* (1975). The values for the three Branford Harbor, CT cores are tabulated in Table II along with the values of Berner (1974) and Murray and Grundmanis (in press) for various estuarine and continental shelf anoxic sediments.

Table II

K_A, K_N and K_P Values from Various Estuarine and Continental
Margin Anoxic Sediments

	$K_A(sec^{-1})$	$K_N(sec^{-1})$	$K_P(sec^{-1})$
Branford, Conn. (August)	1.0×10^{-10}	0.51×10^{-10}	3.3×10^{-10}
Branford, Conn. (February)	1.6×10^{-10}	0.70×10^{-10}	17×10^{-10}
Branford, Conn. (May)	1.8×10^{-10}	0.60×10^{-10}	10×10^{-10}
Santa Barbara Basin (Berner, 1974)	–	0.13×10^{-10}	0.09×10^{-10}
Somes Sound, Maine (Berner, 1974)	–	14×10^{-10}	–
Long Island Sound (Berner, 1974)	–	–	95×10^{-10}
Saanich Inlet, B.C. (Murray and Grundmanis)	3.7×10^{-10}	2.1×10^{-10}	
Saanich Inlet, B.C. (Murray and Grundmanis)	3.9×10^{-10}	2.1×10^{-10}	

CONCLUSIONS

The K_A's and the K_N's computed from our data are very
similar and differ little in the three cores studies. The K_P's,
however, are higher by as much as two orders of magnitude and
differ considerably from core to core. This would suggest, contrary to Berner's (1974) data from the Santa Barbara Basin, that
the anoxic formation of ammonia and phosphate may not be completely coupled. Experiments (Kamatani, 1969) have shown that
phosphate is mineralized from organic matter at a faster rate
than nitrogen, which may explain the higher K_P values.

It is also possible that the K_P reflects the formation
of dissolved phosphate from the dissolution of ferric phosphate
compounds in the anoxic zone of the sediments. Suess (1976) has
shown that "excess" phosphate in anoxic pore waters of Baltic
Sea sediments may indeed be due to this process. If this is
also the case for the Branford sediments, the K_P's reflect not
only the phosphate derived from the decomposition of organic

matter but also the phosphate derived from inorganic redox reactions, *e.g.*, $FePO_4 + e \rightleftharpoons Fe^{2+} + PO_4^{3-}$. Thus, the difference in the K_p values from core to core may reflect either a difference in the phosphorus content of the organic matter or a difference in the ferric phosphate content of the sediments.

Berner (1974) suggests that, due to the differences in K values between sulfate reduction (the production of carbonate alkalinity) and ammonia production in Santa Barbara basin sediments, there is no direct coupling between the two processes. Our calculated K values for alkalinity production and ammonia production differ by a factor of two to three. Ammonia produced by anoxic decomposition processes can also be associated with clay minerals on cation exchange sites (Rosenfeld and Berner, 1976). Even when the amount of ammonia found in association with the sediment is taken into account, the calculated K_N values remain approximately the same (*e.g.*, 0.6×10^{-10} sec^{-1}).

Our data suggest that phosphate is regenerated three to ten times faster than ammonia in the anoxic zone of these sediments. These results are in general agreement with the short term laboratory studies conducted on the aerobic decomposition of organic matter (Grill and Richards, 1964; Vaccaro, 1965; Kamatani, 1969). These workers have shown that phosphate is more rapidly regenerated from organic matter than is nitrogen. Field studies (Ketchum *et al.*, 1967; Holm-Hansen *et al.*, 1966) confirm the laboratory results regarding the rapid regeneration of phosphorus compared to carbon or nitrogen but suggest that under aerobic conditions nitrogen is also regenerated faster than carbon. Our data suggest that under anoxic conditions where many types of microbial metabolism take place (*i.e.*, sulfate reduction, carbonate reduction and fermentation), the rate of nitrogen production is lower than that of carbon production, contrary to prevailing conditions when oxygen is present.

The values for K_A, K_N and K_p differ widely with sedimentary regime (Table II). Berner (1974) and Murray and Grundmanis (in press) have pointed out that the differences in these rates are undoubtedly due to differences in the type of organic matter that reaches the anoxic zone of the sediment. This is, of course, related to the source of the organic material as well as the sedimentation rate of the system. If the organic matter being deposited at the sediment–water interface is not buried rapidly enough, the easily metabolized compounds may be lost before anoxic decomposition can commence, lowering the anoxic rate constants. The rate constants computed from our data show that the rates of production of alkalinity, phosphate and ammonia are lower than the values from other nearshore environments yet higher than those of continental margin sediments. The tops of our sediment samples were always exposed at low tide, and the rates of aerobic respiration, both microbial and macrobenthic, were probably extensive. We have observed large populations of the mud snail, *Nassarium obsoletus*, grazing at the sediment surface. These factors suggest that much of the organic matter deposited at the sediment surface is undoubtedly consumed before burial, indirectly producing the lower rate constants observed by us.

It appears that the rate of anoxic decomposition of organic matter of an exposed tidal flat is intermediate between estuarine and continental margin environments. This is consistent with Berner's (1974) proposal that the higher the burial rate of the more rapidly decomposable organic matter, the higher the rate constants of anoxic decomposition. Even though large amounts of organic detritus are deposited at the sediment-water interface of Branford Harbor, the majority of this material is apparently decomposed aerobically and may not be buried, thereby producing rate constants lower than those from the nearby deeper water estuarine sediments.

ACKNOWLEDGMENTS

We are deeply appreciative to J. W. Murray and V. Grundmanis for providing us with their unpublished data from Saanich Inlet. We thank C. Hunt, T. Fogg, J. Crowell and S. Hornor for their help in obtaining and processing the cores. The senior author is grateful to H. E. Gaudette for his continuing support and interest.

REFERENCES

Berner, R. A. "An Idealized Model of Dissolved Sulfate Distribution in Recent Sediments," *Geochim. Cosmochim. Acta* 28: 1497-1563 (1964).

Berner, R. A. "Sedimentary Pyrite Formation," *Am. J. Sci.* 268: 1-28 (1970).

Berner, R. A. "Kinetic Models for Anoxic Marine Sediments," in *The Sea,* Vol. 5, E. D. Goldberg, Ed. (New York: John Wiley and Sons, 1974), pp. 427-450.

Berner, R. A. "The Benthic Boundary from the Viewpoint of a Geochemist," in *The Benthic Boundary Layer,* N. McCave, Ed. (New York: Plenum Press, 1976), pp. 33-35.

Bray, J.T. "The Behavior of Phosphate in the Interstitial Waters of Chesapeake Bay Sediments," Ph.D. Thesis, Department of Earth and Planetary Science, The Johns Hopkins University (1973).

Bray, J. T., O. P. Bricker and B. N. Troup. "Phosphate in Interstitial Waters of Anoxic Sediments: Oxidation Effects During Sampling Procedure," *Science* 180:1362-1364 (1973).

Gieskes, J. M., and W. C. Rogers. "Alkalinity Determination in Interstitial Waters of Marine Sediments," *J. Sed. Petrol.* 43:272–277 (1973).

Gilbert, T. R., and A. M. Clay. "Determination of Ammonia in Aquaria and in Sea Water Using the Ammonia Electrode," *Anal. Chem.* 45:1757–1759 (1973).

Goldhaber, M. B., and I. R. Kaplan. "The Sulfur Cycle," in *The Sea,* Vol. 5, E. D. Goldberg, Ed. (New York: John Wiley and Sons, 1974), pp. 569–655.

Goldhaber, M. B., and I. R. Kaplan. "Controls and Consequences of Sulfate Reduction Rates in Recent Marine Sediments," *Soil Sci.* 119:42–55 (1975).

Grill, E. V., and F. A. Richards. "Nutrient Regeneration from Phytoplankton Decomposing in Sea Water," *J. Mar. Res.* 23: 51–69 (1964).

Grundmanis, V., and J. W. Murray. "Organic Matter Decomposition and Bioturbation in Puget Sound Sediments," *Trans. Am. Geophys. Union* 57:151 (1976).

Holm-Hansen, D., J. D. H. Strickland and P. M. Williams. "A Detailed Analysis of Biologically Important Substances in a Profile off Southern California," *Limnol. Oceanog.* 11:548–561 (1966).

Kamatani, A. "Regeneration of Inorganic Nutrients from Diatom Decomposition," *J. Oceanog. Soc. Japan* 25:63–74 (1969).

Ketchum, B. H., N. Corwin and C. S. Yentsh, in "Biological, Chemical, and Radiochemical Studies of Marine Plankton," *Woods Hole Oceanographic Institution Ref.* 67-27 (1967), pp. 21–25.

Lyons, W. B., and W. F. Fitzgerald. "Iron and Manganese Geo-chemistry of Tidal Flat Pore Waters: A Thermodynamic Approach," *Abst. Annual Meeting Geol. Soc. Am.* (1976), p. 990.

Lyons, W. B., A. D. Hewitt, A. Rutter, T. R. Fogg and H. E. Gaudette. "Influence of Organic Carbon Character on Sulfate Reduction Rates in Estuarine Sediments," (submitted to *Geology*).

Matisoff, G., O. P. Bricker, G. R. Holdren and P. Kaerk. "Spatial and Temporal Variations in the Interstitial Water Chemistry of Chesapeake Bay Sediments," in *Marine Chemistry in the Coastal Environment,* T. M. Church, Ed., ACS Symp. Series 18 (Washington, D.C.: American Chemistry Society, 1975), pp. 343–363.

244 The Aquatic Environment

Murphy, J., and J. P. Riley. "A Modified Single Solution Method
for the Determination of Phosphate in Natural Waters," *Anal.
Chim. Acta* 27:31-36 (1962).

Murray, J. W., and V. Grundmanis. "Interstitial Water Chemistry
in the Sediments of Saanich Inlet," (submitted to *Geochim.
Cosmochim. Acta*).

Patterson, C. C., and D. M. Settle. "The Reduction of Orders
of Magnitude Errors in Lead Analyses of Biological Materials
and Natural Waters by Evaluating and Controlling the Extent
and Sources of Industrial Lead Contamination Introduced During Sample Collection and Analysis," in The National Bureau
of Standards Special Publication: *Accuracy in Trace Analysis,
Proceedings of the 7th Materials Res. Symp.,* P. La Fleur,
Ed. (1974).

Redfield, A. C., B. H. Ketchum and F. A. Richards. "The Influence
of Organisms on the Composition of Sea Water," in *The Sea,*
Vol. 2 (New York: John Wiley and Sons, 1963), pp. 26-77.

Rosenfeld, J. K., and R. A. Berner. "Ammonia Adsorption in
Nearshore Anoxic Sediments," *Abstr. Annual Meeting of Geol.
Soc. Am.* (1976), p. 1076.

Sholkovitz, E. "Interstitial Water Chemistry of the Santa
Barbara Basin Sediments," *Geochim. Cosmochim. Acta* 37:
2043-2073 (1973).

Siever, R., K. C. Beck and R. A. Berner. "Composition of Interstitial Waters of Modern Sediments," *J. Geol.* 73:39-73 (1965).

Suess, E. "Nutrients Near the Depositional Interface," in
The Benthic Boundary Layer, N. McCave, Ed. (New York: Plenum
Press, 1976), pp. 57-80.

Thomson, J., K. K. Turekian and R. J. McCaffrey. "The Accumu-
lation of Metals in and Release from Sediments of Long Island
Sound," in *Estuarine Research,* Vol. 1, L. E. Cronim, Ed.
(New York: Academic Press, 1975), pp. 28-44.

Troup, B. N., O. P. Bricker and J. T. Bray. "Oxidation Effect
on the Analysis of Iron in the Interstitial Water of Recent
Anoxic Sediments," *Nature* 249:237-239 (1974).

Vaccaro, R. F. "Inorganic Nitrogen in Sea Water," in *Chemical
Oceanography,* Vol. 1, J. P. Riley, and G. Skirrow, Eds.
(New York: Academic Press, 1965), pp. 356-408.

CHAPTER 21

SULFATE REDUCTION IN COASTAL SEDIMENTS AND THE RELEASE OF H$_2$S TO THE ATMOSPHERE

B. BARKER JØRGENSEN
M. H. HANSEN
K. INGVORSEN

Institute of Ecology and Genetics
University of Aarhus
Aarhus C, Denmark

INTRODUCTION

During the past few years a number of estimates have been made of the global sulfur budget. These all emphasize the atmosphere as an important component (*e.g.*, Eriksson, 1963; Friend, 1973; Kellogg *et al.*, 1972). One source of atmospheric sulfur is biogenic H$_2$S produced by the decomposition of organic matter in anoxic environments. Areas that may potentially contribute to the atmospheric sulfur include tidal flats, salt marshes and swamps. The H$_2$S is formed here partly during the hydrolytic breakdown of proteinaceous material and partly as an end product of anaerobic respiration in sulfate-reducing bacteria. In marine environments rich in sulfate the last process tends to dominate (Jørgensen, 1977).

Previously published estimates of the rate of H$_2$S released to the atmosphere have not been based on directly measured values but have been calculated by difference from other parts of the global sulfur cycle in order to balance the budget. Thus, there is still a lack of independent measurement of the biogenic contribution.

In the present study the rate of bacterial sulfate reduction has been determined in different types of sediment along the Danish coast. On some shores where H$_2$S escapes into the atmosphere, the rate of release has been directly measured by a simple technique in which the ascending H$_2$S is quantitatively collected. Some of the factors regulating the H$_2$S release have been studied.

MATERIALS AND METHODS

The investigated localities, Limfjorden and Aarhus Bay, are situated in northern Jutland, Denmark. There is no significant tide in the areas but only wind-induced fluctuations in the water level. The productivity is high, partly due to large stands of eelgrass (*Zostera marina*), which contribute significantly to the organic content of the sediments.

Measurements of bacterial sulfate reduction have been made in sediments both right on the beach and a few km offshore at 5-20 m depth. The sediments vary in grain size from coarse sand to silt and clay, with an organic content between 0.3 and 30 percent dry wt. The rate of sulfate reduction was determined with a radiotracer technique described by Jørgensen and Fenchel (1974). A radioactive sulfate solution was injected directly into undisturbed sediment cores and the amount of radioactive sulfide produced was determined. Other chemical methods were applied as described by Jørgensen (1977).

The release of H_2S to the atmosphere was studied only on beach localities with a few cm water covering. The rate of release was measured by placing a transparent Plexiglas box, open in the bottom, on the sediment surface (Hansen *et al.*, 1977). The air inside the box was rapidly pumped through a sulfide trap in a closed circuit. The trap quantitatively collected the H_2S that had been released from the underlying sediment. A control of the trapping efficiency for the whole setup showed that more than 75 percent of artificially added H_2S was found again in the traps. By renewing the traps at 1-2 hr intervals, the diurnal variation in the H_2S release could be followed. This was supplemented by regular measurements of other parameters such as light intensity, temperature, pH, O_2 and H_2S concentrations in the thin water layer, and the redox profile of the sediment.

RESULTS AND DISCUSSION

A Survey of Sulfate Reduction Rates

The theoretical limits for the amount of H_2S that may be released from coastal marine sediments to the atmosphere are governed by: (1) the total production of sulfide in the sediments and (2) the efficiency with which the sulfide is transferred from the sediment to the air. This transfer may be direct or via a shallow water layer.

The bacterial sulfide production takes place mainly in the uppermost part of the anoxic sediment, and the rate rapidly decreases with depth. In the investigated sediments more than half of the total sulfate reduction per unit area was found in the uppermost 10 cm. Of all the H_2S produced, an estimated average of 10 percent is trapped within the anoxic zone by precipitation with iron and other metal ions (Jørgensen, 1977).

The remaining 90 percent are again lost from the sediment.
Most of this is reoxidized when the H_2S reaches the surface or
when the sediment is stirred and percolated by oxic water during
tides and storms. Only under special circumstances may it
reach up into the atmosphere.

A summary of the measured sulfate reduction rates in the
0-10 cm layer is given in Table I. Individual measurements
yielded results ranging from less than 1 up to 3000 nmol SO_4^{2-}
cm^{-3} day^{-1}. On an areal basis, however, the variation is less
extreme.

On beach localities the sandy sediments generally have
a low metabolic rate. On exposed beaches sulfate reduction may
even be absent within the upper 10 cm. In sheltered areas where
the sand is mixed with fresh organic material, sulfate-reducing
bacteria may be quite active, with reduction rates ranging from
3 to 50 mmol m^{-2} day^{-1} during the summer. The highest values
are reached in the thick masses of decomposing eelgrass and
macroalgae, which drift together along the coast during winter
storms.

In the more offshore waters at 5-20 m depth, less geographical variation in the sediment metabolism has been found.
Thus, the difference between sandy sediments and mud is less
than twofold, although there is a tenfold difference in the
organic content on a dry weight basis. The relation between
the concentration of organic matter and the rate of anaerobic
mineralization is quite complex. In shallow waters the detritus is mixed into the anoxic sediments in an earlier stage of
decomposition than in deeper waters. Thus, there is a tendency
of a higher turnover rate of the organic pool near the coast,
while the organic matter that reaches more offshore sediments
is more refractory to bacterial attack.

Seasonal Variations

In addition to the geographical variation there is also
a strong seasonal variation in the sedimentary metabolism. During a two-year study of the sulfur cycle in Limfjorden sediments
a four- to sixfold difference was found between the rate of
sulfate reduction per m^2 in winter and in summer (Jørgensen,
1977). The rate varied parallel to the temperature with a Q_{10}
of 3.4. This is shown in Figure 1, which also shows the seasonal changes in the dark oxygen uptake of the sediment, the
oxygen concentration in the water right above the bottom, and
the thickness of the oxidized surface layer of the sediment
(Eh $\geqslant$ 0 mV).

In winter the uppermost 3 cm of sediment are oxidized
and the bottom water is saturated with oxygen. During summer
the water masses become stratified and extensive oxygen depletion occurs at the bottom. The high rate of oxygen consumption
in the sediment at this season in combination with the poor
oxygen availability causes the reduced sediment zone to rise

Table I

General Characteristics and Sulfate Reduction Rates in the Upper 10 cm of Danish Coastal Sediments

Locality	Sediment Type	Organic Matter (% dry wt)	Temperature (°C)	SO_4^{2-} Red. Rate (mmol m^{-2} day^{-1})
Limfjorden				
Sheltered beach	Medium sand	0.3–1	18–30	3–10
5–15 m depth	Fine sand	1 –2	10	5– 6
5–15 m depth	Mud	10 –13	2–4	2– 3
5–15 m depth	Mud	10 –13	20	12–20
Aarhus Bay				
Sheltered beach	Decomposing eelgrass	20 –30	16–28	40–50
Sheltered beach	Fine sand and silt	2 –3	20	20–40
10–20 m depth	Mud	4 –8	13	5–10

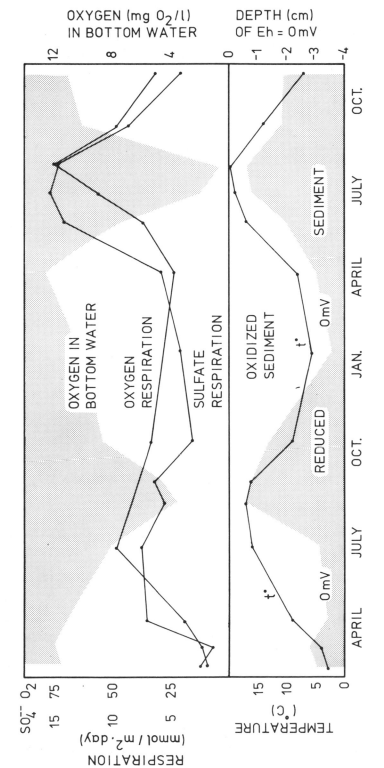

Figure 1. Seasonal variations in Limfjorden of: (upper part) the oxygen concentration in the sea water just above the sediment, the aerobic (oxygen) respiration of the benthic community, the anaerobic (sulfate) respiration in the upper 10 cm of the sediment; (lower part) the temperature at the sediment surface, and the thickness of the oxidized zone of the sediment (Eh ≥ 0 mV).

towards the surface. In some periods the sediment and the overlying water may become completely anoxic. This, however, does
not lead to an immediate release of H_2S into the stagnant water.
Large amounts of ferric iron at the sediment surface functions
as a buffer, which may bind one or two weeks of sulfide production in the form of FeS.

Even when H_2S does appear in the bottom water it will
seldom reach through the surface water and into the atmosphere.
Östlund and Alexander (1963) have calculated that an oxic water
layer of only one m will normally constitute a complete barrier
to the release of H_2S, and even within a 10-cm stagnant layer
all the sulfide may be oxidized. When looking for areas of H_2S
release, one should therefore focus on shore localities.

H_2S Release

Two such localities were selected, one in Limfjorden and
one in Aarhus Bay. Those beach sediments that were most likely
to release H_2S were identified by a visible growth of purple
sulfur bacteria. This indicates that the sulfide zone reaches
within a few mm of the sediment surface. The smell of H_2S was
often noticed, especially at night, during work in these localities.

Transparent boxes with sulfide traps were placed on the
sediments that were covered by only a few cm of water. Through
periods of 24 hr the changes in H_2S release and other sediment
parameters were followed. In Figure 2 the typical course of a
diurnal cycle has been summarized. The sun sets at 19.30 and
rises at 04.30. One hour before sunset the first traces of H_2S
have already started to ascend from the sediment, and as the
light fades the rate of release rapidly increases. It reaches
a maximum soon after midnight, and around sunrise the release
rapidly decreases again.

Since the H_2S reaches the air via the thin water layer
above the sediment, a diurnal variation in the water chemistry
is expected. Figure 2 shows the changes in O_2, dissolved sulfide and pH. The oxygen concentration reaches 150 percent sat-
uration in the afternoon due to an intensive photosynthesis by
the benthic microalgae. As the light intensity decreases so
does the photosynthetic O_2 production, and due to a high rate
of heterotrophic and chemical O_2 consumption, the concentration
reaches zero or very low levels soon after the onset of dark-
ness. Oxygen does not reappear until an hour after sunrise.

Already before O_2 is depleted, H_2S appears in the water.
Through the night its concentration varies rather parallel to
its rate of release. There is a change in the balance between
the gas form (H_2S) and the ionized form (HS^-) caused by changes
in the pH of the water. During the day, light processes produce a high pH. At sunset the pH is 8.5, and only 2 percent of
the sulfide is in gas form. During the night the pH decreases
to a minimum of 7.6 and 25 percent of the sulfide is dissolved

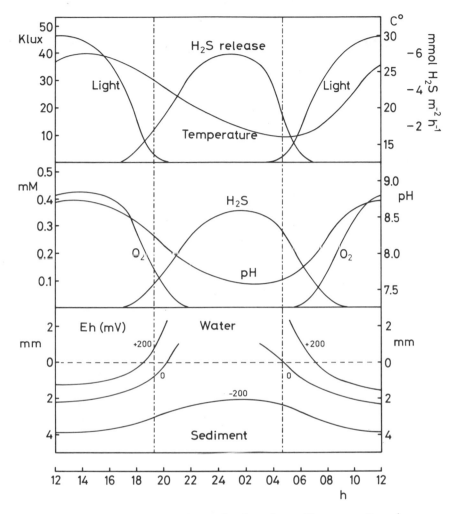

Figure 2. Diurnal variations in beach sediments of: (upper part) light intensity, water temperature, H_2S release from the sediment to the air; (middle part) oxygen and total dissolved sulfide concentrations and pH of the 2-cm water layer; (lower part) and redox isovolts in the sediment. Summer: summary of results.

as gas. Since sulfide can only reach the air as H_2S, the pH variations will strongly influence its rate of release. There is not, however, a clear relationship between the two parameters. This is due to the complexity of the system in which biological factors, such as periodical microturbulence caused by the benthic fauna, and physicochemical factors, such as exchange enhancement by HS^- ions, all affect the rate of H_2S release.

The diurnal variations can also be traced in the redox profile a few mm down into the sediment. The isovolts in Figure 2 show that during the day the oxidized surface layer with

positive redox potentials reaches 2 mm depth. This corresponds
approximately to the penetration depth of daylight (Fenchel and
Straarup, 1971). During the night the sediment becomes reduced
to the very surface and the sulfide zone extends up into the
water.

Evidently it is only a 2-mm thick surface layer that in
the daytime constitutes a complete barrier to the release of
H_2S from the sulfide zone to the water. In this layer dense
populations of photosynthetic and colorless sulfur bacteria,
cyanobacteria, and diatoms are found. Together they catalyze
the oxidation of H_2S, either with CO_2 or with O_2. A chemical
oxidation with O_2 produced by the algae may also be of importance.

The peak emission rates of H_2S during the night reach
up to 0.30 mmol m^{-2} h^{-1} on the Limfjorden beach and up to 6.7
mmol m^{-2} h^{-1} on the Aarhus Bay beach. Over 24 hr, the corresponding release is 1.4 and 38 mmol m^{-2} day^{-1}, respectively.
These figures, however, represent only very restricted areas.
On a larger scale the daily release will be much less. Still,
a comparison with Table I shows that it is a significant fraction of the H_2S produced in the sediment that may reach into
the atmosphere.

The rate of release may be compared with published estimates of the contribution of biogenic sulfur to the atmospheric budget. Rodhe (1972) gives a figure of 250 mg S m^{-2}
yr^{-1} for the "background" flux in northern Europe. Recalcula-
tion of the present results shows that the measured maximum
rates are 1000-fold higher. Thus, the investigated sediments
may indeed be potential sources of atmospheric sulfur. A real
quantitative evaluation of their importance will require a more
extensive field survey.

REFERENCES

Eriksson, E. "The Yearly Circulation of Sulfur in Nature,"
  J. Geophys. Res. 68:4001-4008 (1963).

Fenchel, T., and B. J. Straarup. "Vertical Distribution of
  Photosynthetic Pigments and the Penetration of Light in
  Marine Sediments," *Oikos* 22:172-182 (1971).

Friend, J. P. "The Global Sulfur Cycle," in *Chemistry of the
  Lower Atmosphere,* S. I. Rasool, Ed. (New York: Plenum Press,
  1973), pp. 177-201.

Hansen, M. H., K. Ingvorsen and B. B. Jørgensen. "Mechanisms
  of Hydrogen Sulfide Release from Coastal Marine Sediments to
  the Atmosphere," *Limnol. Oceanog.* (in press).

Jørgensen, B. B. "The Sulfur Cycle of a Coastal Marine Sediment
  (Limfjorden, Denmark)," *Limnol. Oceanog.* (in press).

Jørgensen, B. B., and T. Fenchel. "The Sulfur Cycle of a Marine Sediment Model System," *Mar. Biol.* 24:189-201 (1974).

Kellogg, W. W., R. D. Cadle, E. E. Allen, A. L. Lazrus and E. A. Martell. "The Sulfur Cycle," *Science* 175:587-596 (1972).

Östlund, H. G., and J. Alexander. "Oxidation Rate of Sulfide in Sea Water, a Preliminary Study," *J. Geophys. Res.* 68: 3995-3997 (1963).

Rodhe, H. "A Study of the Sulfur Budget for the Atmosphere over Northern Europe," *Tellus* 24:128-138 (1972).

CHAPTER 22

HYDROCARBON AND FATTY ACID DISTRIBUTIONS IN RECENTLY DEPOSITED ALGAL MATS AT LAGUNA GUERRERO, BAJA CALIFORNIA

R. P. PHILP
S. BROWN
M. CALVIN

Department of Chemistry
University of California
Berkeley, California 94720 USA

S. BRASSELL
G. EGLINTON

Organic Geochemistry Unit
University of Bristol
Bristol BS8 1TS, UK

INTRODUCTION

The results from our study on the lipid content of various samples from the algal mat deposits at Laguna Mormona, Baja California, have been reported previously. The main reasons why we believe studies such as these are of geochemical importance have also been described (Cardoso *et al.*, 1975). In summary, any study involving an examination of the lipid content of ancient sediments will be enhanced if a clearer understanding as to the initial fate of organic matter being deposited in sediments can be obtained. A study of recent algal formations, or mats, should prove particularly useful in this case since the contribution of algal deposits to several ancient sediments is well documented (Traverse, 1955; Thorne *et al.*, 1964).

Laguna Guerrero is about 300 miles further south of the previously described algal mats at Laguna Mormona, Baja California. The algal mats are found in shallow ponds of hypersaline water, of pH around 8.4. The mats were partially covered with water when sampled, although as a result of tidal movement and flooding from heavy rains they experience periods of being both covered and uncovered by water. The algal mat environment

255

appears to be relatively free from any obvious human or industrial contamination and the major contributions of organic material to the deposits are from the algal and bacterial debris.
The lower layer also contains fragments of higher plant cutin.

　　The Laguna Guerrero mats possess a layered structure
that is more clearly defined than those observed at Laguna
Mormona. The upper layer (~1.3 cm thick) of the Laguna Guerrero
mats consists almost entirely of *Microcoleus chthonoplastes*,
with small quantities of *Lyngbya aestuarii*. Aerobic heterotrophic bacteria and a chemoautotrophic bacterium, *Beggiatoa*,
were also detected. Beneath this upper layer was a second
layer (~0.7 cm) of purple photosynthetic bacteria and sulfate-
reducing anaerobic bacteria. This middle layer was in turn
underlain by a lower layer (~7.5 cm) of dark ooze, rich in H_2S,
containing anaerobic bacteria (Javor and Castenholz, 1977).
The most attractive feature of this environment is that the
effects of bacterial action on the algal debris should be clearly evident by observing the changes in the hydrocarbon and
fatty acid composition of these three different layers.

METHODS

　　The individual layers were separated from each other at
the sampling site. The different appearance and coloration of
the three layers made it a relatively simple task to peel off
each layer from a sample taken to a depth of about 10 cm, despite the lateral variation in their individual thicknesses.
The three layers were stored in separate glass containers after
collection, returned to the laboratory as quickly as possible,
and kept at 1°C until they were extracted.

　　Each sample was extracted with solvent (methanol/toluene,
1:1, 3 x 100 ml) by sonication, after initial centrifugation to
remove the aqueous layer. The dried residues were analyzed to
determine their elemental compositions. Each extract was separated into acidic and neutral fractions by repeated partition
between aqueous KOH (6%, 3 x 100 ml) and ethyl acetate (150 ml).
After acidifying the KOH layer with HCl (3 M), the free fatty
acids were partitioned into ethyl acetate, and esterified
(BF_3/MeOH). The neutral fractions were chromatographed on alumina (Grade 1, neutral, 40 x 2.2 cm), eluting sequentially
with heptane (200 ml), ethyl acetate (400 ml) and methanol
(200 ml). The heptane fractions (total hydrocarbons) were further separated by urea adduction into normal and branched/cy-
clic hydrocarbon fractions. The ethyl acetate and methanol
eluants from the alumina column were not examined further.

　　The extraction and fractionation methods cited above
have been more fully documented elsewhere (Eglinton, 1973;
Eglinton *et al.*, 1974; and Cardoso *et al.*, 1975). Gas chromatographic analysis (GC) of the fatty acid fractions (as their
methyl esters) indicated they were sufficiently simple for
direct analysis by computerized-gas chromatography—mass

spectrometry (C–GC–MS). All analytical gas-liquid chromatography
was carried out on a Varian 2700 gas chromatograph. The total,
normal and branched/cyclic hydrocarbon fractions were chromatographed on a 8 m x 75 μm i.d. glass capillary column, packed with
3% Dexcil 300 coated on Gaschrom Q; the oven temperature was
programmed from 70° to 280°C at 4°C/min with helium flow rate
of 6 ml/min. (The same GC conditions were used throughout this
study.) C–GC–MS analyses were carried out on a DuPont 492-1
mass spectrometer interfaced with a Varian Aerograph Model No.
204 gas chromatograph equipped with linear temperature program-
mer. The mass spectral data were acquired and processed using
a DuPont 21-094 data system.

RESULTS

The results of the elemental analyses performed on the
dried residues obtained after the solvent extraction of each
of the three layers and the weights of the hydrocarbon and
fatty acid fractions obtained from the various layers are given
in Table I. The hydrocarbon and fatty acid components identified in the three layers are summarized in Tables II to IV.
The recognition of these compounds was achieved using gas chromatography (on the basis of retention times and coinjection with
standards), mass fragmentography (by key ion monitoring for n-
alkane and n-alkanoic acid series) and low resolution mass
spectrometry. Their quantitation is expressed as relative percentages of the most abundant component of the appropriate fraction (*i.e.*, total hydrocarbons, adducted hydrocarbons, nonadducted hydrocarbons or total fatty acids), measured on peak
heights.

n-Alkanes, n-Alkanoic and n-Alkenoic Acids (Table II)

The major hydrocarbon of the upper layer of the Laguna
Guerrero algal mats in $n-C_{17}$. A small proportion of $n-C_{23}$ to
$n-C_{35}$ alkanes is also present in the upper layer, while in the
middle and lower layers these long chain alkanes are the major
hydrocarbons, maximizing at $n-C_{27}$ and $n-C_{29}$.

The gas chromatogram of the fatty acid fraction of the
upper layer showed n-hexadecanoic acid ($n-C_{16}$) as the major
component. The second major peak was a partially resolved mixture of $C_{18:1}$, $C_{18:2}$ and $C_{18:3}$ acids. Small amounts of $C_{16:1}$
were also detected, together with n-alkanoic acids in the range
C_{12} to C_{20}. The total fatty acid fraction of the middle layer
was dominated by $C_{18:1}$ and $n-C_{18}$ acids. $n-C_{14}$, $n-C_{15}$, $n-C_{16}$,
$n-C_{17}$ and $n-C_{19}$ fatty acids were also identified as prominent
components. The C_{12}, C_{13} and C_{20} to C_{28} normal carboxylic acids
were present in trace amounts. The complex mixture of fatty
acids of the lower layer of the algal mat shows n-octadecanoic
acid ($n-C_{18}$) as its major component. Other normal carboxylic
acids in the range C_9 to C_{30} and C_8, C_9 and C_{16} straight chain

258 The Aquatic Environment

Table I

Elemental Analysis of Air-Dried Residues and Extracted Fraction Weights

Fraction	Dried Residues							Hydrocarbons (mg)		Free Fatty Acids (mg)
Layer	Weight (g)	Org.C%	H%	N%	O%[a]	S%	Ash %	Adducted	Non-Adducted	
Upper	13.1	29.6	4.2	3.7	38.5	1.6	22.4	6	14	24
Middle	28.5	9.62	1.17	1.10	41.3	0.25	46.6	8	8	19
Lower	35.6	9.10	1.10	0.97	37.4	0.42	51.4	6	4	11

[a]By difference.

Table II

Solvent-Extracted Lipids: Relative Distributions of n-Alkanes, n-Alkanoic and n-Alkenoic Acids

N-alkanes

Carbon No. / Layer	17	18	19	20	21	22	23	24	25	26	27	28	29	30	31	32	33	34	35	CPI	Range
Upper[a]	100	<1	<1	<1	<1	<1	<1	<1	<1	1	6	1	4	<1						16.3	C_{17}–C_{30}
Middle[a]	38	24	33	1.8	1.5	<1	4.2	3.8	8.2	7.3	83	33	100	7.5	21	2.7	15	1.3	7.1	3.4	C_{17}–C_{35}
Lower[a]	11	7.2	3.8	1.1	3.4	1.8	12	7.8	20	14	100	29	98	6.8	18	1.0	7.8	<1	2.6	3.6	C_{17}–C_{35}

N-alkanoic and n-alkenoic acids (as methyl esters)

Carbon No. / Layer	9	10	11	12	13	14	15	16	16:1	17	18	18:1	18:2	18:3	19	20	21	22	23	24	25	26	27	28	29	CPI	Range
Upper[a]				1.8	4.1	11	12	100	34	4.7	15	28	14	21	12	<1	<1	<1	<1			<1	<1			3.9	C_{12}–C_{20}
Middle[a]			<1	<1	<1	4.3	83	77		46	54	100			37							<1	<1			1.1	C_{12}–C_{27}
Lower[a]	<1	3.9	1.5	10	4.4	16	12	50	15	7.8	18				4.2	1.4	2.8	2.8	<1	2.8	3.1	<1	<1	<1	<1	2.8	C_{9}–C_{29}

[a] Quantitation expressed as a percentage of the major component of the appropriate extracted fraction.

α,ω-dicarboxylic acids were also detected (see Table III).

Branched Hydrocarbons and Fatty Acids (Table III)

The major hydrocarbon of the upper layer is a branched $C_{17}H_{34}$ alkene. Other major components are 8-methylhexadecane and 7- and 8-methylheptadecanes. The presence of the branched heptadecanes in both adducted and nonadducted hydrocarbon fractions is a reflection of the inefficiency of the urea adduction process in separating normal from mono-methyl branched hydrocarbons. In the middle layer the 7- and 8-methylheptadecanes are present in smaller amounts, while the relative proportion of 8-methylhexadecane is increased. The $C_{17}H_{34}$ branched alkene was not detected in either the middle layer or the lower layer.

In the upper layer three phytenes ($C_{20}H_{40}$ isoprenoids) were detected. The major isomer was identified as phyt-1-ene (3,7,11,15-tetramethylhexadec-1-ene) on comparison with a standard mass spectrum (Urbach and Stark, 1975). Tentative identification of a phytadiene was also made. Phyt-1-ene was not detected in the middle layer, although the other two phytenes present in the upper layers were found in significantly increased proportions. Phytadiene was not observed but phytane appeared as the major component of the adducted hydrocarbon fraction. The phytenes present in the middle layer were both observed in the extract from the lower layer, together with two other phytene isomers, one of which was identified by mass spectrometry (Urbach and Stark, 1975) as phyt-2-ene (3,7,11,15-tetramethylhexadec-2-ene). The major isoprenoid hydrocarbon of this layer was phytane and no phytadiene was detected.

In the fatty acid fraction of the upper layer the branched components detected were C_{17}- and C_{19}-cyclopropanoid acids, iso-C_{14} and C_{15} acids, and anteiso-C_{15} acid. The iso-C_{15} and anteiso-C_{15} acids were present in small amounts in the middle layer. The lower layer contained two C_{19}-cyclopropanoid acids and C_7, C_8 and C_9 mono-methyl branched α,ω-dicarboxylic acids together with iso- and anteiso-C_{15} acids.

No isoprenoid fatty acids were found in the upper layer, whereas the middle layer contained a series (C_{16} to C_{20}) of branched fatty acids with a methyl substituent in the 2 position. In the lower layer a C_{17}-branched acid and two enantiomeric γ-lactones were detected.

Cyclic Hydrocarbons and Fatty Acids (Table IV)

The only cyclic hydrocarbon detected in the upper layer of the algal mat was hop-22(29)-ene, which was present in minor amounts. An increased proportion of this triterpene was found in the middle layer where cholest-2-ene and 24-methylcholest-2-ene were also identified. The lower layer contained cholest-2-ene, hop-22(29)-ene, and hop-21(22)-ene together with several unusual and possibly novel cyclic hydrocarbons, namely two

Table III

Solvent-Extracted Lipids: Relative Distributions of Branched Hydrocarbons and Fatty Acids
(including α,ω-dicarboxylic acids)

Branched Hydrocarbons

	Mono-methyl Alkanes			Branched Alkene	Isoprenoid						
Carbon No.	17	18	18	17	phyt-2-ene	phytene	phyt-1-ene	phytene	phytene	phytadiene	phytane
Methyl position	8	7	8	17							
Upper[a] — adducted	2						7.1		<1	<1	
Upper[a] — non-adducted	3.4	16	30	100			34	9.1	5.9	<1	
Middle[a]	29		6					69	51		65
Lower[a] — adducted					15	12		7.7	17		
Lower[a] — non-adducted					44	79		62	64		100

Branched Fatty Acids (as methyl esters) and **α,ω-Dicarboxylic Acids (as methyl esters)**

	Iso-(i) and Anteiso-(a)			Cyclo-propanoidal		2-methyl substituted branched					Branched	γ-lactones		Straight-chain			Mono-methyl branched	
Carbon No.	14i	15i	15a	17	19	16	17	18	19	20	17	20	20	8	9	16	9	10
Methyl position	12	13	12							20								
Upper[a]	1.5	15		7.0	7.0										4		4	5
Middle[a]			10			7.8	4.3	2.6	2.3									
Lower[a]			30		18[b]						6.7	2.9	4.4	2.0	3.9	21	4.0	2.0

[a] Quantitation expressed as a percentage of the major component of the appropriate extracted fraction.
[b] Two isomers present.

Table IV
Solvent–Extracted Lipids: Relative Distributions
of Cyclic Hydrocarbons

| | Cyclic Hydrocarbons | | | | | | | |
| | Hopenes | | Sterenes | | Unsaturated Polycyclics | | | |
Layer	hop-22(29)-ene	hop-21(22)-ene	cholest-2-ene	24-methylcholest-2-ene	$C_{20}H_{32}$	$C_{24}H_{38}$	$C_{24}H_{38}$	$C_{24}H_{38}$
Upper[a]	8							
Middle[a]	15		19	<1				12
Lower[a]	5	6	16		29[b]	81	6.4	37

[a]Quantitation expressed as a percentage of the major component of the nonadducted hydrocarbon fractions.

[b]Two unresolved isomers present.

$C_{20}H_{32}$ and three $C_{24}H_{38}$ isomers. Figure 1 shows the mass spectra (numbers 1 and 2) of the $C_{20}H_{32}$ isomers, which were only partially resolved by gas chromatography, and the mass spectra of two of the $C_{24}H_{38}$ compounds (numbers 3 and 4). The third $C_{24}H_{38}$ isomer was detected in both the middle and lower layers of the algal mat.

DISCUSSION

In the Laguna Guerrero algal mat the microorganisms characterized in the upper layer are blue-green algae and aerobic bacteria, while the middle layer is composed of both photosynthetic and anaerobic bacteria, and the lower layer of anaerobic bacteria. The presence of blue-green algal cells in the middle layer and dead photosynthetic cells in the lower layer suggests that the algal mat is a continuously evolving system where the living generation on the surface is underlain by the debris of the previous generation undergoing bacterial modification. Therefore, the differences in hydrocarbon and fatty acid content between the layers will reflect the initial algal input and its subsequent conversion by processes of bacterial degradation, assuming that the environment of the algal mat has not changed significantly in recent years. However, if major alterations in the biolipid input to the mat, or its depositional environment, have occurred, then they should be indicated by deviations from this expected lipid pattern. For example, a higher plant input, such as is indicated by the presence of cuticle fragments in the lower layer, would be characterized by the presence of long-chain ($>C_{24}$) n-alkanes and n-alkanoic acids (Eglinton *et al.*, 1962; Eglinton, 1968).

The absence of data on the carbonate content of each layer means that the extent of possible conversion of organic matter to inorganic residue by degradation and diagenetic processes cannot be determined.

n-Alkanes, n-Alkanoic and n-Alkenoic Acids

The n-alkanes of the upper layer are dominated by $n-C_{17}$, which is typical of blue-green algae (*e.g.*, Gelpi *et al.*, 1970; Han *et al.*, 1968). The minor quantities of normal hydrocarbons in the range C_{24} to C_{30} suggest that any contribution of higher plant input (Eglinton *et al.*, 1962) to the mat at the present time is small. The n-alkanoic and n-alkenoic acid distributions in the upper layer are also characteristic of blue-green algal contribution (Schneider *et al.*, 1970; Parker and Leo, 1965; Parker *et al.*, 1967), with $C_{16:0}$ and $C_{18:1}$ as the major components. The increased proportion of long-chain alkanes in the middle and lower layers is explicable either as an indication of an increased higher plant contribution in the past, reflected by the presence of fragments of higher plant cuticle in the lower layer, or as a result of their relative resistance

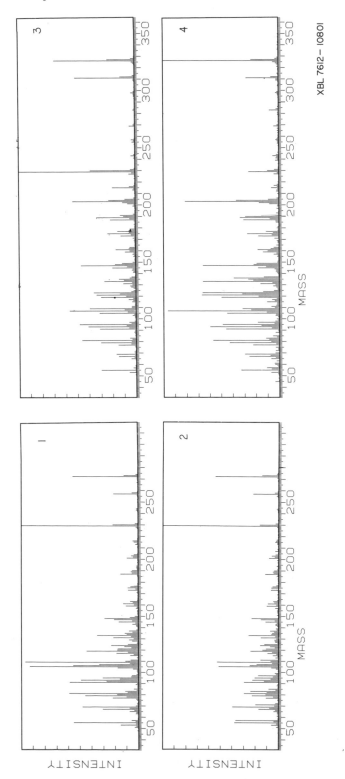

XBL 7612-10801

Figure 1. Mass spectra of unidentified components from the lower layer. Spectra numbers 1 and 2 are those of the unresolved $C_{20}H_{32}$ isomers; numbers 3 and 4 are two of the $C_{24}H_{38}$ isomers.

(compared to n-C_{17}) to bacterial degradation (Cranwell, 1975; Johnson and Calder, 1973). The n-alkanoic acids of the middle and lower layers resemble the n-alkane distributions in showing an enhanced proportion of higher homologues, similarly attributable to an increased higher plant contribution and/or preferential bacterial degradation of lower homologues. The presence of normal carboxylic acids in the C_9 to C_{13} range supports the latter hypothesis, since this range is typical of bacterial fatty acids (Oro *et al.*, 1967; Blumer *et al.*, 1969), which implies that they may therefore be formed as products of the inferred bacterial degradation. The observed decrease in the proportion of alkenoic acids in the lower layer relative to the upper and middle layers indicates a preferential removal of unsaturated components as reported previously (Parker and Leo, 1965). The presence of α,ω-dicarboxylic acids in the lower layer is noteworthy since they have not been widely reported in Recent sediments. However, they were detected in mangrove swamps (Johns and Onder, 1975) where they were suggested as possible indicators of microbial action at the time of deposition and in Esthwaite sediment (Eglinton *et al.*, 1968). They may be derived diagenetically from ω-hydroxy acids (Eglinton *et al.*, 1968).

The calculated CPI value of the n-alkanes shows a characteristic high figure for the upper layer, typical of algae, while the middle and lower layers show significantly reduced values, attributable to microbial degradation of the original input. The CPI of 1.1 for the n-alkanoic acids in the middle layer is unexpected. One possible explanation is that a prominent bacterial contribution, not observed in the n-alkane distribution, is giving rise to this low value.

Branched Hydrocarbons and Fatty Acids

The 7- and 8-methylheptadecanes detected in the upper and middle layers are ubiquitous components of blue-green algae (Han, 1970), and the $C_{17}H_{34}$ branched alkene has also been reported as a major blue-green algal component (Han, 1970). The presence of these compounds in the upper layer is, therefore, in accord with the microbiological data. Their absence in the lower layer further suggests that they are relatively easy to degrade by bacteria. 8-Methylhexadecane has not been reported as a major constituent of blue-green algae and may therefore be a degradation product of the 8-methylheptadecane or the $C_{17}H_{34}$ alkene.

The phytenes detected in all three layers have not been widely reported in Recent sediments, although heating of sediment from the Tanner Basin produced phytenes as thermal degradation products of dihydrophytol (Ikan *et al.*, 1975). However, a $C_{20}H_{40}$ alkene was detected in the Laguna Mormona algal mat (Cardoso *et al.*, 1975). The tentative identification of phytadiene in the upper layer and the presence of phytane in the

middle and lower layers suggests that reductive processes are
occurring. The inferred precursor of phytane, phytenes and
phytadienes is phytol, derived from the phytyl side-chain of
chlorophyll a. Dehydration of phytol forms phytadiene, which
can be subsequently reduced to phytenes and then phytane. The
changes in the relative proportions of the five phytenes observed in the three layers suggests that interconversion of
the isomers may occur. This process is dependent on the original migration of double bonds in phytadiene and/or on the ease
of transformation of the isomers.

The iso- and anteisoacids found in all three layers are
characteristic of bacteria, as are the cyclopropanoid acids also
detected (Cranwell, 1973). The relative proportions of these
acyclic fatty acids in the three layers shows that the largest
bacterial input is found in the lower layer. The mono-methyl
branched α,ω-dicarboxylic acids identified in the lower layer,
by analogy with their straight-chain counterparts, could be
formed by diagenetic oxidation of branched ω-hydroxy acids and
have not been previously reported in Recent sediments.

The branched C_{17} acid observed in the lower layer and
the series of 2-methyl isoprenoid acids are probably derived
from phytol. The branched C_{16} acid was tentatively identified,
by mass spectrometry, as 2,6,10-trimethyltridecanoic acid, suggesting that its precursor is pristanic acid rather than phytan-
ic acid and is therefore indicative of an oxic environment
(Ikan *et al.*, 1975), in contrast to the evidence of the isoprenoid hydrocarbon distribution.

The mass spectra of the two enantiomeric γ-lactones from
the lower layer are identical to those obtained from two components of a fatty acid extract from Rostherne sediment. These
γ-lactones have been postulated as diagenetic products of 2-hy-
droxymethyl-6,10,14-trimethylhexadecanoic acid (Brooks, 1974).

Cyclic Hydrocarbons

The upper layer of the algal mat contains minor amounts
of hop-22(29)-ene, an abundant alkene constituent of *L. aestuarii* (Gelpi *et al.*, 1968 and 1970) and one that was identified
in the Laguna Mormona ooze (Cardoso *et al.*, 1975). Its detection at Laguna Guerrero is a further reflection of the dominant
blue-green algal input to the upper layer. A second hopane-type
triterpene, hop-21(22)-ene was detected in the lower layer and
may have been formed by isomerization of hop-22(29)-ene. The
presence of triterpenes in algal mats agrees with their almost
universal occurrence in Recent and ancient sediments (Kimble
et al., 1974; Eglinton *et al.*, 1974).

The $C_{20}H_{32}$ and $C_{24}H_{38}$ hydrocarbons found in the lower
layer do not appear to have been previously reported in the
literature. The origin of these components is unclear. The
C_{20} isomers may be derived from diterpenoids or, like the C_{24}
components, from steroids or triterpenoids. The major

difference in the mass spectra of two of the $C_{24}H_{38}$ isomers is the ratio of m/e 229 to m/e 203 (Figure 1, numbers 3 and 4), which suggests that these hydrocarbons are stereoisomers derived from similar degradation paths. These novel hydrocarbons may be sterenes representing various stages of sterol degradation by bio- and/or geochemical processes. The presence of cholest-2-ene and 24-methylcholest-2-ene in greater proportions in the middle layer compared to the lower layer supports this hypothesis as it suggests that these sterenes are being further degraded. Cholest-2-ene has been shown to form as a result of dehydration of 5α-cholestan-3β-ol under simulated conditions of geological diagenesis (Rubinstein *et al.*, 1975). However, the mechanism of its formation may be different in an algal mat environment where the temperature is significantly lower. The 5α-cholestan-3β-ol can, in turn, be derived from cholesterol (Gaskell and Eglinton, 1975).

Partial and then complete degradation of the side chain or of the A-ring of cholest-2-ene by bacterial action could give rise to the C_{20} and C_{24} compounds. An alternative precursor would be a triterpene, since hop-22(29)-ene is found in lesser proportions in the lower layer relative to its occurrence in the top and middle layers, suggesting that it may be undergoing microbial degradation.

CONCLUSIONS

The major differences in the lipid composition between the three layers can be rationalized in terms of degradative and diagenetic alteration of a blue-green algal and bacterial input, which corroborates with the microbiological data. The n-alkane and n-alkanoic acid distributions indicate an increased higher plant input in the past, which is in agreement with the observation of cuticle fragments.

The salient features to emerge from analysis of the hydrocarbons and free fatty acids are the presence of $C_{20}H_{32}$ and $C_{24}H_{38}$ polycyclic alkenes, the diversity of the phytene isomers detected, the absence of bishomohopanoic acid in all three layers and the occurrence of α,ω-dicarboxylic acids. The apparent absence of bishomohopanoic acid only implies that it is not present in quantities greater than the detection limit, and investigation of the ω-hydroxy acid content of the three layers might help to explain the presence of their postulated diagenetic products, α,ω-dicarboxylic acids. Further investigations of the polycyclic alkenes and the phytene isomers utilizing additional separation techniques and derivatization are being undertaken at present. The alcohols, especially sterols and isoprenols, of the three layers are also being analyzed to provide further evidence of the bio- and geochemical pathways occurring in the Laguna Guerrero algal mat system. These investigations are being supplemented by radiolabeled incubations of sterols in these algal mats, and similar work is envisaged to investigate the fate of phytol and triterpenoids.

ACKNOWLEDGMENTS

We wish to thank Barbara Javor for the microbiological identifications and Sue Lomas for help in interpretation of mass spectra.

This work was supported by a grant from the National Aeronautics and Space Administration (NGL-05-003-003), the A. L. Day Fund (National Academy of Science), the Nuffield Foundation, the Natural Environment Research Council (GR3/2420) and the Petroleum Research Fund.

REFERENCES

Brooks, P. W. "Isoprenoids and Other Lipids in Recent Sediments," Ph.D. Thesis, University of Bristol (1974).

Blumer, M., T. Chase and S. W. Watson. "Fatty Acids in the Lipids of Marine and Terrestrial Nitrifying Bacteria," *J. Bacteriol.* 99:366-370 (1969).

Cardoso, J., P. W. Brooks, G. Eglinton, R. Goodfellow, J. R. Maxwell and R. P. Philp. "Lipids of Recently Deposited Algal Mats at Laguna Mormona, Baja California," in *Environmental Biogeochemistry,* J. Nriagu, Ed. (Ann Arbor, Michigan: Ann Arbor Science Publishers, 1975).

Cranwell, P. W. "Branched-Chain and Cyclopropanoid Acids in a Recent Sediment," *Chem. Geol.* 11:307-313 (1973).

Cranwell, P. W. "Environmental Organic Chemistry of Rivers and Lakes, both Water and Sediment," in *Environmental Chemistry,* 1 (London: The Chemical Society, 1975).

Eglinton, G., R. J. Hamilton, R. A. Raphael and A. G. Gonzalez. "Hydrocarbon Constituents of the Wax Coatings of Plant Leaves: A Taxonomic Survey," *Nature* 193:739-742 (1962).

Eglinton, G. "Hydrocarbons and Fatty Acids in Living Organism and Recent and Ancient Sediments," in *Advances in Organic Geochemistry,* P. A. Schenck and I. Havenaar, Eds. (Oxford: Pergamon Press, 1968).

Eglinton, G., D. H. Hunneman and K. Douraghi-Zadeh. "Gas Chromatographic-Mass Spectrometric Studies of Long Chain Hydroxy Acids. II. The Hydroxy Acids and Fatty Acids of a 5000-year-old Lacustrine Sediments," *Tetrahedron* 24:5929-5941 (1968).

Eglinton, G. "Chemical Fossils: A Combined Organic Geochemical and Environmental Approach," *Pure Appl. Chem.* 34:611-632 (1973).

Eglinton, G., J. R. Maxwell and R. P. Philp. "Organic Geochemistry of Sediments from Contemporary Aquatic Environments," in *Advances in Organic Geochemistry,* B. Tissot and F. Bienner, Eds. (Paris: Editions Technip, 1974), pp. 941-961.

Gaskell, S. J., and G. Eglinton. "Rapid Hydrogenation of Sterols in a Contemporary Lacustrine Sediment," *Nature* 254:209-211 (1975).

Gelpi, E., J. Oro, H. I. Schneider and E. O. Bennett. "Olefins of High-Molecular Weight in Two Microscopic Algae," *Science* 161:700-701 (1968).

Gelpi, E., H. Schneider, J. Mann and J. Oro. "Hydrocarbons of Geochemical Significance in Microscopic Algae," *Phytochemistry* 9:603-612 (1970).

Han, J., E. D. McCarthy, W. Van Hoeven, M. Calvin and W. H. Bradley. "Organic Geochemical Studies II. Preliminary Report on the Distribution of Aliphatic Hydrocarbons in Algae, in Bacteria and in a Recent Lake Sediment," *Proc. Nat. Acad. Sci. USA* 59:29-33 (1968).

Han, J. "Chemical Studies of Terrestrial and Extraterrestrial Life," Ph.D. Thesis, University of California, Berkeley (1970).

Ikan, R., M. J. Baedecker, and I. R. Kaplan. "Thermal Alteration Experiments on Organic Matter in Recent Marine Sediment II. Isoprenoids," *Geochim. Cosmochim. Acta* 39:187-195 (1975).

Javor, B. J., and R. W. Castenholz. *Carbonate Precipitation in Algal Mats in a Silicoclastic Environment: A Quantitative Analysis* (in preparation).

Johns, R. B., and O. M. Onder. "Biological Diagenesis: Dicarboxylic Acids in Recent Sediments," *Geochim. Cosmochim. Acta* 39:129-137 (1975).

Johnson, R. W., and J. A. Calder. "Early Diagenesis of Fatty Acids and Hydrocarbons in a Salt Marsh Environment," *Geochim. Cosmochim. Acta* 37:1953-1955 (1973).

Kimble, B. J., J. R. Maxwell, R. P. Philp, G. Eglinton, P. Albrecht, A. Ensminger, P. Arpino and G. Ourisson. "Tri- and Tetraterpenoid Hydrocarbons in the Messel Oil Shale," *Geochim. Cosmochim. Acta* 38:1165-1181 (1974).

Oro, J., T. G. Tornabene, D. W. Nooner and E. Gelpi. "Aliphatic Hydrocarbons and Fatty Acids of Some Marine and Freshwater Microorganisms," *J. Bacteriol.* 93:1811-1818 (1967).

Parker, P. L., and R. F. Leo. "Fatty Acids in Blue-Green Algal Mat Communities," *Science* 148:373-374 (1965).

Parker, P. L., C. Van Baalen and L. Maurer. "Fatty Acids in Eleven Species of Blue-Green Algae: Geochemical Significance," *Science* 155:707-708 (1967).

Rubinstein, I., O. Sieskind and P. Albrecht. "Rearranged Sterenes in a Shale: Occurrence and Simulated Formation," *J. Chem. Soc., Perkin Trans. I.* 1833-1836 (1975).

Schneider, H., E. Gelpi, E. O. Bennett and J. Oro. "Fatty Acids of Geochemical Significance in Microscopic Algae," *Phytochemistry* 9:613-617 (1970).

Thorne, H. M., K. E. Standfield, G. U. Dinneen and W. I. Murphy. "Oil Shale Technology: A Review," *Information Circular 8216,* US Bureau of Mines, Washington, D.C. (1964).

Traverse, A. "Occurrence of the Oil-Forming Alga *Botryococcus* in Lignites and Other Tertiary Sediments," *Micropaleontology* 1:343-348 (1955).

Urbach, G., and W. Stark. "The C-20 Hydrocarbons of Butterfat," *J. Agric. Food Chem.* 23:20-24 (1975).

CHAPTER 23

CAROTENOIDS IN AN ALGAL MAT AND OOZE
FROM LAGUNA MORMONA, BAJA CALIFORNIA

P. J. C. TIBBETTS
J. R. MAXWELL

Organic Geochemistry Unit
University of Bristol
Bristol BS8 1TS, UK

S. GOLUBIC

Biological Science Center
Boxton University
Boston, Massachusetts 02215 USA

INTRODUCTION

One aim of the study of the lipids of recent environments is to relate the distributions to the sources of input of organic matter. An understanding of these distributions and an evaluation of different lipid classes as indicators of specific inputs should allow extrapolation to paleoenvironmental situations. Carotenoids occur widely in all photosynthetic organisms and in some nonphotosynthetic organisms such as fungi. Many of the individual components are distributed widely in these organisms but others are found as characteristic components of specific types of organisms (see *inter alia* Weedon, 1971; Goodwin, 1976, and references therein). As such, the presence of the characteristic acyclic methoxylated carotenoids spheroidene (1), spheroidenone (2), and 2,2'-diketospirilloxanthin (3) at a particular level in a lacustrine sediment core was used to determine a specific contribution from a former population of purple photosynthetic bacteria (Brown, 1968, 1969). Comparison of the distributions in three distinct types of environment of deposition (eutrophic, lacustrine, algal mat, marine) has also demonstrated the potential of carotenoids as environmental indicators (Watts *et al.*, 1977). As an extension of this survey approach, the carotenoids of a blue-green algal mat situation in a hypersaline, coastal pond at Laguna Mormona (Baja California, Mexico) have been examined in the present study. A

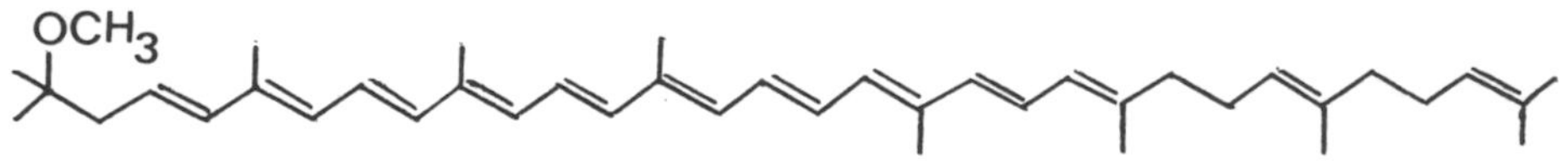

(1)

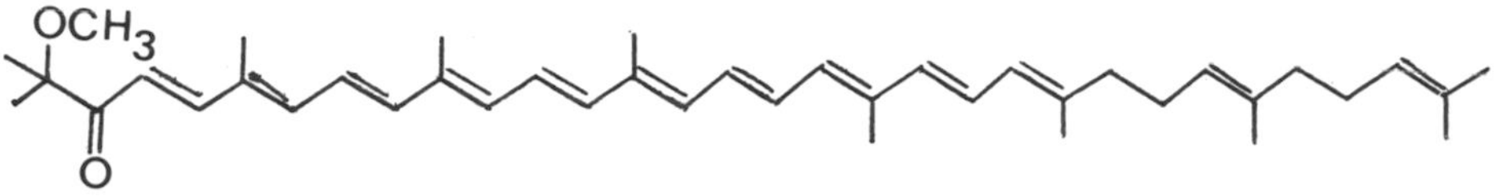

(2)

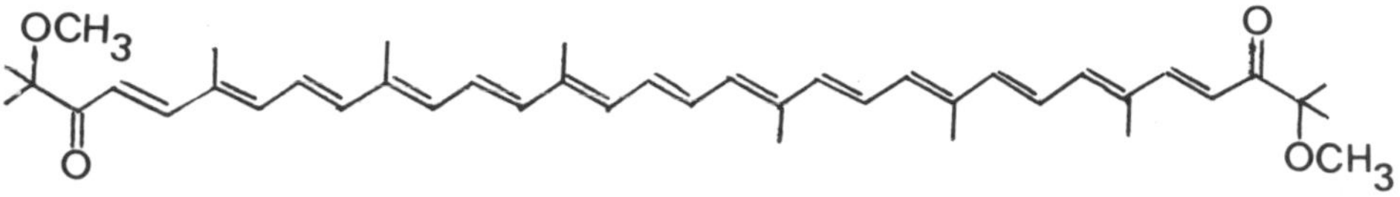

(3)

description of the mat community and the surrounding environment are given elsewhere (Horodyski and Von der Haar, 1975;
Philp and Calvin, 1976; Cardoso et al., 1976). In the community the surface of the mat is dominated by Lyngbya aestuarii
above a layer of diatoms. A second cyanophyte Microcoleus
chthonoplastes dominates the next layer above layers thought to
contain Chloroflexis and sulfur purple photosynthetic bacteria,
although no detailed biological studies have been reported.
Below these is a gelatinous partially layered level that over-
lays a reduced black organic ooze inhabited by various bacterial decomposers.

     The hydrocarbons, carboxylic acids, alcohols and sterols
of the mat layer of a core sample from this simplified environmental situation have been examined previously (Cardoso et al.,
1976). The distributions are explicable in terms of the expected blue-green algal and bacterial contributions with little
input from higher plants or pollutant sources. Comparison of
the two layers provided evidence of the operation of diagenetic
processes in the ooze layer by way of the appearance of steroidal alkenes in the ooze along with a decrease in the ratio of
monounsaturated to saturated carboxylic acids. Degradative
studies of the solvent-insoluble organic matter in the ooze have
suggested the presence of kerogen-like or kerogen precursor
material (Philp and Calvin, 1976).

     In the present study the carotenoids in both the mat and
the associated ooze from an adjacent pond have been examined in
an attempt to: (a) correlate the distributions with the expected
input sources, (b) compare the distributions with those of other
lipid classes examined previously, (c) search via specific components for possible inputs not reported previously in biological studies, and (d) search for evidence of diagenetic changes.

MATERIALS AND METHODS

Sample Collection and Storage

Samples of the mat (*ca.* 2 cm) and ooze were collected with a scoop from a pond adjacent to that from which core samples were collected previously (30°30'N; 116°00'W) (Cardoso *et al.*, 1976). Isopropanol was added and the samples were stored at 0°C for one week before shipping at ambient temperature (*ca.* 1 day in the dark) and reaching the laboratory where they were stored in the dark at -20°C.

Isolation of Carotenoids

Exposure to air and light was minimized throughout and where possible operations were carried out in a nitrogen atmosphere. All fractions were stored in the dark at -20°C. The total nonsaponifiable carotenoids in the hexane/isopropanol (1:4) extract were separated initially by preparative-scale thin layer chromatography (TLC, Silica Gel G, ethyl acetate/methylene chloride, 1:4 as developer); mixtures of acetone (0-50%) in hexane as developer afforded further separation into individual components. The procedures are described in detail by Watts *et al.* (1977). The dry extracted weights of the samples were: 150.9 g (mat) and 45.5 g (ooze).

High Pressure Liquid Chromatography (HPLC)

HPLC analyses were carried out as described previously (Watts *et al.*, 1977) except that separations were obtained using a concave solvent gradient of acetone (2-75%) in hexane over 30 min and a flow rate of 1 ml/min, and a stainless steel column (25 cm x 4.6 mm i.d.) containing irregular silica particles (5 µ Partisil, Whatman Ltd.) and packed by a precise balanced density method using a benzene/1,2-dibromoethane mixture (Martin *et al.*, 1975).

Spectrophotometry

Electronic spectra were recorded on a Unicam SP800 spectrophotometer in ether, ethanol or mixtures of both, in quartz cells (1 cm). Spectra were recorded over 250-500 nm at a fast scan speed using a 0.002-mm slit width; λ max values are uncorrected for differences in solvent effects. Quantitation was obtained from the absorbance at λ max by using literature data (Davies, 1965) for $E_{1cm}^{1\%}$; for unknown carotenoids an average value of 2500 for $E_{1cm}^{1\%}$ was used.

Mass Spectrometry

Spectra were obtained from a Varian Mat CH7 spectrometer

coupled via a Carrick Interface to a DEC PDP8-3 computer, under
conditions described previously (Watts *et al.*, 1977).

RESULTS

As far as possible assignment of individual components
was based on comparison of UV/vis and mass spectra with those
of authentic standards and by TLC and HPLC co-chromatography
with the standards.

Mat Carotenoids

A complex mixture of components absorbing at 451 nm was
observed for the total nonsaponifiable carotenoids (92 ppm)
of the mat (Figure 1). The components labeled β-carotene (4),
torulene (5), spheroidenone (2), echinenone (6), spirilloxanthin (7), canthaxanthin (8) and zeaxanthin (9) coeluted with
authentic standards on both HPLC and TLC analysis. These assignments were confirmed by comparison of the electronic and
mass spectra with those of the standards. As an example, Figure 2 shows the mass spectrum of the isolated zeaxanthin and
that of a standard. The components labeled 3,4,3',4'-tetrahy-
drospirilloxanthin (10), okenone (11), 3,4-dehydrorhodopin (12),
rhodopin (13), 3'-hydroxyechinenone (14) in Figure 1A were not
co-chromatographed on HPLC or TLC but their electronic and mass
spectra compared favorably with those of authentic standards or
of literature examples (Foppen, 1971; Vetter *et al.*, 1971;
Davies, 1976). Myxoxanthophyll (15) was assigned by acetylation
of the most polar band (Rf = 0.0) from preparative-scale TLC
(ethyl acetate/methylene chloride 1:4) of the total nonsaponifiable carotenoids, by TLC co-chromatography of the acetate
with a standard (acetone/hexane 1:3) and by comparison of its
electronic spectrum with that of a standard. Figure 3 shows
the concentrations of the individual fractions isolated by preparative-scale TLC. Separation of spheroidenone from 3,4,3',4'-
tetrahydrospirilloxanthin, echinenone from spirilloxanthin, and
dehydrorhodopin from rhodopin was not achieved under these TLC
conditions. Eleven minor bands were also observed by TLC.

Ooze Carotenoids

The distribution in the total nonsaponifiable fraction
(75 ppm) is shown in Figure 1B. β-Carotene (4), spheroidenone
(2), 3,4,3',4'-tetrahydrospirilloxanthin (10), echinenone (6),
spirilloxanthin (7), okenone (11), canthaxanthin (8) and zeaxanthin (9) were assigned as above by HPLC and TLC co-chromatography with standards and by comparison of electronic and
mass spectra with standards. The mass and electronic spectra
of torulene (5), 3,4-dehydrorhodopin (12) and rhodopin (13)
compared favorably with those of standards. 3'-Hydroxyechine-
none (14) was tentatively assigned from comparison of its

electronic spectrum with a literature example and by comparison of the elution order of carotenoids in the mat and ooze (Figures 1A and 1B). Preparative-scale TLC also afforded nine other minor fractions that could not be assigned.

DISCUSSION

Correlation of Carotenoids with Input to the Mat (Table I)

The major component of the mat layer, β-carotene (4) is

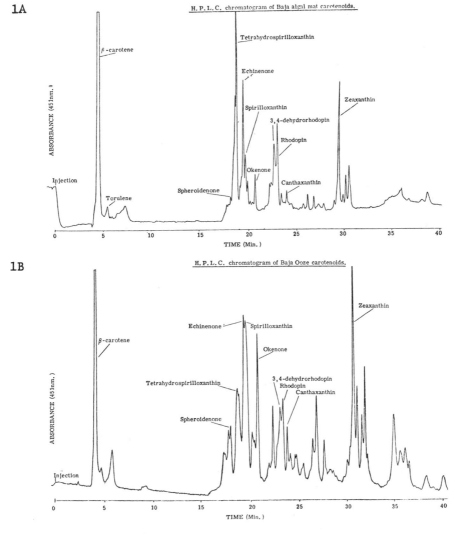

Figure 1. High pressure liquid chromatograms of the total nonsaponifiable carotenoids from Baja algal mat (A) and ooze (B). For conditions see text.

widely distributed and cannot be used as a specific indicator
of input (*cf.* Watts *et al.*, 1977).   The expected blue-green
algal contribution is reflected in the presence of the characteristic glycoside myxoxanthophyll (Züllig, 1960;   Pinevich
and Vasil'era, 1972), although surprisingly it is not one of
the most abundant components.   Although echinenone (6) and
zeaxanthin (9) are not specific blue-green algal components,
they have been found in a number of species (Hertzberg *et al.*,

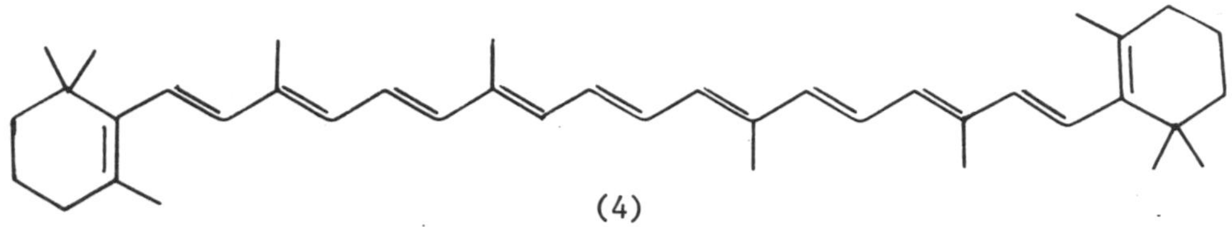

(4)

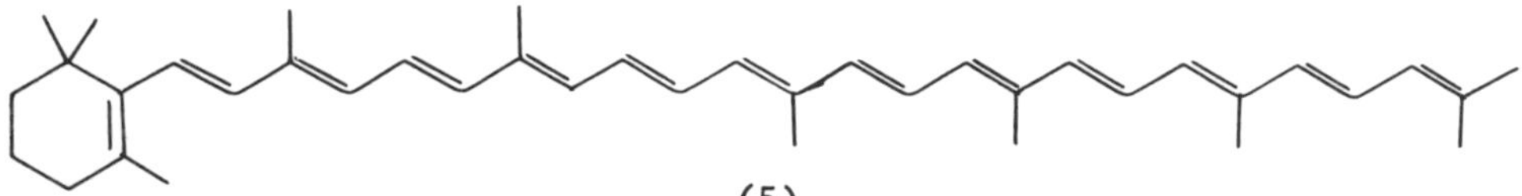

(5)

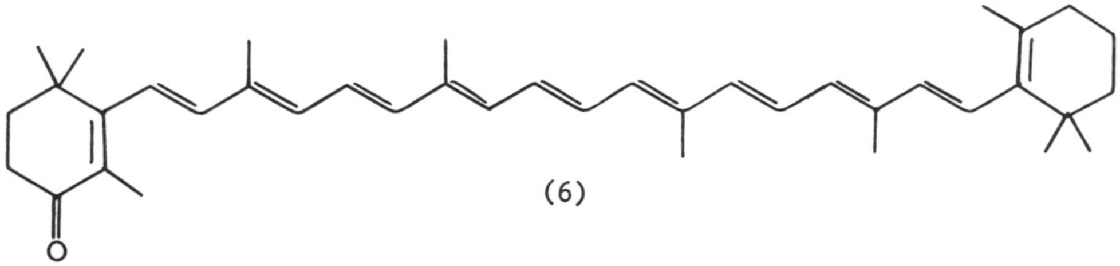

(6)

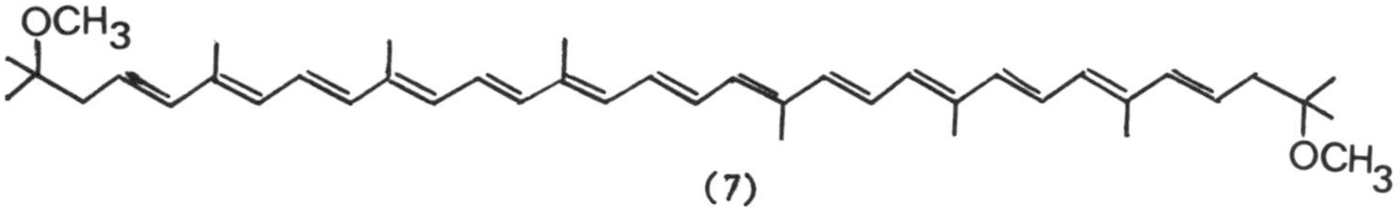

(7)

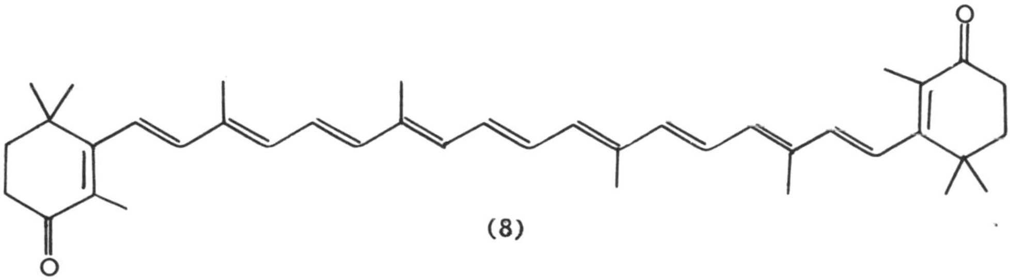

(8)

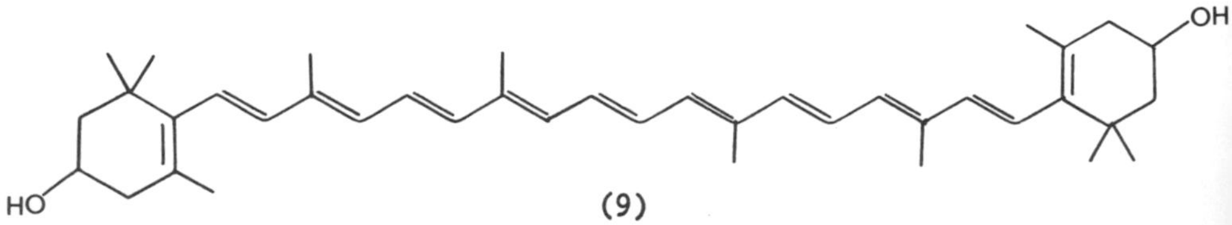

(9)

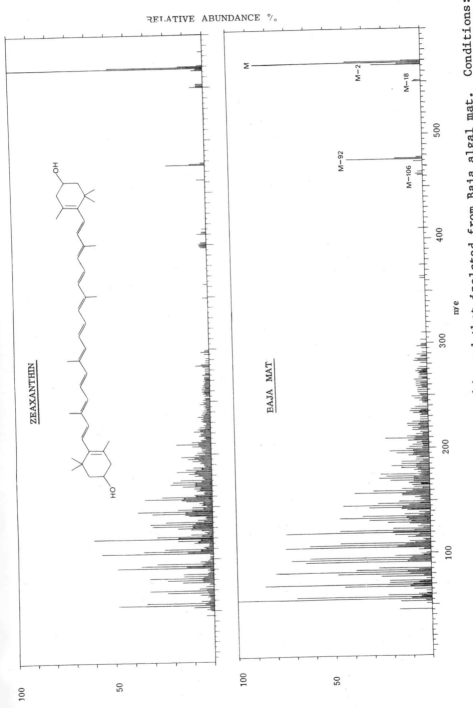

Figure 2. Mass spectra of authentic zeaxanthin and that isolated from Baja algal mat. Conditions: ionizing voltage 70 ev, filament current 100 μa, source temperature 160°C.

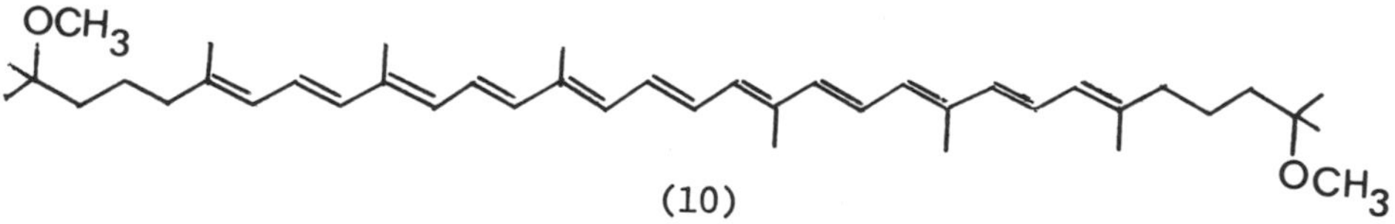

(10)

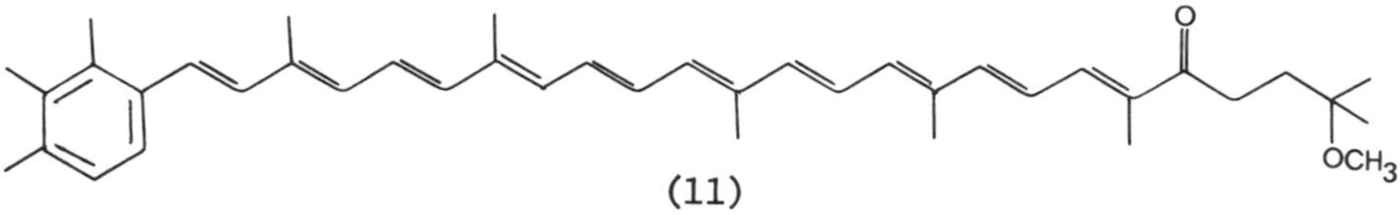

(11)

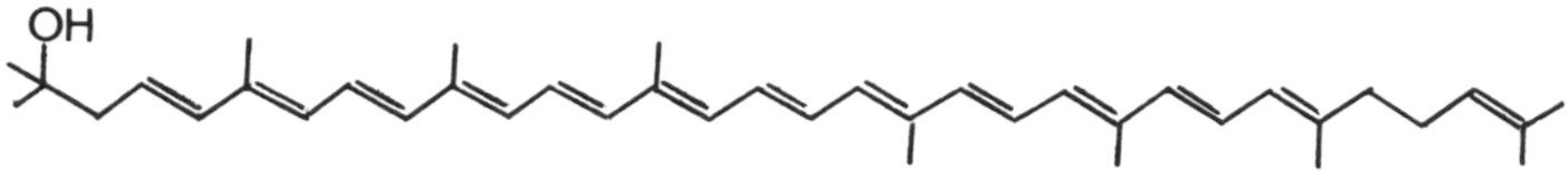

(12)

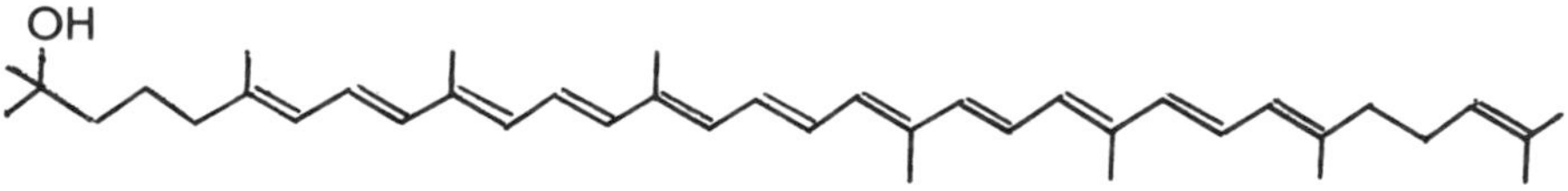

(13)

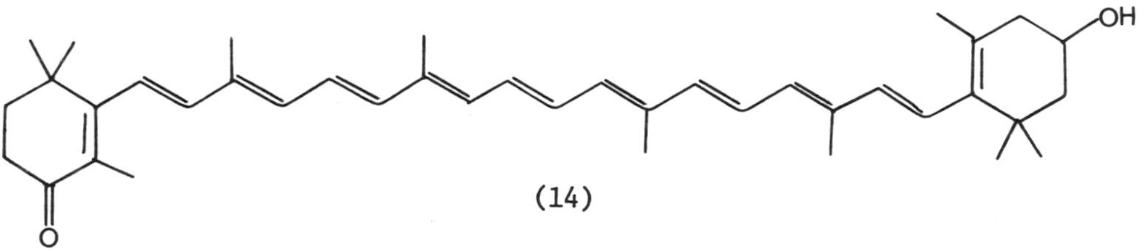

(14)

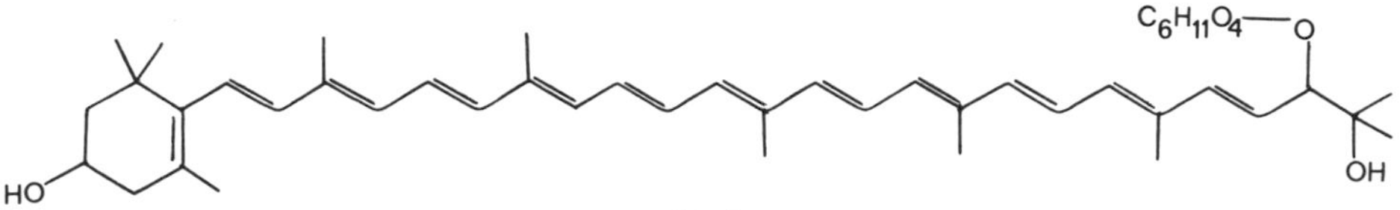

(15)

1971; Goodwin, 1976) and it seems likely that in this situation they derive, at least in part, from this source; they have not been reported in purple photosynthetic bacteria (see below). The blue-greens may also account for the presence of canthaxanthin (8) and 3'-hydroxyechinenone (14) because they have been found in a few species (Hertzberg *et al.*, 1971). Unfortunately, there is no report of the carotenoid distributions of the particular species of blue-greens in the mat.

The presence of the xanthophylls, spirilloxanthin (7), rhodopin (1) and dehydrorhodopin (12) reflects a specific input from purple photosynthetic bacteria, since they appear to be characteristic components (Schmidt *et al.*, 1965; Weedon, 1971). These components do not allow a distinction to be made between sulfur and nonsulfur species. The presence of 3,4,3', 4'-tetrahydrospirilloxanthin (10) and okenone (11) indicates, however, that sulfur purple photosynthetic bacteria make a contribution because these pigments have only been observed in *Thiorhodaceae* (Aasen and Liaaen-Jensen, 1967; Weedon, 1971; Schmidt, 1975). Among the *Athiorhodaceae*, the occurrence of spheroidenone (2) is restricted under aerobic conditions to *Rhodopseudomomas* spp., and its presence may relate to an origin from these organisms. There is one report, however, of the

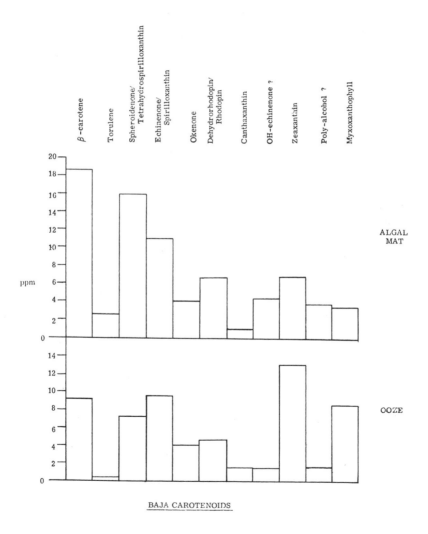

Figure 3. Distribution of major carotenoids in Baja algal mat and ooze (listed in elution order of discrete fractions isolated by preparative-scale TLC).

Table I
Baja Mat Carotenoids

Component		Inferred Input	
Present	Absent (or neg.)	Present	Absent (or neg.)
Torulene	–	Fungi	–
Tetrahydrospirillox-anthin	–	S-Purple Photosynthet-ics	–
Spheroidenone	–	Non-S Photosynthet-ics?	–
Echinenone	–	Blue-green Algae?	–
Spirilloxanthin	–	Purple Photosynthet-ics	–
Okenone	–	S-Purple Photosynthet-ics	–
Rhodopin	–	Purple Photosynthet-ics	–
Dehydrorhodopin	–	Purple Photosynthet-ics	–
Canthaxanthin	–	Blue-green Algae?	–
Hydroxyechinenone	–	Blue-green Algae?	–
Zeaxanthin	–	Blue-green Algae?	–
Myxoxanthophyll	–	Blue-green Algae	–
–	Lutein	–	Plants, Green Al-gae
–	Diatoxan-thin	–	Diatoms
–	Peridinin	–	Dinoflag-ellates
–	Astaxanthin	–	Crustaceans?

occurrence of spheroidenone in a *Thiorhodaceae* sp., although in this case its presence may be the result of adaptation to a habitat of minimal light (Czeczuga, 1974).

The carotene torulene (5) appears to be restricted to fungi, so it is likely that its presence reflects a minor con-tribution from this source (Wolf, 1973). The absence, or very low abundance, of the specific pigments astaxanthin, diatoxan-thin and peridinin indicates little or no input from crustaceans, diatoms, or dinoflagellates respectively (Fox, 1972; Goodwin, 1976 and references therein), although diatoms have been report-ed to occur in the mat (see above). Although lutein (16), the major xanthophyll of higher plants and green algae (Goodwin, 1976) was not found, there is a shoulder on the leading edge of the zeaxanthin peak in the HPLC trace (Figure 1A), which elutes at the retention time of lutein. It is possible that this minor component could be lutein; if so, its presence may relate to the very low concentrations of presumed higher plant n-alkanes found previously (Cardoso *et al.*, 1976).

(16)

The earlier study of a variety of other lipid classes on the mat showed that the distributions were compatible with major inputs from blue-green algae and bacteria (Cardoso *et al.*, 1976). The present study confirms these findings but demonstrates that certain carotenoids can be more specifically related to the contributing organisms. This emphasizes the necessity of exam-ining a wide variety of compound types in studies aimed at un-derstanding the lipid distributions of environmental situations.

Comparison with Other Environments

The distribution in the mat contrasts with those ob-served in two eutrophic lacustrine sediments and in a marine sediment (Watts *et al.*, 1977). There are similarities, however, to those in two other mats from Abu Dhabi and Shark Bay (West-ern Australia) in that myxoxanthophyll (15) is present and no higher plant or green algal contribution is observed by way of lutein (Watts *et al.*, 1977). The differences observed relate mainly to the diversity of the characteristic pigments from purple photosynthetic bacteria, although the Abu Dhabi mat is more similar to the Baja mat in this respect than to the Shark Bay mat. Similarly, a fungal input in the form of torulene (5) is apparent in the former two mats but not in the latter, which contains a lower concentration of total carotenoids.

Comparison of Mat and Ooze Carotenoids

The same major components are present in the mat and ooze but the relative abundances vary. Although the increase in absolute concentration of myxoxanthophyll (15) in the ooze is difficult to explain, there is an apparent contradiction to the earlier study (Cardoso *et al.*, 1976), which showed a decrease in the algal-derived n-C_{17} alkane and 7- and 8-methylheptade-canes. It is possible, therefore, that these alkanes can be more readily biodegraded than myxoxanthophyll in the ooze. In addition, the earlier study showed an increased relative contribution from higher plants to the ooze (probably from nearby *Salicornia* and *Distichilis*), via the high molecular weight n-alkanes and fatty acids, although the absolute concentrations showed little difference. This suggests that the higher plant input to both levels is constant and that biodegradation of the lower molecular weight alkanes and acids has occurred in the ooze.

Marked changes in the relative abundances of the bacterial carotenoids are apparent between the mat and ooze. For example, the concentration of okenone (11) remains constant (4.1 ppm), whereas the concentration of 3,4,3',4'-tetrahydro-spirilloxanthin has dropped markedly (Figure 1). This suggests that either the purple photosynthetic population in former mats synthesized these components in different relative abundances, or that there are differences in the extent of biodegradation of different carotenoids in the ooze.

ACKNOWLEDGMENTS

We thank the Natural Environment Research Council (GR3/2420), the Nuffield Foundation and the National Aeronautics and Space Administration (subcontract NGL 05-003-003) for financial support. One of us (P.J.C.T.) is grateful to Hoffmann La Roche Ltd. (Basel) for a maintenance grant. We also thank Dr. R. P. Philp (University of California, Berkeley) for collection of samples.

REFERENCES

Aasen, A. J., and S. Liaaen Jensen. "Bacterial Carotenoids XXIV," *Acta Chem. Scand.* 21:2185-2204 (1967).

Brown, S. R. "Bacterial Carotenoids from Fresh Water Sediments," *Limnol. Oceanog.* 13:233-241 (1968).

Brown, S. R. "Paleolimnological Evidence from Fossil Pigments," *Mitt. Int. Verein. Theor. Angew. Limnol.* 17:95-103 (1969).

Cardoso, J., P. W. Brooks, G. Eglinton, R. Goodfellow, J. R. Maxwell and R. P. Philp. In *Environmental Biogeochemistry,* Vol. 1, J. O. Nriagu, Ed. (Ann Arbor, Michigan: Ann Arbor Science Publishers, 1976), pp. 149-174.

Czeczuga, B. "Spheroidenone--A Dominating Carotenoid in Purple Bacteria *Thiopedia rosea* Winogr. (*Thiorhodaceae*)," *Bull. Acad. Polon. Sci.* 23:181-184 (1975).

Davies, B. H. "Analysis of Carotenoid Pigments," in *The Chemistry and Biochemistry of Plant Pigments,* T. W. Goodwin, Ed. (London: Academic Press, 1965), pp. 489-532.

Foppen, F. H. "Tables for the Identification of Carotenoid Pigments," *Chromatogr. Rev.* 14:133-298 (1971).

Fox, D. L. "Chromatology of Animal Skeletons," *Am. Sci.* 60: 436-447 (1972).

Goodwin, T. W. "Distribution of Carotenoids," in *Chemistry and Biochemistry of Plant Pigments,* Vol. 1, T. W. Goodwin, Ed. (London: Academic Press, 1976), pp. 225-261.

Hertzberg, S., S. Liaaen Jensen and H. W. Siegelman. "The Carotenoids of Blue-Green Algae," *Phytochem.* 10:3121-3127 (1971).

Horodyski, R. J., and S. P. Von der Haar. "Recent Calcereous Stromatolites from Laguna Mormona (Baja California) Mexico," *J. Sediment Petrol.* 45:894-906 (1975).

Martin, M., C. Eon and G. Guiochon. "Trends in Liquid Chromatography," *Res./Devel.* 26:24-31 (1975).

Philp, R. P., and M. Calvin. "Kerogen Structures in Recently Deposited Algal Mats at Laguna Mormona, Baja California: A Model System for the Determination of Kerogen Structures in Ancient Sediments," in *Environmental Biogeochemistry,* Vol. 1, J. O. Nriagu, Ed. (Ann Arbor, Michigan: Ann Arbor Science Publishers, 1976), pp. 131-148.

Pinevich, V. V., and V. E. Vasil'era. "Carotenoids of the Blue-Green Algae. Importance for Understanding Evolution and the Mechanism of Photosynthesis," *Vestn. Leningrad Univ. Biol.* 4:105-122 (1972).

Schmidt, K. "Carotenoids," in *Photosynthetic Bacteria,* R. K. Clayton and W. R. Sistrom, Eds.

Schmidt, R., N. Pfennig and S. Liaaen Jensen. "Carotenoids of *Thiorhodaceae,*" *Archiv. für Mikrobiol.* 52:132-146 (1965).

Vetter, W., G. Englert, N. Rigassi and U. Schwieter. "Spectroscopic Methods," in *Carotenoids,* O. Isler, Ed. (Basel: Birkhäuser-Verlag, 1971), pp. 189-266.

Watts, C. D., H. Kjøsen and J. R. Maxwell. "The Potential of Carotenoids as Environmental Indicators," in *Advances in Organic Geochemistry 1975* (in press).

Weedon, B. C. L. "Occurrence of Carotenoids," in *Carotenoids,* O. Isler, Ed. (Basel: Birkhaüser-Verlag, 1971), pp. 29-59.

Wolf, F. A. "Synthesis of Various Products, Especially Pigments, by Fungi," *J. Elisha Mitchell Sci. Soc.* 89:185-205 (1973).

Züllig, H. "Die Bestimmung von Myxoxanthophyll in Bohrpro-
filen zum Nachweis vergangener Blaualgenfaltungen," *Verh.
Internat. Ver. Limnol.* 14:263-270 (1960).

SECTION IV

DIAGENESIS

DIAGENESIS OF ORGANIC MATTER: SOME MICROBIOLOGICAL, CHEMICAL AND GEOCHEMICAL STUDIES ON SEDIMENTARY ORGANIC MATTER

JIM BROOKS

School of Chemistry
University of Bradford
Bradford, West Yorkshire, BD7 1DP, UK

POLLEN GRAINS AND SPORES

Spores and pollen grains of plants (palynomorphs) can be carried by wind and water into many different physical environments where they may become fossilized. Since each plant may produce many spores of pollen grains, and because the spore and pollen exine (outer wall) has such great chemical and microbiological resistance to decay, spores and pollens frequently occur as microfossils in large numbers in sediments that often lack other evidence of plant life.

Enormous amounts of pollen grains are dispersed at the flowering of wind-pollinated trees and grasses. If airborne pollen grains produced in a wooden temperate country (*e.g.*, Sweden) were to settle uniformly, there would be more than 300 million grains per annum per square meter. A gram of peat may contain several hundred thousand fossil pollen grains—making one hundred thousand million or more per cubic meter.

Pollen and spore analysis depends fundamentally on the fact that pollen and spore exines are generally preserved in peat, lignite, coal, shales and other sediments as morphologically intact organisms even when most other organic materials have been destroyed, distorted or degraded into amorphous material. In addition to chemical and microbiological changes occurring in the pollen, spores and related materials, there are various other important physical-chemical changes that cause changes in the physical appearance and also in their chemical structure. All these factors are important in both palynological and geochemical studies. In addition to giving fuller understanding to palynology and paleobotany, they are important parameters in petroleum geochemistry, assisting in thermal

maturation, organic metamorphism hydrocarbon generation studies
and petroleum exploration (Brooks, 1977).

DIAGENESIS

Studies have been made on the various physical, chemical
and microbiological agents that either in a natural or laboratory setting have been shown capable of altering or totally
destroying organic matter in unlithified sediments at surface
temperatures and pressures. These processes are generally
called *diagenetic processes*.

The physico-chemico-microbiological changes that operate
during deposition and within the first meter of burial are defined as *early diagenesis*. Subsequent alterations of longer
duration and lesser intensity that occur during or after lithification but prior to metamorphism are defined as *late diagenesis* (Ginsburg, 1957). In the period of early diagenesis the
least resistant parts of the organic matter are degraded by
microbiological diagenesis (Brooks and Shaw, 1968). During
late stages of diagenesis changes continue at a slower rate as
additional sediment accumulates and interstitial water is gradually squeezed out of the sediment. After expulsion of most of
the interstitial water by compaction, diagenesis probably
ceases.

Microbiological Diagenesis

The detailed behavior of microorganisms operating in the
complex processes of organic debris decomposition is largely
unknown, and only some broad generalizations of the processes
have been reported (Moore, 1969). In studies on the microbiological degradation of plant debris, there are important processes that result in the preferential degradation of polysaccharide components and related chemical material. They tend
to concentrate the nonpolysaccharide components (sporopollenine,
lignine, cuticles) that are more resistant to decay. Barghoorn
(1952) has shown that pronounced differences occur in the rates
of degradation of the various polysaccharide layers of single
cell walls. This differential degradation of polysaccharide
lamillae is considered (Barghoorn, 1952) to be consistent with
anaerobic decomposition. Alternatively it is suggested (Moore,
1963) that the differential degradation may be due to chemical
differences in the more resistant lamallae of the polysaccharide
frame work and also to the presence of associated substances
(*e.g.*, lignin or sporopollenin), which retard the deposition
of polysaccharide materials (Brooks, 1971).

The mechanism of microbiological attack upon polysaccharides has been described by Siu and Reese (1953) and Reese (1959)
to be partly dependent upon physicochemical actions. The active
fungi produce enzymes ("cellulases") that diffuse into the substrate and digest the polysaccharides. When the hyphae grow

into the digested region, they follow and digest the polysaccharide distributed within the organisms.

There have been few reports on microbiological attack
on fossil materials. Reinsch (1884) described what he believed
to be fungi on spore walls, and Renault (1900) described the
presence of a saprophytic fungus (*Anthracomyces cannellensis*)
on the surface of both micro- and megaspores, and also within
the latter organisms. For a long time botanists have known of
the attack of modern aquatic and soil-inhibiting fungi on whole
pollen grains. Goldstein (1960) gave a summary account of some
of these studies on various modern pollen and spores:

> Phycomycetes, particularly chytrides, were prominent
> among those organisms responsible for the weakening of
> the spore walls. . . . These fungi appear to be involved
> primarily with the contents of the grain rather than
> with the wall material itself, although occasionally
> they were observed to germinate and penetrate the air
> sacs of coniferous spores. The smoothness of the pollen
> wall in the region immediately surrounding the penetra-
> ting rhizoids and the discharge of tubes from these or-
> ganisms suggests that they digest rather than puncture
> the wall. . . .

This study drew attention to the importance and interest of the
degradation and destruction of pollen grains in relation to
pollen analysis, and among his conclusions to the different
modes of attack of various fungi on pollen, and to the greater
susceptibility to attack of some of the different types of pollen grains.

Sangster and Dale (1961) carried out controlled experiments on three genera of pollen—*Populus*, *Pinus* and *Typha*—
placed in four different environments—pond, lake, swamp and
bog. Their results showed considerable variation in the preservation, diagenesis and fossilization of these various pollen
grains under identical conditions. Also, they concluded
that the diagenesis of any given pollen is dependent upon its
environment, which affects not only the rate of decomposition
but also the nature of the processes involved. The degradation
processes were, in part, thought to be microbiological, and in
the case of *Populus* and *Typha* were primarily due to bacteria
attack. Sangster and Dale (1961) also showed that oxidation
was an important factor in the degradation for certain environments and suggested that the resistance of the exines to oxidizing agents favors fossilization. *Pinus* pollen was very resistant to decay and was well preserved in all four environments
(pond, lake, swamp and bog); *Typha* pollen was preserved only
in the bog; *Populus* pollen was degraded in all four environments. These results led to the suggestion that pollen exines
were made up of varying proportions of sporopollenin, which may
result in differences in the percentage frequency of species in
pollen rain spectra and in the fossil pollen pattern. Differences in the spectra and fossil pollen patterns would be due

to the differential preservation of exines from different plant species in different environments.

In the above discussion the words *fossil* and *fossilization* have been used to describe various conditions and processes that pollen grains (and organic matter) undergo. Faegri (1971) points out that the use of such words leads to popular misconceptions that everything that is buried sufficiently deep and for long periods of time is a fossil. This is not the case, and although we cannot discuss in detail the theory of fossilization, it is possible to state in general terms that "if the organic substance is still present in its original composition it is not a fossil, and should be considered a subfossil." Faegri (1971) states that he is not aware of any true fossil pollen grains, which would mean either that the original pollen wall material had been preserved as an imprint or cast or alternatively that the original wall had been replaced by some mineral. Various observations can be made on the subfossilization studies of pollen grains:

1. Time is a relatively minor factor. Given stable conditions, the changes in the sporopollenin structures after the period of incorporation in the sediment and the period immediately following are very slow processes.
2. After the grain has become incorporated into the sediment, the changes are much more regular and usually fewer in number, resulting in diagenesis at a slow rate.
3. Microbiological enzyme breakdown of pollen walls in sediments is usually very slight. Enzymes normally have difficulty digesting material of long-chain carbon molecules (Brooks and Shaw, 1973 and 1977). Although sporopollenin molecules seem rather vulnerable to oxidative chemical attack, apparently only very few enzymes are capable of attacking the material.

Havinga (1971) examined 19 different pollen and spore species in various soils and studied their preservation or decay in different environments. *Lycopodium clavatum* appears very resistant to microbiological attack, whereas *Taraxacum* and *Polypodium* show a fairly good resistance. *Alnus*, *Corylus* and *Myrica* disappeared nearly quantitatively. The frequencies of *Acer*, *Carpinus*, *Fraxinus*, *Populus*, *Salix* and *Ulmus* are strongly reduced. An intermediate position is taken by *Fagus*, *Tilis*, *Juniperus*, *Quercus*, *Pinus*, *Betula* and *Taxus*. Perforation-type corrosion is the main cause of decay of most species in these studied soil types.

The sequence of increasing susceptibility to corrosion obtained in Havinga's experiments in biologically very active soils (river clay soil and leaf mould) differs considerably from the sequence of increasing susceptibility to pure chemical oxidation and that obtained from corrosion in biologically poor soils.

Brooks and Shaw (1973) studied the microbiological degradation of various pollen and spores incorporated into culture plates and impregnated with different soil samples. Examination of the various preparations showed no significant exine degradation, but *Streptomyces* species colonized the culture plates containing pollen wall and exine preparations. Although these experiments did not show wall degradation, the results suggest that the *Streptomyces* were preferentially digesting the sporopollenin components. These results agree with evidence for the microbiological degradation of fossil spores by *Streptomyces* and *Actinomyces* species (Elsik, 1971).

Elsik (1971) reported that microbiological activity may result in definite patterns of removal of the exine from spores, pollen and other organic-walled microfossils. Chemical or physical degradation does not produce these patterns, except in the case of crystal (mainly pyrite) impressions onto or through the exine. Microbiological degradation of sporopollenin that results in definite patterns or scars is attributable to the higher bacteria (*Actinomyces*) and true fungi. Other fungi and bacteria apparently decompose the exine in an orderly fashion but with no set or recognizable microscopic patterns.

Chemical Diagenesis

Suggestions have been made to explain the role of oxidation-reduction potential (Eh) of sediments in the diagenesis of palynomorphs and related sedimentary organic matter (see Tschudy, 1969). Normal marine waters are ozidizing. Only in an euxinic marine environment is the Eh low enough to provide a reducing environment, and these conditions only exist in situations isolated from the atmosphere. Confined waters, particularly in the presence of organic matter, rapidly lose their oxygen content, and chemical hydrolysis of dissolved silicates causes the environment to become alkaline as well as reducing. Biochemical reactions initiated by microorganisms rapidly remove oxygen and produce carbon dioxide and hydrogen sulfide, resulting in a lowering of pH (acidity-alkalinity). Some anaerobic bacteria actually release hydrogen, which causes strongly negative Eh potentials to be developed, thereby creating strongly reducing conditions (see Brooks, Curtis *et al.*, 1977).

The abundances and preservations of pollen, spores and some other organic components in natural depositional environments undergo significant changes due to naturally occurring processes, similar to those outlined above, that interact with each other in a variety of ways that are both favorable and unfavorable to the diagenesis of sedimentary organic matter. The alterations and destruction of organic matter during natural sedimentation prior to lithification of the sediment are complex processes. Oxidation of unlithified sediments under aerobic conditions is certainly a major factor in organic losses, regardless of whether or not the sediment is subsequently

reduced prior to lithification. The common scarcity or sometimes absence of pollen and spores in red bed deposits is considered due to the oxidation and degradation of the sedimentary
organic matter.

The red color in these sediments is caused by the oxidation state of the iron contained in the rock and indicates that
the sediment was either deposited under already oxidized conditions or was later subjected to oxidation by ground water
containing oxygen. Alternatively it could have been caused by
exposure to atmospheric oxygen. This absence of spores, pollen
and related organic matter in red bed deposits is found in many
different areas that have received prelithification oxidation.
Correia (1971) concluded that the absence and loss of spores
in the Polignac Basin of the Sahara was caused by oxidation
during weathering of the rocks. The destruction of organic
matter by oxidation is caused not only by surface weathering,
since oxidation can occur from oxygenated waters that filter
down fault zones (*e.g.*, Dutch coal mines) and oxidize the organic matter (Gray and Boucot, 1975).

Well-preserved palynomorphs and organic matter are more
likely to be found in sediments deposited under conditions of
acid pH (1-6) and negative Eh (*i.e.*, in a reducing-acidic environment). Such conditions usually develop in bogs, lake
bottoms and in the depths of closed sedimentary basins.

In bog environments with reducing acidic environments,
the oxygen available for bacteria degradation of the organic
material decreases progressively with depth. The antibacterial
properties of various organic substances (*e.g.*, phenolic-like
components in humic substances) probably assists the preservation of the sedimenting materials (Brooks and Shaw, 1973 and
1977). Phenols, quinones, phenyl carboxylic acids and phenyl
glucosides have been shown to be present in peat deposits and
lake-bottom sediments (Nissenbaum, 1974).

In ocean-bottom sediments, the number of microbiological
organisms and hence microbial activity decreases rapidly from
the water-sediment interface downwards. A few centimeters below this water-sediment interface the sediments contain no free
oxygen, and living aerobic bacteria decrease at a logarithmic
rate as the depth increases below 5 to 10 cm. Even anaerobic
microbiols show a similar decrease curve below 40 to 60 cm.
Ancient sediments contain almost as much organic matter as the
uppermost 30-40 cm of recent sediments, suggesting that microbiological activity, which would reduce the organic matter concentration, is negligible below depths of about 40 cm.

The alkalinity of some sedimentary conditions (*e.g.*,
Florida Bay; see Williams and Barghoorn, 1963) ranges in high
pH values from 9.8 to 8.0. These are caused by the high rates
of photosynthesis during the day, which reduce carbon dioxide
and increase the oxygen content. At night, respiration con-
sumes oxygen and liberates carbon dioxide, thus reducing the
pH of the waters. Photosynthesis of algae is also responsible

for the precipitation of carbonates from sea water (Williams and Barghoorn, 1963). In the presence of organic acids, these alkaline precipitates redissolve, and the acidity is reduced and sometimes neutralized. These few general points on the chemistry in sediments show that chemical activities, particularly Eh and pH conditions and changes, have very significant roles to play in the preservation or destruction of palynomorphs and other sedimentary organic matter.

SEDIMENTATION, DIAGENESIS AND METAMORPHISM OF ORGANIC MATTER

The chemical and microbiological processes involved in the alteration of organic matter has been studied by many geochemists (see Tissot and Bienner, 1974; Brooks, 1977b) and various definitions and pathways have been given to the processes taking place. It is therefore important to review these processes that directly and indirectly affect the sedimenting organic matter, and to survey and descriptions and definitions that have been proposed.

The nature of the original biological source material, the environment of deposition, microbiological alterations, chemical changes, the temperature, pressure and nature of ground water solutions all play important roles in the sedimentation, diagenesis and thermal alteration of the organic matter.

The changes in the organic matter involve various important steps (Figure 1) and can be summarized as:

1. microbiological degradation
2. chemical degradation (mainly hydrolysis)
3. chemical polymerization
4. organic diagenesis (reduction, decarboxylation, dehydration, demethylation, deamination and cyclization)
5. thermal alteration ("cracking" and disproportionation of the carbon–carbon bonds)
6. organic metamorphism (including further "coalification" and "carbonization").

The organic materials deposited in sediments consist primarily of naturally occurring biopolymers (polysaccharides, lipids, proteins, sporopollenins, lignine, cuticles and pigments) (Figure 2). When these biopolymers are incorporated into the sedimentary cycle, microorganisms partially or fully degrade them through the use of enzymes, breaking down the biopolymer into smaller units, often down to the monomers (polysaccharides to sugars; proteins to amino acids). These microbiological degradation products, which can be identified in recent and ancient sediments, are often called "biological markers" (Eglinton, 1969).

Alternatively, these degradation products can join together chemically (condensation or polymerization reactions) to form geopolymer complex molecules (kerogen, sapropelic matter, humic acids, named depending upon the original source of the organic material). These microbiological and chemical

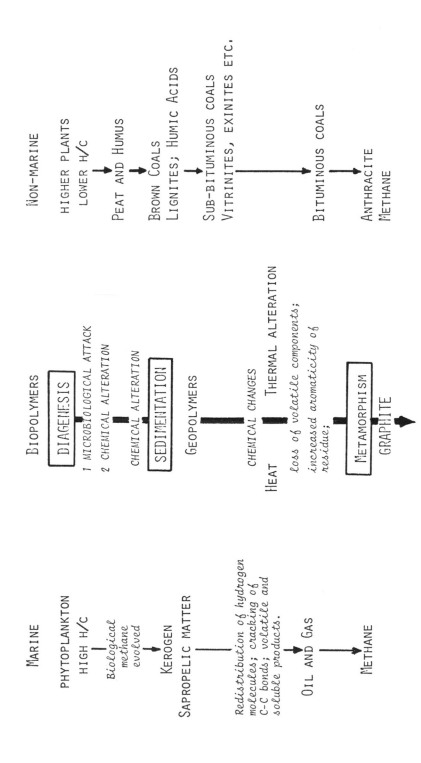

Figure 1. Schematic relationships of the diagenesis and metamorphism of sedimentary organic matter.

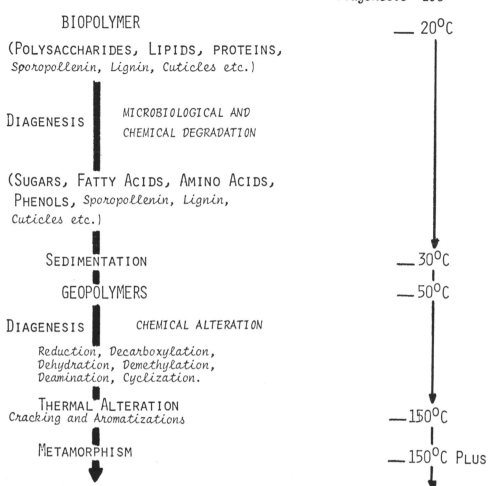

Figure 2. Chemical reactions during diagenesis and metamorphism.

changes appear to take place only in the upper meter of the sediment at near surface temperatures and are considered early diagenesis stages.

Organic diagenesis of the sedimentary organic matter involves a large number of chemical reactions that take place in the upper meters of the sediment at temperatures from surface temperatures to about 50°C. The main chemical reactions taking place are:

1. breaking or cleavage of carbon-carbon bonds (chlorophyll fragments to give one porphyrin and one phytol molecule)
2. reduction of unsaturated carbon-carbon bonds (olefins to saturated alkane molecules)
3. disproportionation reactions (redistribution of the hydrogen atoms within the molecules)
4. aromatization reactions (aliphatic and acyclic hydrocarbons are changes to aromatic structures)
5. loss of ammonia, hydrogen sulfide, carbon dioxide, methane, oxygen, nitrogen and sulfur from the organic

molecules (ammonia and hydrogen sulfide gases are
evolved from nitrogen- and sulfur-containing molecules,
respectively).

Following these initial diagenetic processes are a series
of geothermal reactions leading to products of increasing thermal stability. Thermal alteration of organic matter (often
called "coalification" or "carbonization") involves the cracking of large molecules to form small organic compounds. It
occurs mainly at temperatures from 50° to 150°C. These processes take place in the main zone of petroleum generation. The
major geochemical reactions taking place during thermal alteration of the organic matter may be considered to be:

1. disproportionation and redistribution of the hydrogen
   atoms and breaking of some carbon-carbon bonds, leading
   to smaller molecules of increasing volatility and hydrogen content (with methane as the end product)
2. loss of hydrogen, giving a carbonaceous residue of de-
   creasing hydrogen content and increasing carbon content
   (with graphite as the end product).

The last step, organic metamorphism, occurs mainly at temperatures above 150°C and, ultimately, through these processes,
changes the organic matter to methane and carbon.

COALIFICATION AND CARBONIZATION CHANGES

Probably the most studied thermal alterations of sedimentary organic matter are the coalification and carbonization.
The term "coalification" was proposed by Barghoorn (1952), who
suggested that the term should ". . . designate all physical
and chemical alterations starting with the initial plant substances and ending, perhaps, with graphites." If the plant
material is of higher plant origin, it is considered to undergo
the following coalification processes:

1. When the changes are minimal, peat and humus are formed
   in the first instance (Figure 1).
2. Increasing alterations give successively brown coals,
   lignites and humic acids.
3. Further alterations give subbituminous, bituminous and
   anthracite coals.

These changes involve an increase in fixed carbon content and
a decrease in volatile matter and moisture content (Teichmüller,
1974).

Coalification has been divided into a diagenetic stage,
which ends at soft lignite, and into a metamorphic stage, which
leads to the formation of successively harder coals with higher
carbon contents (Kuyl and Patijn, 1961). Both coalification
and carbonization processes of organic materials involve the
breaking or cleavage of molecular bonds (carbon-carbon linkages;
carbon-hydrogen and carbon-oxygen linkages), with consequent
evolution of volatile components resulting in the organic residue proceeding toward a higher carbon content. Both processes

follow nonreversible reactions and produce major amounts of water, carbon dioxide and methane, but they follow very different chemical routes and result in different spectra of chemical by-products (Figure 3).

Coalification occurs as a low-grade metamorphic process in which the energy responsible for the breakage of some chemical bonds and possible formation of new linkages is provided by:

1. heat sources (geothermal gradients caused by sedimentary and tectonic overburden, igneous activity and tectonic pressure)
2. shear (provided by the overburden pressures and by tectonic pressures in which heat may or may not be a factor).

These reactions are long-term processes (up to millions of years) and involve various different energy sources. Thermal energy, the major source of energy caused by increased depths of burial or frictional heat generated during tectonism, causes chemical changes to take place in the organic matter. Coalification can also occur from local geological perturbations of the geothermal gradient produced from intrusion bodies (Teichmüller and Teichmüller, 1968).

Carbonization processes occur through the rapid charring, thermal degradation or decomposition (pyrolysis) of organic matter (Figure 3). Unlike coalification, carbonization may occur under a variety of pressure conditions from surface/near surface low pressures to very high overburden or tectonic pressures. Carbonization is a pure thermal decomposition of the organic matter that occurs during a short interval, often measured in hours or less. Coalification and carbonization processes both alter the original plant tissue material and, carried to their ultimate end, convert the organic matter into graphitic carbon.

Chemical Reactions

The chemical reactions involved in the coalification process depend mainly on time and temperature, while some effects of pressure cause an increase of coal rank; compression and consolidation are accompanied by losses of volume and moisture. Data accumulated so far support the general physical law that the time taken to attain a given coal rank is halved by an increased temperature of 10°C.

The rates of chemical change with temperature and increasing depths of burial occur at very different rates, and are summarized in Figure 4. The relative amounts of dead carbon, kerogen and asphaltene materials do not change much until the organic matter has been buried a considerable time. When the organic matter reaches certain depths of burial and temperature, rapid chemical changes occur that cause significant degradation of the organic matter, producing gaseous and liquid

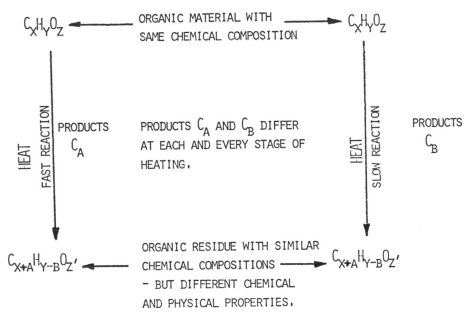

Figure 3.   Alteration of organic matter.

hydrocarbons and increasing the carbon content and stability
of the insoluble organic residue towards graphite. Increased
depths of burial of the organic matter produce relatively minor
changes in the organic components, which are mainly high-carbon
residue. Under certain more extreme thermal conditions they
may produce methane gas.

DIAGENESIS AND METAMORPHISM OF POLLEN AND SPORES

Due to the variation degrees of thermal alteration, pollen grains and spores from different ranks of coal show gradual
color changes in coal, from pale yellow through light brown-brown
to dark brown-black. Although experimental evidence is limited
to reflect all the parameters that can affect the color and
chemical changes in pollen, spores and related organic matter,
it seems that the route to the final color can occur either by
coalification or carbonization. The route depends on the different rates of heating, different times of thermal alteration
and the resulting chemical reactions. It is impossible to consider all these chemical, physical and geological variables.
Generally many of the parameters are considered to be constant,
with only temperature taken as the most influential parameter.
Thermal alterations on the organic matter are considered to be
most important and thus will be discussed in relation to the
chemical and color changes that occur in pollen and spores. It

is essential to note that the effects of hydrostatic pressure
gradients and shear pressure gradient can parallel the effects
of the geothermal gradient in regions subject to deep burial,
and often it is difficult to assess the roles of hydrostatic
pressure and shear separately from thermally produced alterations in pollen and spores (Gray and Boucot, 1975).

    Under laboratory conditions, the chemical effects of ex-
perimental carbonization (Gutjahr, 1966; Correia, 1967 and
1971; Brooks, 1970, 1971 and 1977a; Combaz, 1971; and
Sengupta, 1974) on pollen and spores show that color and chemical changes start at temperatures between 100° and 200°C.

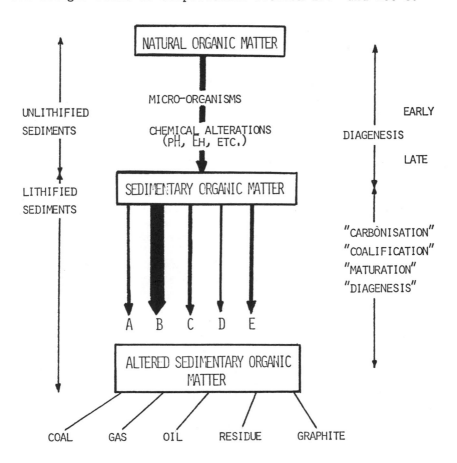

A - CHEMICAL   B - HEAT   C - PRESSURE
D - MICROBIOLOGICAL   E - SHEAR

Figure 4. Alteration of sedimentary organic matter.

Few studies have been carried out on the progressive changes
occurring with the sequential heating of pollen and spores, but
some results (Cook, 1972) suggest that pollen and spores car-
bonize at different temperatures, depending on their previous
geothermal history. Therefore, the possibility exists that
different pollen and spores of the same color may have been
subjected to different initial degrees of coalification and
different subsequent degrees of carbonization. Pollen and
spores of the same color may not have been subjected to the
same amount of bond-breaking energy; alternatively, pollen and
spores of the same color may have been subjected to the same
amount of bond-breaking energy applied from different sources
and at different rates.

    Laboratory experiments (Brooks, 1970, 1971 and 1977a;
McIntyre, 1972; and Sengupta, 1974) in which pollen grains and
spores were heated for varying lengths of time at different
temperatures show that little color or chemical changes occurred
below 180°-200°C, but significant changes occurred above 220°C.
Above 270°C further changes occurred over shorter periods. Laboratory experiments showed that carbonization at temperatures
below 180°C produced little or no color change and only minor
chemical changes (Brooks, 1977a). Above 220°C, the palynomorphs
are readily changed and there are significant color changes from
yellow-light brown to dark brown-black. The color changes are
accompanied by corresponding changes in the pollen and spore
chemical structures. Results showed that the color of the organisms is dependent upon the maximum temperature of heating.
After heating for 60 to 100 hours there appears to be little
additional thermal alteration.

    The experiments also showed that when organic material
(including pollen and spores) are heated at lower temperatures
(less than 180°C), apart from the evolution of water and small
amounts of methane, the sporopollenin residue appears to be
altered little. Spores heated to higher temperatures (greater
than 220°C) produce more volatile and soluble products and show
significant alterations in both color and chemical changes in
relatively short times (Brooks, 1977). These observations suggest that organic carbon-carbon bonds in sedimentary organic
matter may remain unchanged for long periods of geological time
at low temperatures, but may be rapidly broken with higher energy levels.

    Pollen and spores show changes in color and chemical
structure with temperature at different rates than dinoflagellates and acritarchs (Correia, 1971), and these show earlier
changes than chitinozoa. Spores and pollen are the most sensitive indicators of thermal change in any particular region
of a sediment, especially in areas where the temperatures have
been relatively low. This fact has resulted in spore and pollen color changes being used in different geothermal studies
on sediments. Although these techniques have many applications,
the major use has been made in petroleum exploration studies.

In such studies the alteration in the sedimentary organic matter into petroleum-like soluble organic compounds can be paralleled to the *in situ* alteration of spores, pollen and related organic materials (Brooks and Shaw, 1969), provided that the thermal alterations are reacting within the insoluble organic matter (kerogen) in the source rock and not on the generated organic compounds that are subjected to different types of chemical maturations (Connan *et al.*, 1975).

Using these relationships between spore color, translucency and fluorescence, chemical changes and electron spin resonance (ESR) analysis and geothermal conditions, it is now possible for organic geochemists and palynologists to determine the regional thermal properties of sediments (source-rock properties) and their potential for petroleum generation.

ORGANIC DIAGENESIS AND PETROLEUM EXPLORATION

Large research efforts have been devoted to the investigation of organic diagenesis in relation to petroleum occurrences and exploration (see Brooks, 1977b). When sediments undergo diagenesis, the contained organic matter is affected, especially by the influence of heat resulting from increased burial.

Hydrocarbons have probably been more extensively investigated than any other type of compound in rocks, although they constitute only a small fraction of the total organic matter preserved in the sediment. Most of the latter is present in a fine-grained sediment, such as shales or mudstones, and contains up to about 98% insoluble organic geopolymers (kerogen) and generally less than 2% "soluble" organic compounds. Hydrocarbons account for 5-15% of the total soluble organic matter present in these sediments. Correlations of petroleum compositions with the complex mixture of organic compounds present in source-rocks show that crude oils represent a selective accumulation of the less polar constituents of these soluble components.

Early studies on organic diagenesis of sedimentary organic matter (Philippi, 1968) showed that the changes with depth of the particular compositional factors (geochemical parameters) could be used for the general investigation of the petroleum generation processes. The most useful of these parameters were:
1. hydrocarbon/total organic carbon ratio
2. CPI index (odd/even ratio) of n-paraffins
3. naphthene and other hydrocarbon-type variations.
The relationship of these parameters to oil occurrence in sedimentary basins has been generally established, and additional hydrocarbon-type variations have been developed for the investigation of organic diagenetic processes and oil source-rock studies.

The above parameters were concerned primarily with determining the threshold limit of significant petroleum generation

in a sedimentary sequence (Tissot *et al.*, 1973); Brooks
and Thusu, 1976). Other investigations (Hood and Castano,
1974) have been more concerned with establishing the
upper limits for the preservation of liquid petroleum in sediments (the so-called "oil-floor") and have concentrated on
somewhat less direct analytical indicators such as coal-rank
(Stach, 1976), sporomorph color variations, sporomorph translucency (Gutjahr, 1966; Grayson, 1973) and vitrinite reflectivity measurements (see Hood and Castano, 1974). These sporomorph measurements reflect mainly the degree of alteration
(carbonization) of sporopollenin under the influence of temperature, and the reflectivity measurements indicate the changes
in the other components (vitrinite, exinite, resinite) present
in the sedimentary organic matter, which can be correlated with
the occurrence and preservation of petroleum in sediments.

Pyrolysis measurements on kerogens can also be related
to oil occurrence and various methods of determination have
been developed, including the C_R/C_T ratio procedure (Gransh
and Eisma, 1966; Brooks, 1975; Brooks and Thusu, 1976), which
evolved from a consideration of methods for the measurement of
coal volatiles. "Kerogen" decomposition studies are probably
both a direct and an indirect reflection of the petroleum generation process, because kerogens are certainly important precursors of the components found in petroleum.

One of the most used parameters for the correlation with
both the threshold of oil generation and the upper limits of
its preservation is coal rank measurement (Suggate, 1959).
Coal rank studies have been used since 1925 (White, 1925) to
correlate oil and gas occurrences with carbon ratios of associated coals. During the last 25 years, the method has been
revised and applied extensively, due primarily to the development of precise reflectivity methods of rank determination
which utilized only the small quantities of coals that might
be obtained from exploration oil well cuttings. The method
obviously requires the presence of coals in sediments, but the
widespread occurrence of small amounts of vitrinite has enabled
the technique to be used far more widely than had previously
been expected.

The various geochemical parameters that are currently
used to investigate organic diagenesis and petroleum generation are:
1. hydrocarbon/organic carbon variations (Gehman, 1962;
    McIver, 1967; LaPlante, 1974)
2. kerogen pyrolysis studies, including C_R/C_T measurements
    and analyses of evolved products (Gransh and Eisma,
    1966; Correia and Peniguel, 1975; Brooks, 1975;
    Brooks and Thusu, 1976)
3. sporomorph color, translucency (Gutjahr, 1966; Grayson,
    1973), fluorescence (van Gizjel, 1971; Teichmüller,
    1974) and cathodoluminescence (Muir and Grant, 1971)
    measurements

4. coal rank determinations, using vitrinite reflectivity techniques (see Hood and Castano, 1974)
5. thermal alteration index (Staplin, 1969; Burgess, 1974; Correia and Peniguel, 1975)
6. chemical maturation index (Philippi, 1968; Tissot *et al.*, 1975)
7. hydrocarbon-type analysis (see Mead *et al.*, 1974)
8. electron spin resonance (ESR) studies (Pussey, 1973)
9. level of organic metamorphism (LOM) scale (Hood and Castano, 1974).

These parameters probably reflect more accurately the integrated effect of time and temperature, and possible catalytic activity, but many of them are a direct measure of petroleum formation, so other factors are taken into account. The more "indirect" methods have now been sufficiently well correlated with petroleum occurrences to be considered of fairly general application.

The results of organic diagenesis and source-rock studies, using a variety of geochemical parameters, indicate that in a uniform sedimentary sequence significant hydrocarbon generation occurs at a depth that appears to be controlled primarily by temperature. Similarly, geochemical parameters are able to indicate limits in a sedimentary sequence below which liquid petroleum-like deposits are unlikely to occur. Within the "stratigraphic interval" defined by these parameters most petroleum occurrences are likely to be found. However, due to the possibilities of petroleum migration, the geological history of an area must be carefully considered in conjunction with evidence obtained from geochemical studies in order to effectively assess its petroleum exploration potential.

REFERENCES

Barghoorn, E. S. "Degradation of Plant Materials and its Relationship to the Origin of Coal," *Nova Scotia Dept. Mines Conf. Origin and Constitution of Coal* (1952) pp. 181-207.

Brooks, J. "Chemical Constituents of Various Plant Spore Walls," Ph.D. Thesis, University of Bradford, England (1970).

Brooks, J. "Some Chemical and Geochemical Studies on Sporopollenin," in *Sporopollenin,* J. Brooks *et al.*, Ed. (London and New York: Academic Press, 1971), pp. 351-407.

Brooks, J. "Organic Geochemistry and Petroleum Exploration—a Special Report," Continental Shelf Institute, Royal Norwegian Council for Scientific and Industrial Research, Norway (1975).

Brooks, J. "Chemical Studies on the Thermal Products from Sporopol Lenin and Their Probable Geochemical Significance," in *Proc. ICP Congr. "Diagenesis of Miospores and Methods of Palynological Preparations"* (1977a, in press).

Brooks, J. *Coalification and Carbonisation of Sedimentary Organic Matter*, to be published by Academic Press (1977b, in preparation).

Brooks, J., C. Curtis, P. Grant, W. E. Krumbein and M. D. Muir. *Geochemical and Microbiological Processes in Weathering, Sedimentation and Diagenesis*, to be published by Academic Press (in preparation).

Brooks, J., and G. Shaw. "Identity of Sporopollenin with Older Kerogen and New Evidence for the Possible Biological Source of Chemicals in Sedimentary Rocks," *Nature* 220:678-679 (1968).

Brooks, J., and G. Shaw. "Kerogen and Sporopollenin," *Nature* 227:195-197 (1969).

Brooks, J., and G. Shaw. "The Role of Sporopollenin in Palynology," in *Problems in Palynology* (Moscow: Nauka Press, 1973), pp. 80-92.

Brooks, J., and B. Thusu. "Oil-Source Rock Identification and Characterisation of the Jurassic Sediments in the Northern North Sea," *Chem. Geol.* (in press).

Brooks, J., and B. Thusu. "North Sea Oil: Applications of Palynological and Geochemical Studies to an Understanding of the Properties and Potential of Jurassic Source Rocks," in *Stratigraphic Palynology and Applications to Fossil Fuel Exploration,* ICP Conference, Lucknow, India (in press).

Brooks, J., and G. Shaw. "Recent Advances in the Chemistry and Geochemistry of Pollen and Spore Walls," *Trans. Bose Res. Inst., India* (in press).

Combaz, A. "Thermal Degradation of Sporopollenin and Genesis of Hydrocarbons," in *Sporopollenin,* J. Brooks *et al.,* Ed. (London and New York: Academic Press, 1971), pp. 621-658.

Connan, J., K. Le Tran and B. van der Weide. "Alteration of Petroleum in Reservoirs," in *Proc. World Petroleum Congress* (Essex, England: Applied Science Publications, 1975), pp. 171-178.

Correia, M. "Relations possibles entre l'état de conservation des éléments figures de la matière organique (microfossiles palynoplanctologiques) et l'éxistence de gisements d'hydrocarbures," *Rév. Inst. Francais Pétrole* 2:1285-1306 (1967).

Correia, M. "Diagenesis of Sporopollenin and Other Comparable Organic Substances: Application to Hydrocarbon Research," in *Sporopollenin,* J. Brooks *et al.,* Ed. (London and New York: Academic Press, 1971), pp. 569-620.

Correia, M., and G. Peniguel. "Etude microscopique de la matière organique—ses application a l'éxploration pétroliers," *Bull. Centre Rech. Pau—SNPA* 9:99-127 (1975).

Cook, A. C., D. G. Murchison and E. Scott. "A British Metaanthracite Coal of Devonian Age," *Geol. J.* 8:83-94 (1972).

Eglinton, G. "Organic Geochemistry: The Organic Chemists' Approach," in *Organic Geochemistry*, G. Eglinton and M. Murphy, Eds. (Berlin: Springer-Verlag, 1969), pp. 20-73.

Elsik, W. C. "Microbiological Degradation of Sporopollenin," in *Sporopollenin*, J. Brooks *et al.*, Ed. (London and New York: Academic Press, 1971), pp. 480-509.

Faegri, K. "The Preservation of Sporopollenin Membranes under Natural Conditions," in *Sporopollenin*, J. Brooks *et al.*, Ed. (London and New York: Academic Press, 1971), pp. 256-270.

Gehman, H. M. "Organic Matter in Limestones," *Geochim. Cosmochim. Acta* 6:885-897 (1962).

Ginsburg, R. N. "Early Diagenesis and Lithification of Shallow-Water Carbonate Sediments in S. Florida," in *Regional Aspects of Carbonate Deposition*, R. J. LeBlanc and J. G. Breeding, Eds., *Soc. Econ. Paleontologists and Mineralogists Spec. Pub.* 5:80-99 (1957).

van Gizjel, P. "Review of the UV-Fluorescence Microphotometry of Fresh and Fossil Exines and Exosporia," in *Sporopollenin*, J. Brooks *et al.*, Ed. (London and New York: Academic Press, 1971), pp. 659-682.

Goldstein, S. "Degradation of Pollen by Phycomycetes," *Ecology* 41:543-545 (1960).

Gray, J., and A. J. Boucot. "Colour Changes in Pollen and Spores: A Review," *Geol. Soc., America Bull.* 86:1019-1033 (1975).

Gransch, J. A., and E. Eisma. "Characterisation of the Insoluble Organic Matter of Sediments by Pyrolysis," in *Advances in Organic Geochemistry 1966*, G. D. Hobson and G. C. Speers, Eds. (Oxford: Pergamon Press, 1966), pp. 407-426.

Grayson, J. R. "Relationship of Palynomorph Translucency to Carbon and Hydrocarbons in Clastic Sediments," *Col. Interm. Pétrographie de la Matière Organique des Sédiments, CNRS, Paris* 1973:261-273.

Gutjahr, C. C. M. "Carbonisation Measurements of Pollen Grains and Spores and Their Application," *Leidse Geol. Mededel.* 38: 1-29 (1966).

Havinga, A. J. "An Experimental Investigation into the Decay of Pollen and Spores in Various Soil Types," in *Sporopollenin*, J. Brooks *et al.*, Ed. (London and New York: Academic Press, 1971), pp. 446-478.

Hood, A., and J. R. Castano. "Organic Metamorphism: Its Relationship to Petroleum Generation and Application to Studies of Authigenic Minerals," *U.N. ESCAP, CCOP, Tech. Bull.* 8: 85-118.

Kuyl, O. S., and R. J. H. Patijn. "Coalification in Relation to Depth of Burial and Geothermal Gradient," in *Cong. Avanc. Etudes Stratigraphie et Géologie Carbonifère* 2:357-365 (1961).

La Plante, R. E. "Petroleum Generation in Gulf Coast Tertiary Sediments," *Am. Assoc. Petrol. Geol. Bull.* 58(7):1281-1289 (1974).

McIntyre, D. J. "Effect of Experimental Metamorphism on Pollen in a Lignite," *Geoscience and Man* 4:111-117 (1972).

McIver, R. D. "Composition of Kerogen—Clue to its Role in the Origin of Petroleum," in *Proc. 7th World Petroleum Congress, vol. 2* (London: Elsevier, 1967), pp. 25-36.

Mead, W. L., A. R. West, S. A. Knight, G. W. Smith and P. B. Tooke. "New Developments in the Molecular Analysis and their Application in the Petroleum Industry," in *Proc. 8th World Petroleum Congress, vol. 3* (Essex, England: Applied Science Publishers, 1974), pp. 231-241.

Moore, L. R. "Microbiological Colonisation and Attack on Some Carboniferous Miospores," *Palaeontology* 6:349-372 (1963).

Moore, L. R. "Geomicrobiology and Geomicrobiological Attack on Sedimented Organic Matter," in *Organic Geochemistry*, G. Eglinton and M. Murphy, Eds. (Berlin: Springer-Verlag, 1969), pp. 265-303.

Muir, M. D., and P. Grant. "Application of Scanning Electron Microscope Techniques and Optical Microscopy to the Study of Sporopollenin," in *Sporopollenin*, J. Brooks *et al.*, Ed. (London and New York: Academic Press, 1971), pp. 422-439.

Nissenbaum, A. "The Organic Geochemistry of Marine and Terrestrial Humic Substances: Implications of Carbon and Hydrogen Isotope Studies," in *Advances in Organic Geochemistry 1973*, B. Tissot and F. Bienner, Eds. (Paris: Editions Technip, 1974), pp. 39-52.

Philippi, G. T. "Essentials of the Petroleum Formation Process Are Organic Source Material and a Subsurface Temperature Controlled Chemical Reaction Mechanism," in *Advances in Organic Geochemistry,* P. A. Schenck and I. Havenaar, Eds. (Oxford: Pergamon Press, 1968), pp. 25-46.

Pusey, W. C. "The ESR-Kerogen Method—a New Technique of Estimating the Organic Maturity of Sedimentary Rocks," *Petroleum Times* 1973:21-25.

Reese, E. T. "Enzymatic Hydrolysis of Cellulose," *Appl. Microbiol.* 4:37-45 (1959).

Rennault, B. "Recherches sur les bactériacées fossiles," *Ann. Sci. Nat. VIII Ser. Bot.* 275 (1900).

Sangster, A. G., and H. M. Dale. "Degradation of Pollen and Spores in Different Environments," *Can. J. Bot.* 4:35-52 (1961).

Sengupta, S. "The Effects of Temperature and Pressure on Lycopodium Clavatum," in *Advances in Organic Geochemistry 1973,* B. Tissot and F. Bienner, Eds. (Paris: Editions Technip, 1974), pp. 305-306.

Stach, E. *Textbook of Coal Petrology* (Berlin and Stuttgart: Gebrüder Borntraeger, 1975).

Staplin, F. L. "Sedimentary Organic Matter, Organic Metamorphism, and Oil and Gas Occurrence," *Can. Petrol. Geol. Bull.* 17:47-66 (1969).

Suggate, R. P. "New Zealand Coals, Their Geological Setting and Its Influence on Their Properties," *New Zealand Dept. Sci. Industry Res. Bull.* 134:1-113 (1959).

Teichmüller, M., and R. Teichmüller. "Geological Aspects of Coal Metamorphism," in *Coal and Coal-Bearing Strata,* D. G. Murchison and T. S. Westoll, Eds. (New York: Elsevier, 1968), pp. 233-267.

Teichmüller, M. "Generation of Petroleum-Like Substances in Coal-Seams as Seen under the Microscope," in *Advances in Organic Geochemistry 1973,* B. Tissot and F. Bienner, Eds. (Paris: Editions Technip, 1974), pp. 379-395.

Tissot, B., G. Deroo and J. Espitalie. "Etude comparee de l'epoque de formation et d'éxpulsion du pétrole dans diverses provinces géologiques," in *Proceedings of the 9th World Petroleum Congress,* Panel Discussion Paper 3(3) (Essex, England: Applied Science Publishers, 1975), pp. 1-12.

Tissot, B., and F. Bienner. *Advances in Organic Geochemistry 1973* (Paris: Editions Technip, 1974).

Tschudy, R. H. "Relationship of Palynomorphs to Sedimentation," in *Aspects of Palynology*, R. H. Tschudy and R. A. Scott, Eds. (New York: Wiley-Interscience, 1969), pp. 79-96.

White, D. "Progressive Regional Carbonisation of Coal," *Trans. Am. Inst. Mining, Met., Eng.* 71:253-281 (1925).

Williams, M., and E. S. Barghoorn. "Biogeochemical Aspects of the Formation of Marine Carbonates," in *Organic Geochemistry*, I. A. Breger, Ed. (Oxford and New York: Pergamon Press, 1963), pp. 596-604.

CHAPTER 25

DIAGENETIC PROCESSES OCCURRING IN COMPACTING CLAY-RICH SEDIMENT SEQUENCES

C. D. CURTIS

Sorby Laboratory
Department of Geology
The University of Sheffield
Sheffield, S1 3JD, England

INTRODUCTION

This chapter will review the current state of knowledge concerning diagenetic processes in fine-grained and generally clay-rich sediments. These changes are quite dramatic in all but organic-poor sediments, with significant mineralogical alteration starting soon after burial. The fundamental reasons for these changes will be analyzed, as will their environmental control. It is clear that microbiological processes play a very important part in diagenesis. Several different processes can be recognized, some of which are well-documented whereas others are not. It is hoped that this review will bring these important rocks to the attention of workers qualified to investigate microbial mechanisms and thereby stimulate research.

FINE-GRAINED CLASTIC SEDIMENTS AT DEPOSITION

The mineralogical constituents of clay sediments at deposition are derived from two principle sources. The first, and quantitatively most important, is soil horizons. Erosion and transport deliver these to the basin of deposition where sorting is achieved as a result of hydrodynamic factors. Fine-grained materials are separated from coarse clastics and deposited as muds.

Relatively little alteration occurs during transport and deposition, so that the distribution of clay minerals in the present oceans (Rateev *et al.*, 1968) closely follows that in the soils on adjacent continents (Gradusov, 1972). The latter report also clearly demonstrates that the mineralogy of soils is greatly influenced by climate. High temperatures, high

rainfall and high organic productivity lead to intensive
chemical alteration, whereas cold climates promote physical
processes relative to chemical ones.

This analysis of soils is important because diagenetic
alteration can only be documented successfully if sediments
can be fully described *prior* to alteration. Table I demonstrates that fine-grained sediments may have very different
compositions at deposition depending upon the climatic regime
in the source area. Cold climates yield soils (or, in the case
case of glacial environments, regoliths) little affected by

Table I
Environmental Controls on Soil Composition:
Fine Fraction Maturity

Chemical Response	Mineralogy	Climate
Slight	Unaltered "stable" silicates	Cold
	Clays Biotite Chlorite	Slightly oxidized
Significant	Chlorites Vermiculites Hydromicas	Oxidized
	Some hydroxides, degraded illites	Cool, wet to warm, dry
	Organic residues	Wet
	Carbonates, salts	Dry
Massive	Wet tropical soils	Hot, wet

LOW RELIEF, POOR DRAINAGE: Smectites, organic residues

HIGHER RELIEF, GOOD DRAINAGE: Kaolinite, Gibbsite,
                              Amorphous, Si-Al-Fe,
                              Hydroxides

the chemical agencies of the soil environment: oxygen, low
ionic strength waters and soil biota products. At the other
extreme soils of humic, tropical climates contain few traces
of bedrock minerals and are dominated by cation-poor clays,
high oxidation state (ferric, manganic) hydroxides and
amorphous Si-Al compounds. Another soil variable--site
relief--is also important. Well-drained soil situations

promote leaching, whereas poorly drained sites concentrate
soil water solutes that stabilize clays with higher cation
contents and salts. Carbonates, sulfates and halides reflect
increasing dominance of evaporation over precipitation. These
factors are illustrated in Table I and have been analyzed by
various workers (Strakhov, 1967; Curtis, 1976a,b). The
organic content of soils also depends on climatic and site
controls. Arid soils are organic poor, but some cool and some
warm climatic situations may lead to significant enrichment.

Various sediment components are also derived from
depositional waters, which constitute the second principle
source. Table II lists the most important of these. Certain
depositional conditions can lead to significant concentration.
Relatively slow sedimentation of detrital clays within oceanic
waters of high nutrient status will lead to organic rich
sediments with potentially high hydrocarbon yield. Deep sea
sediments today demonstrate other situations with accumulation
of siliceous or calcareous oozes.

Table II

Precipitate Input	Depositional Waters
'Biogenic' silica	
'Biogenic' carbonates	Aragonite High Mg-calcite
Organic residues	
Volcanic ash	Reactive silicate glass

POTENTIAL REACTIVITY

It is useful to analyze some possible sediment
constituents in terms of their potential reactivity once they
are buried. Redox reactions tend to dominate early diagenesis,
which is not surprising at the simplest approach since very
large free energy changes accompany them. The most reactive
sediments, therefore, must be anticipated to contain large
amounts of both oxidants and reducing agents. High valence
state iron and manganese compounds, derived directly from
soils, constitute the only real source of the former, and
organic material is the only significant reducing agent. The
sedimentational conditions leading to highly reactive sediments
can be readily anticipated on this basis.

Other unstable sediment constituents include biogenic
carbonates, which tend to recrystallize to more stable forms,
and aluminium hydroxides. These rapidly "silicify" to

aluminosilicates (Curtis and Spears, 1971). Volcanic ash is also unstable and may be a significant source of metal cations, especially in the case of basic compositions.

DIAGENETIC MINERALS

Mineralogical examination of ancient mudrocks reveals a host of phases that, with very few exceptions, do not form within soil profiles nor precipitate from depositional waters. These include metal sulfides, calcium phosphates, numerous carbonates and various clay silicates. These are listed in Table III. Many rarer minerals could be added here (zeolites, for example) but only the most widespread and well-documented diagenetic reactions can be discussed in a review of this kind. Although organic derivatives are not strictly minerals, they must be included for their common occurrence and crucial economic importance.

Table III
Common Diagenetic Minerals Formed within Sediment Pore Space
(at greater depths by replacement reactions)

Sulfides	Pyrite most common: usually after replacement of earlier, less stable sulfides	FeS_2
		FeS, Fe_3S_4?
Carbonates	Low magnesian calcite ferroan calcite	$CaCO_3$
	Dolomite Ferroan dolomite	$CaMg(CO_3)_2$
	Ankerite	$Ca(Mg.Fe)(CO_3)_2$
	Siderite Magnesian siderite	$FeCO_3$
Phosphates	Amorphous carbonate: hydroxy apatite most common: "collophane"	$Ca_5(PO_4)_3(OH,CO_3)$
Clays	Kaolinite Illite Chamosite } Fe-rich Glauconite	
Organic derivatives	Kerogen, coal, oil chert	

Burial diagenesis, therefore, includes all processes whereby the constituents of soils and precipitate sediments are converted to the diagenetic minerals listed in Table III.

DEPTH-RELATED DIAGENETIC ZONES

In recent papers, Curtis (1977 a,b) proposed that distinctive diagenetic zones could be recognized within mudstone burial sequences. Each is characterized by a particular reaction or reactions that may be responsible for triggering other reactions in response to solutes fed into the sediment/ porewater system. Zone I, termed the oxidation zone, is present as a thin (mm to cm) "skin" over most present day marine sediments, resulting from oxidizing bottom waters and downward diffusion of oxygen into very porous (> 80% porosity; Preiss, 1968) sediment. Under these conditions, ferric compounds are stable and the principle effect is degradation of organic matter. This can be represented by Equation 1. Such

$$CH_2O + O_2 \rightarrow CO_2 + H_2O \qquad HCO_3^- + H^+ \qquad (1)$$

a representation obviously is an oversimplification, since numerous intermediate oxidation state organic compounds will probably form. A consequence of good diffusive contact with overlying depositional waters will be the almost certain loss of most reaction products by back diffusion. Reaction with mineral constituents of the sediment is unlikely to be significant. The efficiency of this process insofar as degradation of organic matter is concerned is attested to by complete removal from extremely slowly deposited clays (red clays).

In virtually all organic-rich sediments, Zone I reactions totally consume dissolved oxygen within a few mm burial and reducing conditions are established. Oxidate minerals are rendered thermodynamically unstable. In marine sediments sulfate reduction commences and can be traced to be operative (by porewater depletion) to depths of a few meters. This is true for deep sea cores (Sayles and Manheim, 1975) as well as for shallow marine and estuarine environments. The overall reaction (again simplified) for Zone II, termed the sulfate reduction zone, can be expressed as:

$$2CH_2O + SO_4^{2-} \rightarrow HS^- + H_2CO_3 + HCO_3^- \qquad (2)$$

Ferrous iron, produced by reduction of oxidate phases (especially surface active soil colloids) is rapidly precipitated as iron sulfides (Berner, 1970). Their very low solubility ensures low ferrous iron activities in porewaters. The build-up of bicarbonate derived from organic matter has been confirmed by Presley and Kaplan (1968), who showed that the isotopic composition of porewater carbonate changed with depth from values close to those of marine reservoir to those of organic matter (2.5% enrichment in ^{12}C).

Early diagenetic carbonate concretions also reveal ^{12}C enrichment (Galimov and Girin, 1968). This suggests that both principle solute products of sulfate reduction precipitate readily to give typical diagenetic minerals. Other products of organic matter degradation include phosphorous and nitrogen compounds. The former precipitate as amorphous carbonate apatites.

Below the depth of effective sulfate penetration, sulfide species are no longer generated and organic matter ceases to be degraded by reactions like Equation 2. Here abundant evidence of "dry" gas generation has been gathered. Isotopically "heavy" (^{13}C-enriched) bicarbonate (Nissenbaum, 1972; Claypool *et al.*, 1973) has also been documented. Fermentation has been suggested to account for these products according to Equation 3. Since "shallow" methane invariably shows massive

$$H_2O + 2CH_2O \rightarrow HCO_3^- + H^+ \qquad (3)$$

enrichment in ^{12}C, the bicarbonate produced must be depleted in this isotope. Other "oxidized" compounds, however, are likely to result from this process also. Once again, carbonates must be anticipated to precipitate. Now, however, they they will be isotopically heavy and likely to contain iron since activity levels are not being suppressed by sulfide availability. Carbonates of this type have been described: siderites (Curtis *et al.*, 1972) and dolomites/ankerites (Irwin *et al.*, 1977).

Several environmental factors could limit fermentation at depth. Excessive temperatures, exhaustion of suitable substrate and poisonous solutes all might act in this way. The depth interval over which fermentatative degradation of organic matter is important was termed the fermentation zone (Zone III) in Curtis (1977b).

At depths and temperatures greater than those supporting fermentation, degradation by organic matter continues, presumably by largely abiotic mechanisms. Kerogen maturation studies, such as those of Laplante (1974) and Tissot *et al.* (1974), identify fermentation at relatively shallow depths followed by decarboxylation (Zone IV) and liquid hydrocarbon evolution (Zone V). More carbon dioxide will be introduced to the sediment/porewater system in Zone IV according (very approximately) to Equation 4. The isotopic composition of

$$R.CO_2H + H_2O \rightarrow R.H + H^+ + HCO_3^- \qquad (4)$$

bicarbonated produced by this type of process will be isotopically light, although less so than the organic starting materials. Carbonates precipitated at these depths will reflect this in marked contrast to those from Zone III.

At even greater depths, environments transitional to metamorphism will be encountered (Zone VI). Residual organic matter will then evolve towards graphite. It seems unlikely that much carbon dioxide will be released below Zone IV. Diagenetic carbonates fromed at these depths (mostly in re-placement reactions) almost certainly represent dissolution and reprecipitation of primary or early diagenetic minerals.

One further reaction type, however, continuously pro-duces carbon dioxide throughout the sediment column. Muddy sediments at deposition contain oxidized iron minerals that are reduced during diagenesis. Oxidation must accompany reduction and the only sensible expression of this fact lies in reactions such as Equation 5. This type of reaction is of very great significance because hydroxyls are produced that compensate the hydrogen ions produced in reactions 1 to 4.

$$2FE_2O_3 + CH_2O + 3H_2O \rightarrow 4FE^{2+} + HCO_3^- + 7OH^- \qquad (5)$$

Precipitation of carbonates is the logical consequence. Silicate hydrolysis reactions are thus seen to be only one source of hydroxyls and need not be important. This is just as well since wholesale silicate hydrolysis in the uppermost few meters of buried sediments is not very attractive.

The zonal model described here is based on organic matter degradation reactions. Reduction of iron minerals and precipitation of sulfides and carbonates are the most obvious direct mineralogical consequences. Amorphous calcium phos-phates (collophane) are commonly associated with these assemblages and almost certainly the phosphate source is, in part at least, organic. Tables IV and V summarize different

Table IV

Zone	Process Description	Zone Base Depth (m)	$\Delta T°C$	Average Porosity	$\delta^{13}C_{PDB}\%$ Carbonate
I	Bacterial oxidation	10^{-2}	0	80	−25
II	Bacterial sulfate reduction	10	0.3	75	−25
III	Bacterial fermentation	10^3	75	15	+15
IV	Decarboxylation	2.5×10^3	75	15	−20?
V	Liquid hydrocarbon generation	4×10^3	120	10	Variable: may include carbon from primary or early diage-netic carbonates
VI	Gas graphite metamorphism	$> 4 \times 10^3$	120^+	<10	

Table V

Zone	Carbonates Precipitated	Other Minerals Precipitated	Mineral modifications
I	None: Diffusion of solutes into overlying depositional waters		Partial destruction of organic matter
II	Calcite Low Fe,Mn	Pyrite	Rapid destruction of colloids, Fe,Mn,Al,Si
III	Ferroan Calcite	Amorphous Carbonate Apatites	Clay exchange reactions especially $Fe^{2+}/Mg^{2+}/Ca^{2+}$
IV	Ferroan Dolomite or Siderite	Kaolinite	Montmorillonite Mixed layer clays
V	Calcite Dolomite Ferroan Dolomite	Illite	Illite
VI	Siderite Depending upon instability of earlier carbonates		Mica development Chlorite Biotite

aspects of the zonal model assuming a thermal gradient of approximately 30°C/km, similar to values recorded for boreholes offshore of Louisiana and Texas in Gulf Coast sediments. The ΔT°C values refer to increments over the sediment/water interface value. The transition between the diagenesis and metamorphism probably is to be found in the 160–200°C region and is thought by this author to be defined by wholesale silicate recrystallization.

Porewaters expressed from mudstones migrate through sandstones, and evidence of diagenetic clay minerals is best found therein where detrital clays may not be present. There is ample evidence of early kaolinite precipitation in many different sandstones. Diagenetic carbonate concretions also can contain very pure kaolinite. Diagenetic mixed-layer and illitic clays also occur in sandstones. As yet, however, it is not possible to establish sequence relationships because porewater composition, expecially if controlled by meteoric water input, could radically affect silicate precipitation.

ANCIENT SEDIMENT EVIDENCE

Perhaps the best evidence supporting some kind of diagenetic depth zonation is offered by distinctive mineral
assemblages that crop up time and time again as common rock
types in the Phanerozoic. The link between these assemblages
and depth zonation, however, is not entirely simple. The
extent to which chemical reactions characteristic of a
particular zone will modify a sediment depends very much on
the time that a specific unit spends within a given depth
interval. Rate of detrital sedimentation governs rate of
burial, which is the critical factor. This control is analyzed
in Figure 1. Thus, essentially similar starting materials can
end as very different (but common) rock types in consequence
of a single rate factor interaction with a zoned environmental
sequence. The other obvious variable of consequence is the
relative proportions of different sediment components at
deposition. It is simple to anticipate trends: a good oil
prospect, for example, would be rich in organic matter and
low in oxidized iron compounds at sedimentation, and the
realization of that prospect would necessitate fairly rapid
burial.

One very positive piece of evidence supporting the
zonal model (or something like it) was recently reported by
Irwin *et al.* (1977). Three different types of carbonate
were sampled from the Kimmeridge Clay (Dorset Coast Section).
These were: (a) impure coccolith limestones, (b) early
diagenetic calcite concretions, and (c) iron-rich dolomitic
cementstones. All were analyzed for stable C and O isotope
composition, and the results are summarized in Table VI.

Table VI
Kimmeridge Carbonates: Isotopic Composition[a]

	Number of Samples	$\delta^{13}C_{PDB}$	$T^{\circ}C$ (from $^{18}O/^{16}O$)
Coccolith-rich limestones	16	−0.31±0.70	26.4±1.6
Calcite concretions	6	015.54±1.03	17.1±4.1
		+9.28	15.6
Cementstones	33	smooth trend from positive ^{13}C at low T to negative $\delta^{13}C$ at high T	
		−6.46	40.9

[a]from Irwin *et al.*, 1977.

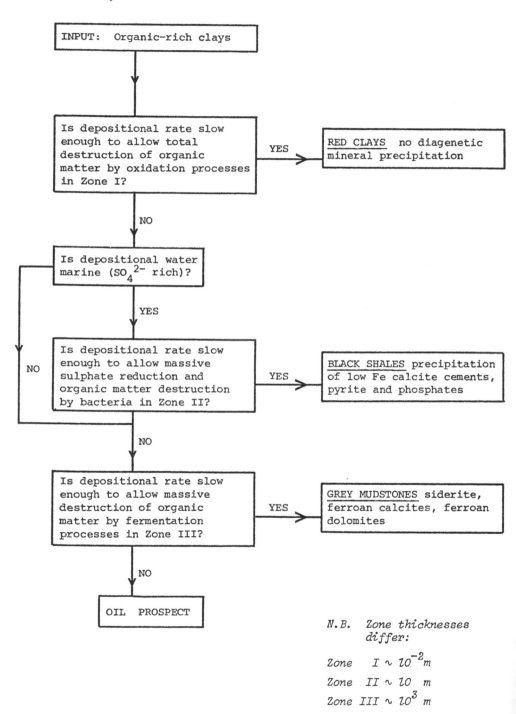

Figure 1. Dependence of final sediment mineralogy on rate
of burial (sedimentation).

Group (a) values are precisely those expected for surface precipitated marine organisms. The carbonate in group (b) has very light carbon and precipitated at much lower temperatures. The values obtained are sensible for precipitation in the sulfate reduction zone not far below the sediment/water interface. Abundant pyrite occurs in these mudstones. Group (c) shows a remarkable trend from extremely heavy carbon at low temperatures to light carbon at high temperatures. This correlation is easily associated with precipitation spanning Zones III and IV. This work certainly proves the impact of organic degradation products on carbonate precipitation and strongly supports some aspects of the zonal model.

DISCUSSION

The purpose of this chapter has been to draw attention to a mass of evidence linking organic matter degradation in compacting mud sediments with a whole range of diagenetic mineral transformations. A rather complex zonal model has been described that accounts for many observations of diagenetic alteration in both recent and ancient clay-rich sediment sequences.

This model is merely a starting point. Its value can only lie in directing further research effort. It should at least underline the necessity for integrated investigations of biological, inorganic, organic, porewater and mineralogical aspects of diagenesis.

In the context of this symposium, the most important observation is that the very important reactions of Zone I, II and III, all of which have very significant consequences insofar as the total diagenetic process is concerned, are almost certainly dominated by microbiological activity. The questions of uppermost importance are what factors control the rate and extent of microbiological activity in these environments. A great deal is known about sulfate reduction, but much less about deeper processes. Information relating to suitability of different organic substrate as nutrients, limiting temperature ranges and toxicological factors all would be valuable. So also would be further studies aimed at identifying all the microorganisms involved.

REFERENCES

Berner, R.A. "Sedimentary pyrite formation," *Am. J. Sci.* 268:1-23 (1970).

Claypool, G., B.J. Presley and I.E. Kaplan. "Gas analyses in sediment samples from legs 10, 11, 13, 14, 15, 18 and 19," in *Initial Reports of the Deep Sea Drilling Project, Vol. XIX,* (1973), pp.879-884.

Curtis, C.D. "Free Energy Changes in Surface Weathering
  Reactions," *Earth Surf. Processes* 1:22-29 (1976a).

Curtis, C.D. "Chemistry of Rock Weathering; Fundamental
  Reactions and Controls," in *Geomorphology and Climate*,
  E. Derbyshire, Ed., (New York: J. Wiley and Sons, 1976b).

Curtis, C.D. "Sedimentary Geochemistry: Environments and
  Processes Dominated by Involvement of an Aqueous Phase,"
  Phil. Trans. R. Soc. Lond. A:123-141 (1977a).

Curtis, C.D. "Possible Links Between Sandstone Diagenesis and
  Depth Related Geochemical Reactions Occurring in Enclosing
  Mudstones," *J. Geol. Soc. Lond.* (in press).

Curtis, C.D., C. Petrowski and G. Oertel. "Stable Carbon
  Isotope Ratios within Carbonate Concretions: a Clue to
  Place and Time of Formation," *Nature, Lond.* 235:98-100
  (1971).

Curtis, C.D., and D.A. Spears. "Diagenetic Development of
  Kaolinite," *Clays & Clay Minerals* 19:219-227.

Galimov, E.M. and Yu. P. Girin. "Variation in the Isotopic
  Composition of Carbon During the Formation of Carbonate
  Concretions," *Geokhimiya* 2:228-233 (1968).

Gradusov, B.P. "Raxmescheniye Osnovnykh Tipov Profiley
  Glinistogo Materiala v Pochvaka," *Dokl. Akad. Nauk. SSSR*
  202:1164-1167 (1972).

Irwin, H., M. Coleman and C.D. Curtis. "Isotopic Evidence
  for Several Sources of Carbonate and Distinctive Diagenetic
  Processes in Organic-Rich Kimmeridgian Sediments," *Nature,
  Lond.*, submitted (1977).

Laplante, R.E. "Hydrocarbon Generation in Gulf Coast
  Tertiary Sediments," *Bull. Amer. Assn. Petrol. Geol.*
  58:1281-1289 (1974).

Nissenbaum, A., B.J. Presley and I.R. Kaplan. "Early Diagenesis in a Reducing Fjord, Saanich Inlet, British Columbia
  --I. Chemical and Isotopic Changes in Major Components of
  Interstitial Water," *Geochim. et Cosmochim. Acta* 36:1007-
  1027 (1972).
Preiss, K. "*In-situ* Measurement of Marine Sediment Density
  by Gamma Radiation," *Deep-Sea Res.* 15:637-641 (1968).

Presley, B.J., and I.R. Kaplan. "Changes in Dissolved Sulphate,
  Calcium and Carbonate from Interstitial Water of Near-Shore

sediments," *Geochim. et Cosmochim. Acta*   32:1037-1048 (1968).

Rateev, B.J., and I.R. Kaplan.   "Changes in Dissolved Sulphate, Calcium and Carbonate from Interstitital Water of Near-Shore Sediments," *Geochim. et. Cosmochim. Acta* 32:1037-1048 (1968).

Sayles, F.L. and F.T. Manheim.   "Interstitial Solutions and Diagenesis in Deeply Buried Marine Sediments: Results from the Deep Sea Drilling Project," *Geochim. et Cosmochim. Acta* 39:103-127 (1975).

Strakhov, N.W.   *Principles of Lithogenesis* (New York: Consultants Bureau, 1967).

Tissot, B., B. Durand, J. Espitalie and A. Combaz.   "Influence of Nature and Diagenesis of Organic Matter in Formation of Petroleum," *Bull. Amer. Assn. Petrol. Geol.* 58:499-506 (1974).

CHAPTER 26

IMPORTANCE OF MICROORGANISMS IN SEDIMENTATION

GERALD M. FRIEDMAN
Rensselaer Polytechnic Institute
Troy, New York 12181 USA

Actual fossil remains of microorganisms, such as bacteria, have been recognized in rocks as old as the Precambrian and have been credited as effective geologic agents. Their influence is still not clearly understood, and generally it is impossible to distinguish reactions in which microorganisms are involved from those that are purely chemical. What is more, we usually find the products of reactions in which microorganisms were important rather than finding the microorganisms themselves. Bacteria function as catalysts at ordinary temperatures in reactions which, if purely inorganically chemical, would require the addition not only of considerable time but also of considerable heat, pressure or ultraviolet light (Horne, 1969; Wood, 1967).

Weathering of rocks is in part caused or accelerated by bacteria. Other simple organisms, such as fungi, algae and lichens, participate in weathering processes (Krumbein, 1972). Soils contain dense populations of bacteria; minerals, such as certain feldspars and micas, decompose twice or many times as rapidly in sediment in which bacteria are active as in sterile sediment that lacks bacteria. Fungi and heterotrophic bacteria, that is bacteria which obtain their energy through the oxidation of organic matter, produce simple organic acids (oxalic acid, acetic acid, lactic acid and keto-gluconic acid) that affect the decomposition of feldspars and other silicate minerals during weathering. Autotrophic bacteria, that is bacteria which obtain their energy through oxidation of inorganic matter, produce inorganic acids (H_2SO_4, HNO_3) that dissolve mostly limestone. Bacteria acidize the soil by introducing CO_2 and various organic acids, all of which promote the breakdown of solid rock to masses of particles. Boring algae degrade only limestones, but the kind of acid and the exact mechanism of degradation are not known.

Among the most important geologically active bacteria
are sulfate reducers, especially *Desulfovibrio*. These bacteria
are involved in the formation of H_2S, calcium carbonate,
native sulfur and pyrite, and in the reduction of the sulfate
ion in the waters in the pores of sedimentary strata, known
as formation waters.

By bacterial action calcite forms at the expense of
gypsum in the waters of the modern Dead Sea; in this process
H_2S is evolved. The doughty pioneer-geologist, M. Blankenhorn,
discovered in the early 1890s that gypsum, although precipitated
continuously from the surface waters of the Dead Sea, is deposited and preserved only in shallow waters where the supply
of oxygen is ample. Below the wave-influenced zone of oxidation, sulfate-reducing bacteria break down calcium sulfate;
as a result, calcite forms (Friedman, 1966; Neev, 1963, 1964;
Neev and Emery, 1967). The mechanism for this biochemical
reaction depends on the ability of the bacteria to extract
oxygen from the sulfate in gypsum. With this oxygen they
are able to oxidize organic matter and thus produce energy.
When the HCO_3^- produced in this bacterial oxidation of organic
matter combines with calcium from the decomposed calcium sulfate,
sulfate, calcite forms, as is explained in the following
reaction:

$$CaSO_4 + 2CH_2O = CaCO_3 + H_2O + CO_2 + H_2S$$
$$\text{organic}$$
$$\text{matter}$$

The nonfossiliferous condition of certain carbonate sediments
in modern seas and in some ancient limestones has been attributed
to this biochemical reaction. Examples include modern deep-
water carbonate sediments of the Red Sea, deep-water limestones
of Permian strata in Texas, Devonian shelf carbonates of
western Canada, limestone caprock atop salt plugs in the Gulf
Coast area of the United States, and calcite cement that
forms at the oil/water contact of hydrocarbon reservoirs
(Friedman, 1972; Sanders and Friedman, 1967).

In the absence of solid calcium sulfate, this reaction
can proceed, from the dissolved calcium and sulfate ions in
sea water. In the laboratory, sulfate reduction by *Desulfovibrio*
is usually studied by using soluble compounds, and the bacteria
attack the sulfate ion directly in solution. Chemical precipitation of $CaCO_3$ in the ocean, where Ca^{2+} and HCO_3^- are
buffered, requires a high pH; bacteria living on the degradation
of organic compounds, such as proteins, sugars or their acids
and salts, precipitate $CaCO_3$ at pH values as low as 7.0.

No one who has visited the Netherlands or the city
of Venice at the height of the summer can fail to be impressed
with the stench of H_2S emanating from the canals where the
sulfate-reducing bacteria attack the inorganic sulfates present

in the sewage. In south Florida, the Bahamas, or the algal flats of Abu Dhabi in the Persian Gulf, the smell of H_2S rises when pits are sunk into the sediment or when the interstitial water is pumped to the surface from the shallow-water environments where carbonate sediments are accumulating. When salt-bearing strata or deep-water limestones as old as Paleozoic are freshly broken, H_2S is emitted. H_2S can evolve on the the sea floor from gypsum and erupt violently. Such H_2S has penetrated in the air as far as 65 km inland from offshore exhalations near the coastal town of Swakopmund, Walvis Bay, in southwestern Africa. There, every few years, a stretch of sea bottom, 320 km long and 40 km wide, generates H_2S. In 1951, the exhalation lasted several months. The atmosphere appeared "like a London fog, metal work turned black, public clocks were blotted out by deposit, thousands of fish [were] strewn on beach, [and] sharks came into surf gasping on the evening tide" (newspaper report quoted by K.R. Butlin, 1953). The bottom sediments of this area yielded pure cultures of sulfate-reducing bacteria.

　　Reduction of gypsum or of anhydrite by sulfate-reducing bacteria forms native sulfur, which occurs in modern salt lakes or playas or in caprocks atop salt plugs. In lakes as well as in shallow-water and deep-water marine environments as, for example in the Black Sea, bacteria reduce sulfates to sulfides. The sulfides occur as black, finely disseminated iron monosulfides, and impart a black color to the sediment. Below the water/sediment interface monosulfide changes later to pyrite. Some evidence exists that bacteria not only dissolve quartz and silicate minerals but transfer and precipitate amorphous silica. Thus, we see that a variety of sedimentary material results from bacterial activity; however, most of this material is involved in the sulfur cycle.

REFERENCES

Butlin, K.R. "The Bacterial Sulphur Cycle," *Research* 6:184-191 (1953).

Friedman, G.M. "On the Origin of Aragonite in the Dead Sea," *Israel J. Earth Sci.* 14:79-85 (1966).

Friedman, G.M. "Significance of Read Sea in Problem of Evaporites and Basinal Limestones," *Amer. Assoc. Petrol. Geol., Bull.* 56:1072-1086 (1972).

Horne, R.A. *Marine Chemistry, the Structure of Water and the Chemistry of the Hydrosphere* (New York: Wiley-Interscience, 1969).

Krumbein, W.E. "Role des Microorganismes dans la Genese, la Diagenese et la Degradation des Roches en Place," *Rev. Ecol. Biol. Sol.* 3:283-319 (1972).

Neev, D. "Recent Precipitation of Calcium Salts in the Dead Sea," *Research Council Israel, Bull.* 11G:153-154 (1963).

Neev, D. "Geological Processes in the Dead Sea" (unpubl. Ph.D. Thesis, Hebrew University, Jerusalem).

Neev, D., and K.O. Emery. "The Dead Sea, Depositional Processes, and Environments of Evaporites," *Israel Geol. Survey Bull.* (1967).

Sanders, J.E., and G.M. Friedman. "Origin and Occurrence of Limestones," in *Carbonate Rocks: Development in Sedimentology, 9A* (New York: Elsevier, 1967), p. 169-265.

Wood, E.J.F. *Microbiology of Oceans and Estuaries* (New York: Elsevier, 1967).

CHAPTER 27

MICROBIOLOGICAL FORMATION
OF METHANE IN MARINE SEDIMENTS

S. S. BELYAEV
K. S. LAURINAVICHUS

Institute of Biochemistry and
Physiology of Microorganisms
USSR Academy of Sciences
Puschino, USSR

The presence of methane in the reduced sediments of inland seas and coastal regions has been shown by many investigators (Butkevich, 1938; Emery and Hoggan, 1958; Weber and Turkeltaub, 1958; Nissenbaum *et al.*, 1972; Bagirov *et al.*, 1973; McIver, 1974). It has been found by Emery and Hoggan (1958), Sholkovitz (1973), and Martens and Berner (1974), that methane concentration in marine sediments increases with depth as sulfates are removed by sulfate-reducing bacteria from interstitial waters. In recent years, it was discovered that methane can accumulate in considerable amounts as gas hydrates at low temperature and high pressure (Makagon *et al.*, 1971; 1972). So, there are now real prospects for finding methane industrial deposits in marine sediments.

Evidence is presented in literature of the microbiological origin of methane in marine sediments. It is mainly based on investigations of the chemical composition of interstitial waters and gas phase of sediments, and carbon isotope content of methane and carbon dioxide (Claypool and Kaplan, 1974; Alekseev and Lebedev, 1975; Bernard *et al.*, 1976). Unfortunately, there are few microbiological research works in this field (Butkevich, 1938; Zobell, 1947; Mogilevskii *et al.*, 1975; Belyaev, 1975), and experiments on the determination of the activity of methane-forming bacteria directly in sediments are single (Belyaev, 1975; Oremland, 1975). And, even if geochemical investigations are assumed to be sufficient to determine the microbiological origin of methane, the problem still remains as to whether methane is formed in marine sediments now or was formed as a result of the geochemical activity of methanogenic bacteria in the geological past.

The purpose of this chapter is to report the results of
of the research on the numbers of methane-producing bacteria
and the intensity of the present bacterial methanogenic process in sediments of the Pacific and Indian peripheral regions.
These investigations were carried out during the 9th and 22nd
scientific research cruises of *Dmitrii Mendeleev* and *Academi-
cian Kurchatov*.

METHODS

Investigations were carried out on the reduced sediments of the Gulf of California and the adjacent part of the
Pacific, sediments of the Persian and Oman Gulfs, and the
Arabian Sea. The geographical schemes of the stations where
sedimentary samples were taken are given in Figures 1 and 2.

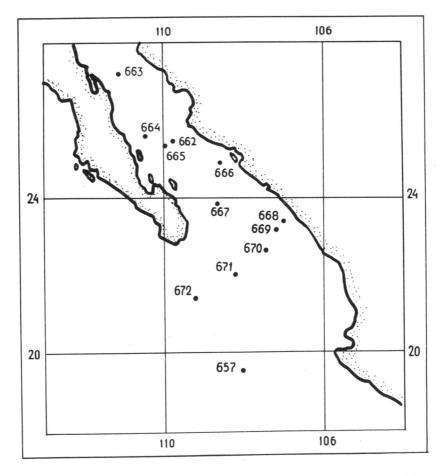

Figure 1.   Geographical scheme of the stations in the Gulf of
California and the adjacent part of the Pacific Ocean.

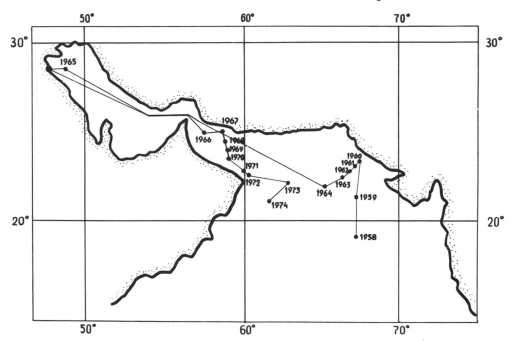

Figure 2.   Geographical scheme of the stations in the Persian
and Oman Gulfs and the Arabian Sea.

Silt samples for microbiological investigations were
taken from the monolith central part and placed in sterile
glass tubes.   Tenfold diluted silt samples were incubated on
nutrient media with acetate or hydrogen (as the energy source)
in order to count the numbers of viable methanogenic bacteria.

The analysis of the gas produced was made by gas
chromatography (Belyaev and Finkelstein, 1976; Belyaev *et al.*,
1976).   The intensity of the bacterial methane production was
determined by the radioisotopic method with $NaH^{14}CO_3$ and
$^{14}CH_3COONa$ (Belyaev *et al.*, 1975).   Samples with radioisotopes
were incubated for 30 days at 2°C.   The radioactivity of the
methane produced was registered on the scintillation counter
with the preliminary methane combustion to CO_2.

The carbon content of bicarbonates in silts was
calculated from the data on the total alkalinity of interstitial waters.   Acetic acid concentration was determined by
thin-layer chromatography (Andreev *et al.*, 1974) with Silufol
UV-254 as the plate sorbent.

Since the initial substrate radioactivity ($NaH^{14}CO_3$
or $^{14}CH_3COONa$), the quantity of the labelled carbon transformed into $^{14}CH_4$, and the content of acetate and bicarbonate
in silt samples was known, we could calculate the intensity
of the bacterial methane production.

RESULTS

        The experimental data presented in Table I indicate
that methanogenic bacteria growing on the medium with molecular
hydrogen were found in all the samples of the reduced sediments
of the Gulf of California and the adjacent part of the Pacific.
Their numbers made up 25-250 cells/1 g of wet silt and did
not clearly depend on the ocean depth. On the nutrient
medium with acetate the bacterial methane formation was
revealed only when inoculation two samples. In all the
other cases the bacterial hydrogen formation was observed.
        A similar distribution pattern of methanogenic
bacteria was obtained when investigating the sediments from
the Persian and Oman Gulfs (Table II). The numbers of
bacteria revealed in the medium with hydrogen decreased with
depth from 250 to 25 cells/g.
        The intensity of the bacterial methane generation
at the expense of the reduction of CO_2 and acetate methyl
groups in the investigated sediments (Tables I and II) made
up $1.4-47.2 \times 10^{-6}$ ml of CH_4 per kg wet silt per day. More
than 74% CH_4 was formed through the bacterial reduction of
CO_2 by hydrogen. The highest intensity of methane formation
was found in the upper horizons of the Gulf of Oman sediments
at stations 1969 and 1971. As sediment depth increased, the
intensity of methane generation calculated per a kg of wet
silt decreased in most cases. However, the decrease in the
intensity was not so pronounced as the decrease in the numbers
of microorganisms per unit of the sediment weight, and if
calculated per one viable cell the intensity of methanogenesis
increased, usually with depth by several times (Tables II and
III).
        Table III presents the data on the distribution of
methanogenic bacteria and intensity of methane generation
in the Arabian Sea sediments. These data show that the
numbers of the investigated bacteria increased from station
1958 to station 1960 (Figure 2) as they approached the
continent. At station 1960, a significant amount (250-600
cells/g) of methanogenic bacteria was revealed on the media
with both hydrogen and acetate. The highest intensity of the
methane generation was also found in the sediments at coastal
stations 1961 and 1960 situated on the continental slope of
the Hindoustan Peninsula. From 37.2 to 96.3% methane in the
sediments at these stations was formed at the expense of acetate
acetate methyl groups.

DISCUSSION

        These investigations have shown that viable cells of
methanogenic bacteria are widely distributed in the reduced
sediments of the Gulf of California and the adjacent part of

Table I

Microbiological Methane Formation in the Gulf of California and the Pacific Ocean Adjacent Part Sediments

Station Number and Depth	Horizon (cm)	Eh (mv)	CH_3COOH (mg/kg wet sediments)	Number of Methanongenic Bacteria (cell/g)		Intensity of Methane Formation (ml $\times 10^{-6}$/kg/day)	
				CO_2/H_2	CH_3COOH	Total	At the Expense of CO_2 Reduction (%)
657;3150 m	45–50	+50	3.2	60	n.d.[a]	3.97	99.5
670;1450 m	70–75	−310	2.4	25	n.d.	1.37	97.8
664;1170 m	150–155	−240	2.0	60	n.d.	2.39	97.1
663;1760 m	50–55	−210	14.0	250	n.d.	2.69	86.2
	165–170	−230	5.2	60	n.d.	2.56	95.7
662;2400 m	35–38	+105	10.0	250	2	3.09	87.4
667;2860 m	35–40	−200	2.0	60	n.d.	2.68	97.8
	95–97	−240	4.7	60	n.d.	5.57	97.8
665;3260 m	40–45	−180	13.0	130	6	5.08	91.1
	95–100	−220	2.4	60	n.d.	4.03	98.0

[a] n.d. – Here and in Tables II and III, means that growth of methanogenic bacteria is not determined when inoculating 1 g of silt.

Table II

Numbers of Methanogenic Bacteria and Intensity of the Present Methane Formation in Sediments of the Persian and Oman Gulfs

Station Number and Depth	Horizon (cm)	Numbers of Bacteria (cells/g wet sediment)		Intensity of Methane Formation		
		CO_2/H_2	CH_3COOH	ml x 10^{-6}/kg/day		ml x 10^{-11}/cell/day
				Total	At the Expense of CO_2 Reduction (%)	
1965;43 m	0-5	250	n.d.	7.02	83.2	2.3
1966;1215 m	0-10	250	n.d.	4.29	97.9	1.7
	40-50	25	n.d.	1.71	100	6.8
1969;2400 m	1-8	250	25	47.18	74.0	17.2
	40-50	25	n.d.	7.30	96.4	29.2
1971;2270 m	0-8	250	25	44.12	84.5	16.0
	20-40	60	n.d.	20.33	98.2	33.9

Table III
Numbers of Methanogenic Bacteria and Intensity of Present Methane
Formation Process in the Arabian Sea Sediments

Station Number and Depth	Horizon (cm)	Numbers of Bacteria (cells/g wet sediment)		Intensity of Methane Formation		
		CO_2/H_2	CH_3COOH	ml x 10^{-6}/kg/day		ml x 10^{-11}/cell/day
				Total	At the Expense of CO_2 Reduction (%)	
1958;3240 m	70-80	6	n.d.	2.64	87.9	38.7
1964;2720 m	50-60	13	n.d.	2.58	85.4	17.1
1959;1890 m	2-10	25	n.d.	7.35	89.3	26.2
	50-60	25	n.d.	6.91	79.6	22.0
1963;1820 m	2-10	25	n.d.	2.92	78.8	9.2
	50-60	13	n.d.	9.20	95.4	67.5
1961;1040 m	0-10	250	25	27.57	28.8	10.0
	150-160	25	25	54.89	9.2	109.8
1960;520 m	0-10	600	250	47.40	62.8	5.6
	45-55	250	250	92.79	3.7	18.6
	190-200	25	25	15.51	20.6	31.0

the Pacific Ocean, in the sediment of the Persian and Oman
Gulfs and Arabian Sea.

The numbers of methanogenic bacteria revealed on the
medium with molecular hydrogen made up from several to
hundreds of cells/1 g wet sediment and were the highest in the
the coastal sediments. But the numbers of bacteria did not
always increase with the decrease in the sea depth. As a
rule, it decreased along the length of the core; however, the
viable cells producing methane on nutrient media occurred up
to 200 cm deep (deeper horizons were not tested).

On the nutrient media with acetate, viable cells of
methanogenic bacteria were found only in 30% of silt samples.
This fact points to a wider distribution of methanogenic
bacteria that utilize hydrogen as the energetic substrate.
Anaerobic bacteria forming hydrogen on media with organic
substrates were revealed in all the sediments investigated
(Belyaev, Finkelstein, 1976). Taking into account that
sediments of the investigated regions had a low redox potential
and a significant amount of organic substances--in particular,
acetic acid up to 14 mg/kg (Table I) (Rozanov *et al.*, 1976),
we could assume that methanogenic bacteria found in the
sediments were in the active state.

The existence of the present bacterial methane
formation process in marine sediments was proved by the radioisotopic method. The methane formation intensity made up
1.4–47.2×10^{-6} ml of CH_4 per kg wet silt per day. More than
74% of CH_4 formed at the expense of the CO_2 reduction; from
0.5 to 26% of methane was produced by acetate degradation.
Somewhat different data were obtained on the sediments at
two stations (1960 and 1961) situated on the continental
slope of the Hindoustan Peninsula in the region of the Ind
River estuary. When the total intensity of the methane production in the sediments at the two points mentioned above
made up 15.5–92.8×10^{-6} ml of CH_4/kg wet silt/day, from
37.2 to 96.3% of methane was produced at the expense of
acetate methyl groups.

Unfortunately, no other data on the intensity of the
microbiological methane production in marine sediments have
been reported elsewhere.

We can compare our data only with those of Oremland
(1975). He has shown that the methane evolution rate from
tropic shallow marine sediments makes up from 0.009 – 0.054
to 0.97 – 1 ml CH_4/m^2 per day. Similar calculations from
the radioisotopic data at stations 1959 and 1960 (the Arabian
Sea) show that 0.014 and 0.102 ml of methane are produced in
1 m^2 of sediments (thickness 2 m) per day, respectively. It
is clear that the methane evolution rate and the intensity of
its formation are not one and the same thing. Nevertheless,
the values obtained are comparable and provide additional
support for our data.

The intensity of methane production per one viable cell in the sediments tested made up 1.1 - 109.8 x 10^{-11} ml per day and increased with the depth of sediments. This may be caused by the change of physicochemical conditions in marine sediments with depth in favor of methanogenic bacteria.

In conclusion, it should be noted that the investigations have convincingly demonstrated the existence of the present process of microbiological methane production in upper horizons of the reduced marine sediments. Kaplan and the other geochemists have shown, and not less convincingly, a wide distribution of the isotopically light methane in deeper (subsurface) horizons of marine sediments and have pointed out the possibility of forming important deposits under such conditions. Therefore, the study on the distribution and activity of methanogenic bacteria in subsurface ocean sediments concerned with the deep-sea drilling is a pressing problem for the next years.

ACKNOWLEDGMENTS

The authors express their gratitude to Professor Mikhail V. Ivanov (Institute of Biochemistry and Physiology of Microorganisms, USSR Academy of Sciences, Pushchino) whose criticism and valuable advice assisted in the studies and writing of this paper.

REFERENCES

Alekseev, F.A., and V.S. Lebedev. "The Carbon Isotope Composition of Carbon Dioxide and Methane in the Bottom Sediments of the Black Sea," in *Dispersed Gases and Biochemical Conditions of Sediments and Rocks* (Moscow: 1975), pp. 49-53 (in Russian).

Andreev, L.V., Z.I. Finkelstein and S.S. Belyaev. "The Detection of Low Molecular Fatty Acids in Natural Objects by the Thin Layer Chromatography Technique," *Appl. Biochem. and Microbiol.* 10:308-312 (1974) (in Russian).

Bagirov, V.I., L.M. Zor'kin and L.V. Chertkova. "Hydrocarbon Gases of the Black Sea Bottom Waters," *DAN USSR (geochem.)* 212(4):976-977 (1973) (in Russian).

Belyaev, S.S. "Gasforming Bacteria in the Pacific Ocean Bottom Sediments," in *Dispersed Gases and Biochemical Conditions of Sediments and Rocks* (Moscow: 1975), pp.162-168 (in Russian).

Belyaev, S.S., Z.I. Finkelstein and M.V. Ivanov. "The Intensity of Bacterial Methane Production in Bottom Deposits of Some Lakes," *Microbiol.* 47:309-312 (1975) (in Russian).

Belyaev S.A., and Z.I. Finkelstein. "Anaerobic Gas Forming Bacteria in Sediments of the Gulf of California and the Pacific Ocean Coastal Regions," in *Biochemistry of Diagenesis of Ocean Sediments* (Moscow: Nauka Press, 1976), pp. 75-82 (in Russian).

Belyaev, S.S., M.V. Ivanov, E.I. Chebotarev and A. Yu. Lein. "Distribution of Saprophite Bacteria in Different Sediments of the Pacific Ocean Tropic Zone," in *Biochemistry of Diagenesis of Ocean Sediments* (Moscow: Nauka Press, 1976), pp. 59-67 (in Russian).

Bernard, B.B., J.M. Brooks and W.M. Sackett. "Natural Gas Seepate in the Gulf of Mexico. Earth and Planet," *Sci. Lett.* 31(1):48-54 (1976).

Butkevich, V.S. "On Bacterial Population of the Caspian and Azov Seas," *Microbiol.* 7:1005-1021 (1938) (in Russian).

Claypool, G.E., and I.R. Kaplan. "The Origin and Distribution of Methane in Marine Sediments," in *Natural Gases in Marine Sediments,* I.R. Kaplan, Ed. (New York: Plenum Press, 1974), pp. 99-139.

Emery, K.O., and D. Hoggan. "Gases in Marine Sediments," *Amer. Soc. of Petr. Geol. Bull.* 42(9):2174-2188 (1958).

Makagon, Yu. F., F.A. Trebin, A.A. Trofimuk, V.P. Tsarev and N.V. Cherskii. "Detection of Natural Gas Deposits in Solid (Gasohydrate) State," *DAN USSR (geol.)* 196(1):203-206 (1971) (in Russian).

Makagon, Yu. F., V.P. Tsarev and N.V. Cherskii. "To the Problem of the Formation of Large Gas Deposits in Low Temperature Zones," *DAN USSR (geol.)* 205(3):700-703 (1972) (in Russian).

Martens, Ch.S., and R.A. Berner. "Methane Production in the Interstitial Waters of Sulfate-Depleted Marine Sediments," *Science* 185(4157):1167-1169 (1974).

McIver, R.D. "Hydrocarbon Gas (Methane) in Canned Deep Sea Drilling Project Core Samples," in *Natural Gases in Marine Sediments,* I.R. Kaplan, Ed. (New York: Plenum Press, 1974), pp. 63-69.

Mogilevskii, G.A., V.M. Bogdanova and Z.P. Telegina. "Peculiarities of the Distribution of Some Physiological Groups of Microorganisms in the Bottom Sediments and Waters of the Black Sea West Part," in *Dispersed Gases and*

Biochemical Conditions of Sediments and Rocks (Moscow: 1975), pp. 149-154 (in Russian).

Nisenbaum, A., B.J. Presley and I.R. Kaplan. "Early Diagenesis in a Reducing Fjord, Saanich Inlet, British Columbia--I. Chemical and Isotopic Changes in Major Components of Interstitial Water," *Geochim. et Cosmochim. Acta* 36(9):1007-1027.

Oremland, R.S. "Methane Production in Shallow-Water, Tropical Marine Sediments," *Appl. Microbiol.* 30(4):602-608 (1975).

Rozanov, A.G., I.I. Volkov, V.S. Sokolov, Z.V. Pushkina and M.F. Pilipchuk. "Redox Processes in Sediments of the Gulf of California and the adjacent Part of the Pacific Ocean," in *Biochemistry of Diagenesis of Ocean Sediments* (Moscow: Nauka Press, 1976), pp. 96-135 (in Russian).

Sholkovitz, E. "Interstitial Water Chemistry of the Santa Barbara Basin Sediments," *Geochim. et Cosmochim. Acta* 37:2043 (1973).

Weber, V.V., and N.M. Turkeltaub. "Gaseous Hydrocarbons in Present Sediments," *Geol. Petr. and Gas* 8:39-44 (1958) (in Russian).

Zobell, C.E. "Microbial Transformation of Molecular Hydrogen in Marine Sediments, with Particular Reference to Petroleum," *Bull. of the Amer. Assoc. of Petrol. Geol.* 31(10):1709-1751 (1947).

CHAPTER 28

FORMATION OF CARBONATE AND SULFIDE MINERALS DURING DIAGENESIS OF REDUCED SEDIMENTS

ALLA YU. LEIN

Institute of Biochemistry and
Physiology of Microorganisms
USSR Academy of Sciences
Pushchino, USSR

INTRODUCTION

The present work is devoted to the study of the peculiarities of the formation of sulfide and carbonate minerals in the process of microbial sulfate reduction in the reduced sediments of the Gulf of California and in laboratory experiments.

It is acknowledged by all the investigators, beginning with Beyerinck (1895) that H_2S and CO_2 are formed during the bacterial reduction of sulfates. H_2S in terrigenous sediments, rich in the reactive iron, is fixed as a number of sulfide minerals: hydrotroilit FeS, mackinawite greigite $Fe_3S_4 \xrightarrow{S^0}$ pyrite FeS_2 (Sweeney and Kaplan, 1973.)

The role of microbial carbon dioxide in the formation of carbonates in the reduced sediments is a debatable question. Strakhov (1972) suggests that a major part of carbon dioxide, formed in the process of the bacterial oxidation of the organic matter in the form of HCO_3-ion, diffuses from muds into superbottom water. Other investigators (Bavendam, 1932; Berner, 1969) consider that the products of H_2S and CO_2 bacterial metabolisms acidify the medium of the sedimentation and transfer the shell carbonate to the solution, a carbonate that can be precipitated from the solutions under favorable conditions. Therefore, the majority of investigators think that microbial carbon dioxide does not form carbonate minerals in the reduced sediments.

LABORATORY EXPERIMENTS

    We tried to model the process of the precipitation of
carbonates in gypsum columns during bacterial sulfate reduction under the conditions of continuous culture on sodium
lactate. The scheme of modelling is given in Figure 1.

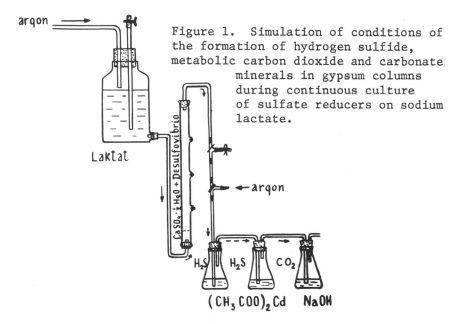

Figure 1. Simulation of conditions of
the formation of hydrogen sulfide,
metabolic carbon dioxide and carbonate
minerals in gypsum columns
during continuous culture
of sulfate reducers on sodium
lactate.

The dynamics of the processes of sulfate reduction and formation
of dissolved H_2S and CO_2 is shown in Figure 2. The pH of the
medium was maintained at 7.5 - 9.0. Eh was equal to -180÷
-220 mv. During the experiment 0.767 - 0.899 g of sulfur of
hydrogen sulfide and 0.962 - 1.093 g of dissolved CO_2 and HCO_3
were formed (Table I). The gypsum columns were disconnected
from the nutrient medium after 397 days, blown through with
argon, and dried at room temperature. Then the content of
carbonates ($CO_2/CaCO_3$ in Table I) was determined. The microscopic analysis and calculations show that in these gyps
columns 41-48% of metabolic carbon dioxide is fixed as idiomorphic calcite crystals (Figure 3-1). The content of the
measured total carbon dioxide (CO_2 exper) is less than the
CO_2 value calculated by 12.7 - 16.4%. The calculated CO_2
value was determined by the quantity of H_2S from the reaction:

$$SO_4^{2-} + 2C = S^{2-} + 2 CO_2$$

    The fractionation of carbon isotopes during the
bacterial oxidation of the organic matter in the process of
sulfate reduction is still a debatable question. A more

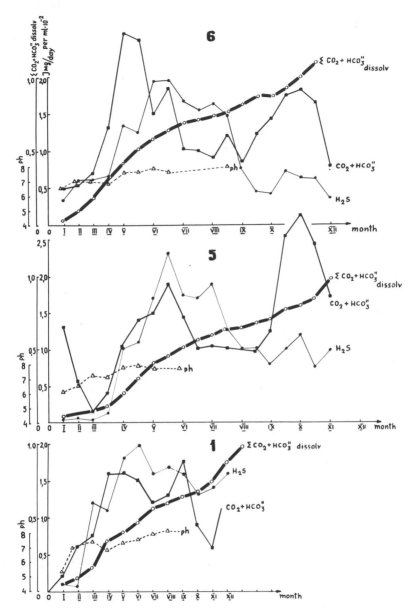

Figure 2. Quantity and rate of the formation of hydrogen
sulfide, dissolved carbon dioxide and bicarbonate during
lactate oxidation by Desulfovibrio desulfuricans;
temperature 19-22°C.

widespread opinion holds that metabolic carbon dioxide inherits
the isotopic content of the initial organic matter (Galimov,
1974).

In our experiments, the dissolved carbon dioxide contains, on the average, 6‰ less isotope C^{12} than the initial

650X

7000X

2000X

Figure 3. Textures of carbonate minerals and pyrite developed
during the process of sulfate reduction in laboratory
experiments (1) and biogenic marine sediments (2-7).

(1) Micrograph of idiomorphic calcite crystals formed on the
gypsum grain; (2) Station 667 (95-100 cm): SEM micrograph of
zenomorphic and idiomorphic Mg-calcite crystals with the irregular grain size; (3) Station 666 (140-170 cm): SEM micrograph of framboid pyrite aggregate on a shell fragment. Small
aggregates of protodolomite and Mg-calcite crystals are visible.

3000X

2000X

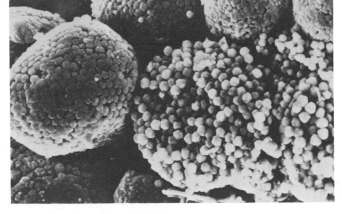

3000X

(4) Station 672 (490–510 cm): SEM micrograph of pyrite crystals
and collomorphic mackinawite in the sulfide framboid, size 0.01
mm; (5) Station 668 (50–100 cm): SEM micrograph of pyrite framboids in different shells, usual type; (6) SEM micrograph of
pyrite framboid composed of pentagon-dodecahedron crystals.
The left framboid crystals are packed in membranes of the chitin
type: the other framboid has a disturbed membrane. One of the
framboids with membrane starts to convert into a hexahedron.

Table 1

Concentration (G) and Isotopic Composition of Carbon (%o) in Products of
Sulfate Reducers Metabolism (laboratory experiment)

Column (N)	CO_2 of Lactate Used (%)	Products of Sulfate Reducers Metabolism				ΣCO_2		$\delta^{13}C$ (%o)		
		S/H_2S	CO_2+HCO_3^{2-} Dissolved	CO_2/$CaCO_3$	C of Organic Matter	Experiment	Calculated by S/H_2S	CO_2 Dissolved	CO_2/ $CaCO_3$	C of Organic Matter
1	33.8	0.83	0.99	0.85	0.07	1.84	2.18	-22.7	-19.3	-23.7
5	27.4	0.77	0.96	0.89	0.10	1.85	2.12	-22.8	-16.9	-23.4
6	28.6	0.80	1.10	0.75	0.05	1.84	2.20	-22.1	-18.2	-26.5

Results are given relative to the PDB standard.

Σ- total content of carbon dioxide.

$\delta^{13}C$ value of the carboxyl-carbon of starting lactate is equal to -16.4%o.

Σ CO_2 calculated by S/H_2S from equation SO_4 + 2C $\rightarrow$ S^{-2} + 2CO_2.

organic matter--carboxyl-carbon of lactate, the $\delta^{13}C$ value of which is equal to -16.4%o (Table I). This fact confirms Kaplan and Rittenberg's (1964) and Smejkal's *et al.*(1971) conclusions about the fractionation of carbon isotopes during the formation of metabolic carbon dioxide. During calcite precipitation carbon increases its weight by 3-6%o as compared to dissolved carbon dioxide (Table I).

The isotope ^{12}C occurs in the newly formed organic matter of the gyps column apparently containing the biomass of sulfate-reducing bacteria ($\delta^{13}C$ = -23.4÷ -26.5%o).

MARINE SEDIMENTS

General Characteristics of the Medium of Sedimentation

The reduced sediments of the Gulf of California and the adjacent part of the Pacific Ocean are rich in organic matter and contain from 1.0 to 5.8 of organic carbon. Eh value is equal to -200÷ -250 mV (Rozanov *et al.*, 1976) and the total sum of the reduced sulfur compounds may be as great as 1.6% of S/H_2S by dry weight (Volkov *et al.*, 1976).

Ivanov and Chebotarev (1976) reported the presence of 100-1000 cells of sulfate reducers per 1 g mud up to 6 m depth. On addition of Na_2 $^{35}SO_4$ into isolated samples of mud, ^{35}S passed into all the reduced compounds and concentrated during the experiment (6-8 months) in the resulting products of diagenesis pyrite and sulfur organic compounds (Ivanov *et al.*, 1976). The values of the sulfate reduction intensity obtained by this method were used to calculate the rate of sedimentation. The calculated values (60-270 cm for 1000 years) correlate well with the data on the radiocarbon dating of the mud age in this region (Van Andel, 1964).

The highest intensity of sulfate reduction is characteristic of the young sediments of the upper 20-50 cm (Figure 4). The process is observed through the total depth of sediment investigated, as well as sulfate is not exhausted completely in the porewater in any core tested. The irregular granulometric composition of muds and the process of bioturbation promote the sulfate diffusion from the superbottom water through the greater depth of sediments.

Free hydrogen sulfide and elemental sulfur are found in the sediments at the majority of stations (Volkov *et al.*, 1976). The reactive iron content is, on the average, 1.1% in sediments (Rozanov *et al.*, 1976). The terrigenous material predominates in muds. Substantial addition of carbonates (up to 10%) as aleuritic and sandy shell fragments is observed only in stations 664,670,671 sediments. In the muds at stations 665-667, the $CO_2/CaCO_3$ quantity does not exceed 1-3%.

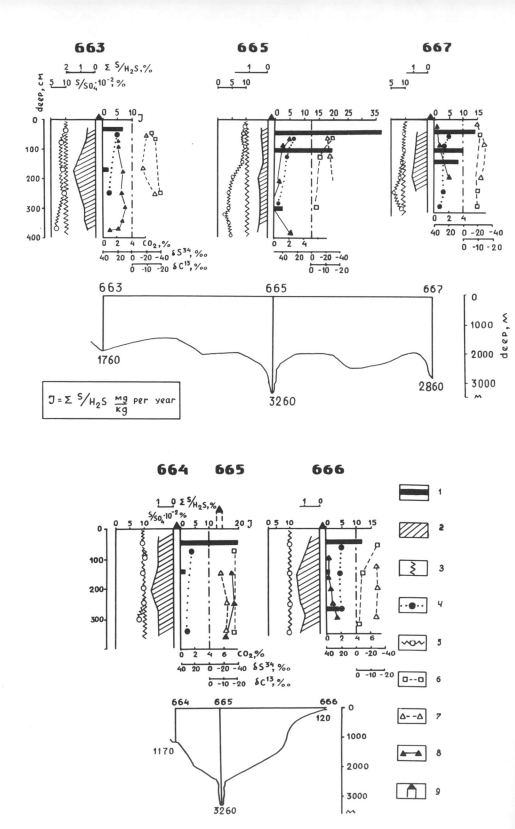

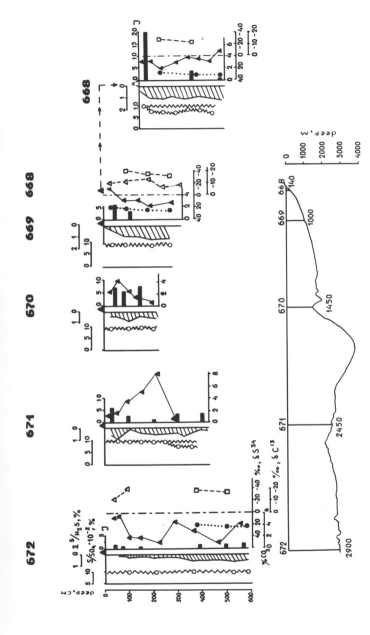

Figure 4. Results of geochemical activity of sulfate reducers in the recent sediments of the Gulf of California on the section across the basins Guaymas-Farallon-Pescadero from the north to south (stations 663-667), and in the shelf and continental slope sediments on the section from Mazatlan (station 668-672).

(1) Rate of the process of sulfate reduction (J) is equal to ratio of sulfur compounds ($\Sigma S/H_2S$ mg/kg of wet mud/yr; (2) Content of $\Sigma S/H_2S$ (%); (3) Content of S in sea water sulfate (%); (4) Content of S in porewater sulfate (%); (5) $\delta^{34}S$ value (%o) of sulfate sulfur of porewater; (6) $\delta^{34}C$ (%o) of total carbonate carbon of sediment; (8) Content of CO_2 in sediment (%); (9) Terrigenous muds with aleuro-pelitic texture.

SULFIDE MINERALS OF SEDIMENTS

It has been stated by mineralogical, chemical and X-ray diffraction analyses that the major part of the reduced sulfur occurs in the form of pyrite in sediments. The pyrite still occurs in the very first tens of centimeters of sediments and increases gradually, reaching its maximum at the depth 1.5-2.0 m. Pyrite in sediments is presented by framboids consisting of aggregates of crystals of the octahedral, pentagon dodecahed one and less frequent cubic forms (Figure 3.3-7). The framboids tend to increase in size up to 0.05 - 0.1 m and more with depth. Most often pyrite is formed *in situ* from the organic matter of foraminifera (Figure 3).

The intensive process of sulfate reduction and the availability of the elemental sulfur in such sediments favor the rapid transformation of all the sulfide minerals to the end product, pyrite. We succeeded in observing mackinawite only at the horizon 490-510 cm at station 672, where the intensity of sulfate reduction is minimal and the free hydrogen sulfide is absent.

The maximal enrichment of pyrite in isotope ^{32}S is observed at the surface horizons of muds with the limitless quantity of sulfate in the zone of reduction processes: $\delta^{34}S$ values vary from -23.8 to -39.0%o (Figure 4). The products of the reduction of porewater sulfate and diffusion sulfate are added to the products of the sulfate reduction on the mud surface at a depth of 20-50 cm. The consumption of sulfate results in the increased content of ^{34}S in the residual sulfate, and hydrogen sulfide and pyrite originated from it with depth. A profound increase in ^{34}S content (18.3%) in the pyrite is observed with depth when only the sulfate of porewaters takes part in the formation of this pyrite without sulfate diffusion from superbottom waters (for instance, station 665, horizon 310 cm) (Figure 4).

In the muds of the majority of other stations, the increase in the content of ^{34}S is not as high. The total value of the reduced sulfur forms (1.0 - 1.6% S on dry weight) in sediments at stations 667-669 considerably exceeds the concentration of sulfate sulfur in the sea water. In that case, the pyrite is enriched little in ^{34}S isotope with depth as compared to pyrite sulfur at the surface horizons (by 4-7%).

CARBONATE MINERALS OF SEDIMENTS

Sulfate reduction processes in sediments are accompanied by the organic matter oxidation, resulting in carbon dioxide formation. The increase in HCO_3 content in porewaters of the Gulf of California is shown in the works of Claypool and Kaplan (1974) and Shishkina and Pavlova (1976). The isotope content of bicarbonate carbon varies from -1% at the surface

horizons to -16%o in the depth with the active process of
sulfate reduction (Claypool and Kaplan, 1974).

We studied the isotope content of the total carbonate
carbon of sediments isolated on the ship from the fresh mud
by the processing of sediment with 3% HCL and distillation of
CO_2 into the alkaline solution. $\delta^{13}C$ Values of the total
carbonate carbon varied in the wide range from -4.1 to -15.1%o
(Table II). This value varied from -25 to -39%o in carbonate
concretions at station 666 (Lein *et al.*, 1975). Organic carbon
in muds had the $\delta^{13}C$ value equal to -23.0%o (the average from
six analyses).

Table II
Isotopic Composition of the Total Carbonate-Carbon
and Calculation of Metabolic (Reduced) Carbon Dioxide Content
in Mud Carbonate Minerals (Gulf of California)

Station N	Horizon (cm)	CO_2 of Total Carbonate (% per dry weight)	$\delta^{13}C$ of Total Carbonate (%o)	CO_2 Reduced[x] Calculated from Equation 1 (%)
663	50	2.00	-10.0	48
	165	1.60	- 7.8	39
	255	2.48	-13.4	61
644	152	7.00	- 7.8	39
	260	8.24	-12.1	48
	340	6.00	-11.8	55
665	40	1.11	-12.3	57
	95	0.88	-13.4	61
667	15	0.50	-10.2	49
	37	0.50	-11.0	52
	97	1.00	-15.1	68
	200	2.40	-12.6	58
669	37	5.10	- 8.1	40
	90	3.20	-10.6	50
	185	1.78	-12.9	60
	280	2.20	- 8.1	40
672	40	4.52	-10.5	50
	75	3.00	-14.7	67

Table III
Isotopic Composition of Carbon of Carbonate Minerals
in Mud / Results Reported in δ^{13}C‰,
PDB Standard

Station N	Horizon (cm)	Autogenic Protodolomite + Mg–Calcite		Aragonite + Calcite of Shells
		MUD CONCREC		
666	5–10	–	–39.0	
	20–45	–	–20.0	
			–24.9	+2.6
	120–140	–14.5	–18.1	
	160–170	–15.6	–19.9	+2.2
	270–280	–	–18.6	+0.1
667	95–100	–19.3		+4.3
669	175–195	–17.6		+1.8
672	75	–23.0		+1.3

The concentration of carbonate minerals of aleurite and sandy classes was carried out in the process of the laboratory study. Foramineferal shells and their fragments were isolated from them. The δ^{13}C values fo the shell carbonate were equal to +2‰ on the average from 11 analyses. Calcite and protodolomite were determined by X-ray diffraction analyses in the composition of xenomorphic fibrous, granular and diamond-shaped crystals of carbonates (Figure 3) which remained after the removal of the major part of the shell carbonate—represented by aragonite and calcite when shell carbonate could be fully removed (for instance, in the fraction > 0.05 mm).

Values δ^{13}C of autigenic calcite and protodolomite varied from –17.6 to –39.0‰ (Table III). Therefore, the isotopically light carbon dioxide takes part in the formation of this autigenic carbonate mineral.

DISCUSSION

The processes of diagnetic sulfide and carbonate formation in the specific ecological environment of the zone of reduced sediment and superbottom water exchange have been presented in the given work. This exchange favors the sulfate diffusion into pore solutions and increases in the quantity of

reduced sulfur compounds, mainly, pyrite in the upper 0.50-
3.0 m of sediments. The complete exhaustion of sulfate at
the depths investigated, even within the range from 5.6 to 6 m
of sediments, was observed nowhere.

We have obtained the chemical, X-ray diffraction, micro-
scopical and isotope evidences for diagenetic carbonates
These carbonates have anomalous high contents of isotope C^{12}
(Table II). Such isotopic composition of diagenetic carbonates
is formed by carbon dioxide produced by methane oxidation or
generated by the bacterial decomposition of organic matter,
for example, during the process of sulfate reduction. The
mechanism of this process has been discussed above when describing the laboratory experiment. Literature contains
examples of isotopically light diagenetic carbonates with
carbon formed on methane oxidation, the so-called methane
derived carbonates (Hathaway and Degens, 1969; Roberts and
Whelan, 1975; Milliman, 1974).

In the reduced sediments investigated, the intensive
processes of sulfate reduction lead to the H_2S generation in
amounts toxic for all the other anaerobic microorganisms.
Thus, methane-generating bacteria are present in muds, but
in the inhibited state. The intensity of methane generation
in the experiments with labelled carbon dioxide in the
muds investigated does not exceed $4 \cdot 10^{-16}$ mg CH_4/kg wet mud/
day (Belyaev and Finkelstein, 1976). Undoubtedly, the
highly reduced sedimentation medium inhibits methane oxidation
formed both *in situ* and, possibly, migratory.

Therefore, the anomalously high isotope ^{12}C content of
the carbon dioxide of porewaters (Claypool and Kaplan, 1974)
and carbon of autigenous protodolomite and magnesian calcite
cannot be related to methane oxidation processes, but is due,
absolutely, to the processes of the anaerobic decomposition
of organic matter, among which the process of sulfate reduction is the main one. Metabolic carbon dioxide produced
has a carbon isotope content approximating that of the mud
organic matter, *i.e.*, about -22%. This carbon dioxide
participates in the formation of diagenetic carbonates.

The method proposed deals with the determination of the
part of diagenetic carbonates formed under the influence of
metabolic carbon dioxide by the carbon isotope content of
total carbonate in the sediment from the equation:

$$A = xB + (1-X) \ C, \qquad . \ . \ . \ I$$

where   A - $\delta^{13}C$, %o of total carbonate carbon in
              sediment
         B - $\delta^{13}C$, %o carbon of organic matter in
              sediment (-23.0%o)
         C - $\delta^{13}C$, %o carbon of foraminiferan shell
              carbonate in sediment (+2.0%o)

X - the portion of carbonate carbon, formed on oxidation of the organic matter by sulfate reduction during the early diagenesis of the sediment (Table II).

The calculations show that in the sediments investigated from 39 to 68% of the total content of carbon mineral forms in the sediment is due to the diagenetic carbonates (Table II). Therefore, the formation of paragenous diagenetic iron sulfides and carbonates is possible under the conditions of intensive microbiological sulfate reduction (from 1.46 to 40.9 mg of H_2S/kg/yr).

ACKNOWLEDGMENTS

Thanks are due to Dr. V. G. Bondar for the analysis of carbon isotope content and Dr. E. V. Kashparova for chemical analyses. Both are with the Institute of Biochemistry and Physiology of Microorganisms.

REFERENCES

Bavendamm, W. "Die Mikrobiologische Kalkfällung in der Tropischen See.," *Arch. Mikrobiol.* 3:205-276 (1932).

Belyaev, S.S., and Z.I. Finkelstein. "Anaerobic Gas Forming Bacteria in Sediments of the Gulf of California and the Pacific Ocean Coastal Regions," in *Biogeochemistry of Diagenesis of Ocean Sediments* (Moscow: Nauka, 1976), pp.7 pp. 75-82.

Berner, R.A. "Chemical Changes Affecting Calcium during the Bacterial Decomposition of Fish and Clams in Sea Water," *Marine Geol.* 7:253-274 (1969).

Beyerinck, M.W. "Ueber Spirillum Desulfuricans als Ursache von Sulfatreduction," *Centr. Bacteriol. Abt. II*, I/(I):1-9; (2):49-59; (3):104-114 (1895).

Claypool, C.E., and I.R. Kaplan. *Natural Gases in Marine Sediments*, I.R. Kaplan, Ed. (New York, London: Plenum Press, 1974), pp. 99-139.

Chebotarev, E.N., and M.V. Ivanov. "Distribution and Activity of Sulphate Reducers in the Bottom Sediments of the Pacific Ocean and the Gulf of California," in *Biogeochemistry of Diagenesis of Ocean Sediments* (Moscow: Nauka, 1976) pp. 68-74.

Deelman, John C. "Bacterial Sulfate Reduction Affecting Carbonate Sediments," *Soil Sci.* 119(1):73-80 (1975).

Galimov, E.M. *Carbon Isotopes in Oil-Gas Geology* (Moscow: Nedra, 1973).

Hathaway, J.C. and E.T. Degens. "Methane--Derived Marine Carbonates of Pleistocene Age," *Science* 165(3894):690-692 (1969).

Ivanov, M.V., A. Yu. Lein and E.V. Kashparova. "The Intensity of Formation and Diagenetic Transformation of Sulfur Reduced Compounds in the Pacific Ocean Sediments," in *Biogeochemistry of Diagenesis of Ocean Sediments* (Moscow: Nauka, 1976), pp. 171-178.

Kaplan, I.R., and S.C. Rittenberg. "Carbon Isotope Fractionation during Metabolism of Lactate by Desulfovibrio Desulfuricans," *J. Gen. Microbiol.* 34:213-217 (1964).

Lein, A. Yu., N.V. Logvinenko, I.I. Volkov and M.V. Ivanov. "Mineral and Isotopic Composition of Diagenetic Carbonate Minerals of Concretions from the Gulf of California Reduced Muds," *DAN USSR* 224(2):426-429 (1975).

Lein, A. Yu., A.I. Kudryavtseva, A.G. Matrosov and A.M. Zyakun. "The Isotope Content of Sulphur Compounds in the Pacific Ocean Sediments," in *Biogeochemistry of Diagenesis of Ocean Sediments* (Moscow: Nauka, 1976), pp. 179-185.

Milliman, J.D. *Recent Sedimentary Carbonates, Part 1. Marine Carbonates* (Berlin: Springer-Verlag, 1974), p. 375.

Roberts, H.H., and T. Whelan. "Methane-Derived Carbonate Cements in Barrier and Beach Sands of a Subtropical Delta Complex," *Geochim. et Cosmochim. Acta* 39:1085-1089 (1975).

Rozanov, A.G., I.I. Volkov, V.S. Sokolov, Z.V. Pushkina and M.F. Pilipchuk. "Redox Processes in the Sediments of the Gulf of California and the Adjacent Part of the Pacific Ocean," in *Biogeochemistry of Diagenesis of Ocean Sediments* (Moscow: Nauka, 1976), pp. 96-135.

Shishkina, O.V., and G.A. Pavlova. "On the Porewaters of the Gulf of California," in *Biogeochemistry of Diagenesis of Ocean Sediments* (Moscow: Nauka, 1976), pp 83-95.

Smejkal, V., F.D. Cook and H.R. Krouse. "Studies of Sulfur and Carbon Isotope Fractionation with Microorganisms Isolated from Springs of Western Canada," *Geochim. et. Cosmochim. Acta* 35:787-800 (1971).

Strakhov, N.M.   "Balance of Reduction Processes in the Pacific
   Ocean Sediments," *Lithol. and Miner. Resourc.*   4:65-92
   (1972).

Sweeney, R.E., and I.R. Kaplan.   "Pyrite Framboid Formation:
   Laboratory Synthesis and Marine Sediments," *Econ. Geol.*
   68:618-634 (1973).

Van Andel, T.H.   "Recent Marine Sediments of the Gulf of
   California," in *Marine Geology of Memoir 3* (Tulsa, Oklahoma
   USA: 1964), pp. 216-310.

Volkov, I.I., A.G. Rozanov, N.N. Zhabina and L.S. Fomina.
   "Sulphur Compounds in Sediments of the Gulf of California
   and the Adjacent Part of the Pacific Ocean," in *Biogeochemistry of Diagenesis of Ocean Sediments* (Moscow: Nauka,
   1976), pp. 136-170.

CHAPTER 29

FATTY ACIDS OF <u>DESULFOVIBRIO DESULFURICANS</u> AS MARKER MOLECULES IN SEDIMENTARY ENVIRONMENTS

JAAP J. BOON, W. LIEFKENS,
W. IRENE C. RIJPSTRA,
MARIANNE BAAS AND J.W. DE LEEUW

Delft University of Technology
Department of Chemistry and Chemical Engineering
Organic Geochemistry Unit
de Vries van Heystplantsoen 2
Delft, The Netherlands

INTRODUCTION

Over the past years it has become clear that reconstruction of the original environment and understanding the diagenetic pathways by means of an inventory of organic compounds present in ancient sediments is a rather speculative affair. Numerous investigations have demonstrated the analytical possiblity of determining in detail the molecular structures of rather complex sedimentary compounds (Ourisson, 1973). However, decoding the information incorporated in these molecular fossils is hampered severely from lack of knowledge of biogeochemical processes operating in the top layers of sediments. For this reason, many organic geochemists now concentrate on "very recent sediment"--chemistry and environmental chemistry.

The goal of our investigations is to demonstrate that some characteristic molecules from organisms in the sedimentary environment can be used as marker molecules in sedimentary ecosystems. The object of understanding the sedimentary ecosystem is to find out which molecules escape from the biocycle and leak into the geocycle. This knowledge is necessary to consider the impact of diagenetic influences on the molecular lag deposits, resulting from biosynthesis and biodegradation in the water column and in the top layers of sediments.

The iso- and anteisomonoenoic fatty acids of *Desulfovibrio desulfuricans*, a sulfate-reducing bacterium, were chosen as potential marker molecules because of their easily recognizable and peculiar structure and because *D. desulfuricans* is a widespread bacterium in marine (sedimentary) environments (Boon *et al.*, 1977b).

The scope and limitations of these molecules as marker molecules were tested in three environments of increasing complexity: the innershelf offshore Walvis Bay (S. W. Africa), the deeper layers of abyssal Black Sea sediments (Unit 2), and a tidal flat of the Wadden Sea (The Netherlands), respectively. Some of the most important differences between these environments are summarized in Table I. The Walvis Bay shelf sediment (Copenhagen, 1953; Calvert and Price, 1971) and the Black Sea sediment (Degens and Ross, 1974) share the absence of an aerobic macrofauna, which would rework the sediment top layer, but they differ in input material and in the location of sulfate reduction in the environmental setting. The tidal flat environment was chosen for the presence of its abundant aerobic macrofauna consisting of suspension-, surface and deposit-feeders (Beukema, 1976), which opened the possibility of tracing the *Desulfovibrio* fatty acids moving up in the food chain.

The complexity of the latter environment--*i.e.*,high primary production, high-low tide periodicity, input of terrigenous detritus, abundant and versatile bacterial activity, presence of macrofauna, dynamic sediment structure--is demonstrated by the occurrence of several biocycles. One of these cycles in which the deposit feeder *Arenicola marina* is the key organism was investigated· in detail. The subenvironment of *Arenicola marina* and the worm itself, known to digest large amounts of the tidal flat sediment, were analyzed for fatty acid-containing lipids, with special attention for the presence of iso- and anteisomonoenoic fatty acids.

EXPERIMENTAL

Method

The isolation of *Desulfovibrio desulfuricans,* the cultural conditions, isolation of lipid material and the identification of fatty acids from extractable lipids have been described earlier (Boon *et al.*, 1977b). The bacterial residue after extraction was stirred with 0.1 N aqueous KOH/ethanol (2:1, v/v) for 24 hours at 20°C. After acidification and extraction with n-hexane and diethyl ether, the extract was washed with water and evaporated to dryness. The extract was methylated by CH_2N_2 and separated by TLC (Skipski, *et al.*, 1965) into methyl esters and hydroxy methyl esters (one additional band is still unidentified). Methyl esters and hydroxy methyl esters, as trimethylsilylether derivatives, were analyzed by GC/MS.

Table I
Some Characteristics of the Investigated
Sedimentary Environments

	Walvis Baai Innershelf Sediment	Black Sea Abyssal Sediment (Unit 2)	Wadden Sea Tidal Flat (*Arenicola* Sand Flat)
Sediment	Diatomaceous ooze	Marly clay, rich in organic matter	Quartz sand and and silt
Water Column	O_2-rich	Upper 200 m: rich; below 200 m: no O_2, abundant H_2S	O_2-rich (at high tide period)
Sediment-Water Interface	No O_2; abundant H_2S, no aerobic macrofauna	No O_2, no aerobic macrofauna	O_2-rich; below ± 1 cm abundant H_2S, abundant aerobic macrofauna
Input Material	Algal remains (98% diatoms)	Algal and bacterial remains, terrigenous detritus	Algal and bacterial remains, macrofaunal elements, terrigenous detritus (partly pollutants)

Walvis Bay

The extraction, isolation and identification of fatty acids and hydroxy fatty acids from Walvis Bay diatomaceous ooze was described by Boon *et al.* (1975, 1977a). The fatty acid methyl esters were reacted with OsO_4, reduced by H_2S and analyzed as a mixture of di-trimethylsilylether derivatives and nonderivitized methyl esters by GC/MS, as described elsewhere (Boon *et al.*, submitted to *J. Org. Geochem.*).

Black Sea Sediment

The Black Sea sediment was sampled by gravity corer in the western part of the euxine abyssal plain at a water depth of about 2150 m (41° 39[1] N, 30° 44[1] E). The recovered core length measured 118 cm. The core section from 27-71 cm, corresponding to Unit 2 of Degens and Ross (1974), was packed and stored at -20°C.

An amount of 1130 g of this sediment (81% H_2O) available for analysis was homogenized in a Waring Blendor, and subsamples of 250 g were used for various analyzes.

A subsample of 250 g wet sediment was saponified by 1 N ethanolic KOH at reflux temperature for 2 hr. The saponified mud suspension was centrifuged. The supernatant solution was pipetted off, acidified and extracted with CH_2Cl_2 extract (basic hydrolysate) was obtained in this way.

Fatty acids were isolated from a portion of 50 mg of this extract by K[+]-impregnated silicic acid column chromatography (McCarty and Duthie, 1962). A diethyl ether-1% formic acid eluate was analyzed after reaction with CH_2N_2 and Bistrimethylsilylacetamide (Merck Chem. Co.) by GC/MS.

Monohydroxy monocarboxylic fatty acids were also isolated separately by TLC (Skipski *et al.*, 1965), reacted with BSA and analyzed by GC/MS. Another subsample of 240 blended wet sediment was stirred in stainless steel centrifuge tubes with methanol, centrifuges and the supernatant pipetted off into a separatory funnel. This procedure was repeated four times with increasing amounts of redistilled analytical grade CH_2Cl_2. The ternary solvent mixture consisting of H_2O, CH_3OH and CH_2Cl_2 was separated into two phases by addition of water into a CH_2Cl_2-layer and a H_2O-CH_3OH-layer. The evaporated CH_2Cl_2-layer yielded a neutral solvent extract of 1220 mg.

A portion of 50 mg of this extract was passed over a K[+]-impregnated silicic acid column and yielded 26.6 mg neutral lipids (diethyl ether eluate) and 14.3 mg acids (diethyl ether-1% formic acid eluate). The free acids were methylated by CH_2N_2 and separated by TLC (Skipski *et al.*, 1965). The monocarboxylic fatty acid methyl esters (extractable complex lipid-bound fatty acids, see Figure 4B) were analyzed by GC/MS. The double bond positions of the monoenoic fatty acids were determined as described above.

The residual sediment after the $H_2O-CH_3OH-CH_2Cl_2$ extraction was saponified with 1 N ethanolic KOH and further treated as described above. A portion of 10 mg of the obtained CH_2Cl_2 and analyzed by GC/MS (residual-bound fatty acids, see Figure 4C).

Balgzand Tidal Flat

The sediments and *Arenicola marina* (see Figure 5) were sampled on the Balgzand tidal flat (Wadden Sea, The Netherlands--52° 55^1 N, 4° 50^1 E). The sediments were transferred into glass-stoppered glass vials and fixed with an adequate amount of chloroform-methanol (1:2, v/v). The anaerobic sediment (2 kg, dry weight), the faeces (700 g, dry weight) and the sediment in front of *Arenicola*'s head (520 g, dry weight) were extracted with methanol and increasing amounts of redistilled CH_2Cl_2.

The solvents were recovered by filtration over a Büchner funnel, pooled into a separatory funnel and separated by the addition of water into a water-methanol-layer and CH_2Cl_2-layer. The extracts were saponified with 1 N KOH in 95% methanol. After acidification and extraction with diethyl ether, the fatty acids were found to be transesterified.

Fatty acid methyl esters of these extracts were resaponified with 0.5 N KOH; nonsaponifiables were removed by extraction with diethyl ether. Acidification and extraction with diethyl ether yielded the fatty acid fraction, which was methylated by CH_2N_2, reacted with BSA and analyzed by GC/MS. The surface sediment was saponified as such with 1 N aqueous KOH-methanol (5:1, v/v), after an initial attempt to obtain an extract with CH_2Cl_2. The saponification was carried out at room temperature by intensive stirring of the sediment for 96 hr. After a sedimentation period of 12 hr, the clear supernatant was decanted into a separatory funnel. The residue was suspended in methanol and CH_2Cl_2, acidified to pH≈2 and filtrated. The residue on the filter was washed with methanol and CH_2Cl_2 and the filtrate was transferred into the separatory funnel. After additional acidification and addition of water, a CH_2Cl_2-layer was obtained, which was washed with water. After drying of the CH_2Cl_2 with Na_2SO_4 and evaporation, 260 mg CH_2Cl_2-extract was obtained. Fatty acids were isolated as methyl esters by TLC from an aliquot of 20 mg after methylation by CH_2N_2 (Skipski *et al.*, 1965). The methyl esters were analyzed immediately by GC/MS.

Ten adult lugworms (*Arenicola marina*) were homogenized in a Waring Blendor and extracted according to Bligh and Dyer (1959); 233 mg of extractable lipids was obtained. An aliquot of the extract (40 mg) was saponified with 1 N methanolic KOH. After acidification and extraction (four times) with diethyl ether, the combined extracts were washed with water, dried over Na_2SO_4 and methylated by CH_2N_2. Separation by TLC (Slipski *et al.*, 1965) yielded a methyl ester fraction, which was analyzed by GC/MS. Double bonds in the monoenoic fatty acid methyl ester were determined by GC/MS analysis of the corresponding disilyloxyderivatives. The separation of the lipid extracts into various lipid classes and their identification are treated elsewhere (W. Liefkens, in preparation).

GC/MS Conditions

The Varian-Mat 111 gas chromatograph/mass spectrometer was used, equipped with a 30-m OV 101 glass capillary column, which was used as carrier gas. Mass spectra were obtained at 80 eV. Methyl esters and trimethylsilylether derivatives were separated by temperature programming from 140°-300° at a rate of 4°C/min.

GLC

Polyunsaturated fatty acid-containing mixtures were also gas chromatographed on a Perkin Elmer 990 instrument, equipped with a 2-m column (i.d. 2 mm) packed with 5% Apolar on Gaschrom Q (80-100 mesh), which was used as a carrier gas. The flow rate was 11.5 ml/min, and the temperature was programmed from 150-250°C/min. The relative retention times and the GC/MS data improved the final identification.

RESULTS

Desulfovibrio desulfuricans

Figures 1 and 2 show the gas chromatograms of the extractable complex lipid-bound and the residual fatty acids from a strain of *Desulfovibrio desulfuricans*, which was isolated from Wadden Sea sediment. The characteristic iso- and anteisomonoenoic fatty acids are almost exclusively present in the extractable lipid fraction, which consists mainly of phospholipids. The double bond position in the monoenoic fatty acids was demonstrated to be almost exclusively at the ω-7 position (Boon *et al.*, 1977b). This is related to their biosynthesis along the anaerobic chain elongation pathway (Bloch, 1969), the only feasible pathway for fatty acid synthesis in these anaerobic bacteria. *D. desulfuricans* is the only organism known to process branched chain precursors via this pathway. Therefore, the presence of iso- and anteisomethyl branches combined with the ω-7 double bond position in monoenoic fatty acids is considered to be indicative of *Desulfovibrio* species.

Other characteristic fatty acids in *D. desulfuricans* are β-hydroxy fatty acids. Iso- (C_{15}, C_{16}, C_{17}) and anteiso- (C_{15}, C_{17}) β-hydroxy fatty acids were found as the major hydroxy fatty acids in extractable lipids (Boon *et al.*, 1977b). In the residual fraction the saturated iso and anteiso fatty acids and the iso-C_{15}-β-hydroxy fatty acid are the major components. The Δ^2-monoenoic fatty acids in this fraction (Figure 2) may be derived from β-hydroxy acids by dehydration.

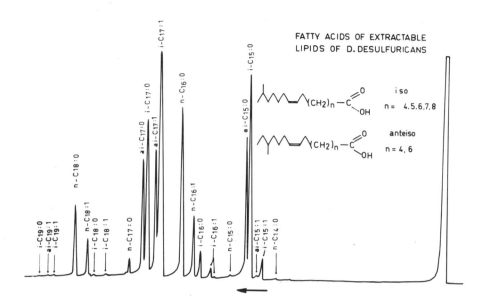

Figure 1. Capillary gas chromatogram of the extractable complex lipid-bound fatty acids of *Desulfovibrio desulfuricans*. The insert shows the structure of the iso- and anteisomonoenoic fatty acids identified. (Redrawn from Boon *et al.*, 1977b).

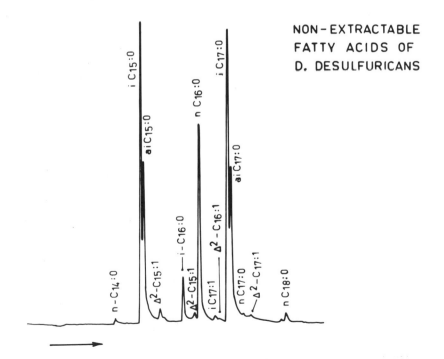

Figure 2. Total ion current trace from capillary GC/MS of the residual fatty acids of *Desulfovibrio desulfuricans*.

Walvis Bay Diatomaceous Ooze

Figure 3 shows the chromatogram of the total fatty acid mixture from the top layer of diatomaceous ooze (3-28 cm) sampled on the innershelf offshore of Walvis Bay (Boon *et al.*, 1975). The branched chain monoenoic fatty acids identified were the iso- (Δ^7-$C_{15:1}$, Δ^9-$C_{16:1}$, Δ^9-$C_{17:1}$, Δ^{11}-$C_{17:1}$, Δ^9-$C_{18:1}$, Δ^{11}-$C_{18:1}$) and anteiso- (Δ^7-$C_{15:1}$, Δ^9-$C_{17:1}$, Δ^{11}-$C_{17:1}$) fatty acids. The major fatty acid isomers belong to the ω^7-series. Saturated iso and anteiso **fatty acids are** relatively abundant. The major β-hydroxy fatty acids present in this sediment are the normal (C_{14}, C_{16}, C_{18}, C_{20}), iso- (C_{15}, C_{16}, C_{17}) and anteiso- (C_{15}, C_{17}) isomers (Boon *et al.*, 1977b).

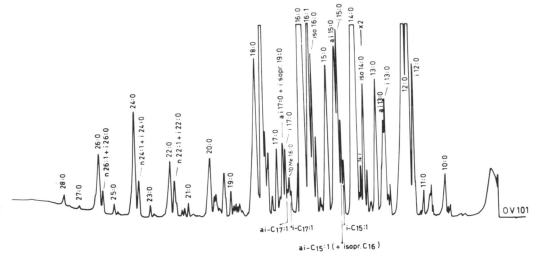

Figure 3. Capillary gas chromatogram of the total fatty acids of a surface sample of Walvis Bay diatomaceous ooze (core KF6:3-28 cm). The separation was achieved on a Perkin Elmer 990 gas chromatograph equipped with a 20-m stainless steel capillary column (i.d. 0.25 mm) temperature programmed from 120-300°C at a rate of 4°C/min.

Black Sea Sediment

The sediment investigated is 3000-7000 years old and is identical to the Unit 2 type sediment described by Ross and Degens (1974). Figure 4 (A,B and C) shows the compositions of the free, the extractable complex lipid-bound, and the residual fatty acids ranging from C_{13}-C_{19}. The medium-sized peaks are emphasized in the figure. Iso- and anteiso- ω-7 monoenoic fatty acids are found almost exclusively in the extractable complex lipid fraction. The variations between the saturated iso and anteiso fatty acids in the three fractions in comparison with the odd straight chain saturated fatty acids are notable. The β-hydroxy fatty acids found in the

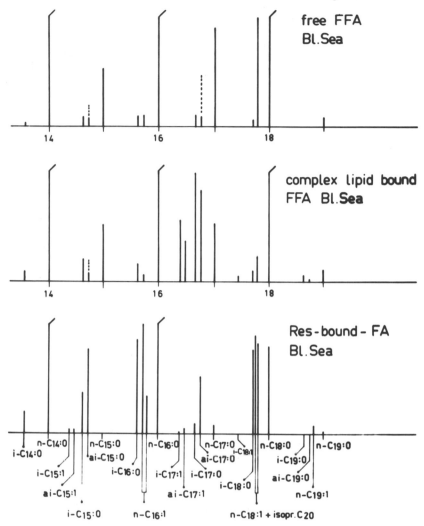

Figure 4. Fatty acids composition in the chain length from
$C_{13}-C_{19}$ of the free (A), extractable lipid-bound (B) and
residual-bound fatty acids (C), isolated from Black Sea
sediment (Unit 2).

total hydroxy fatty acid mixture of this sediment are the
normal ($C_{12}, C_{14}, C_{16}, C_{18}, C_{20}$), the iso- ($C_{14}, C_{18}$) and a branched-
chain (C_{15}) β-hydroxy fatty acid.

The Environment of *Arenicola marina*

The environment of *Arenicola marina* (Figure 5) was
divided into five parts:

> •sediment surface (a)
> •aerobic sediment in front of the mouth of the
> the worm (b)
> •the worm itself (discussed below) (c)

- the anaerobic sediment around the living tube (d)
- sediment that passed the gut and is deposited on
  the sediment surface as faeces (e).

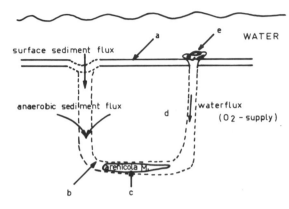

Figure 5.   Habitat
of the lugworm
Arenicola marina.

The gas chromatograms of the fatty acids of a, b, d and e are
shown in Figures 6, 7, 8 and 9.   Iso- and anteisomonoenoic
fatty acids are present in b, c and d.   Traces of these acids
are present in e.   The saturated iso and anteiso fatty acids
are relatively abundant in b, c and d.   Algal fatty acids
($nC_{20:5}$ and $nC_{22:6}$) are very abundant in a and present in b,
c and e.

The Lugworm *Arenicola marina*

Figure 10 shows the gas chromatogram of the fatty acid
methyl esters obtained from the extractable lipid material of
the marine polychaete *Arenicola marina*.   Major components are
the normal $C_{14:0}$, $C_{16:0}$, $C_{18:0}$, $C_{20:5}$ and $C_{22:6}$ acids.   Iso-
and anteisomonoenoic fatty acids are components of medium
intensity in this total fatty acid mixture.   The double-bond
locations in the monoenoic fatty acids were determined by
GC/MS analyses of the di-trimethylsilyl derivatives.   The
branched chain $C_{17:1}$ component has the double bond at the Δ^9
position.   The straight chain monoenoic fatty acids ($C_{16:1}$,
$C_{18:1}$, $C_{20:1}$) belong almost exclusively to the ω-7 series.
Iso and anteiso fatty acid moieties were found to be present
in sterolesters, triglycerides, ether lipids and phospholipids
of *A. marina*.   They are enriched with respect to their saturated counterparts in the sterol-ester fraction.

DISCUSSION

Desulfovibrio Lipids and the Geocycle

The mode of occurrence of saturated and monoenoic fatty
acids in the bacteria is of direct importance to their fate in
the geocycle.   The characteristic iso- and anteisomonoenoic
fatty acids are found almost exclusively in extractable lipids,

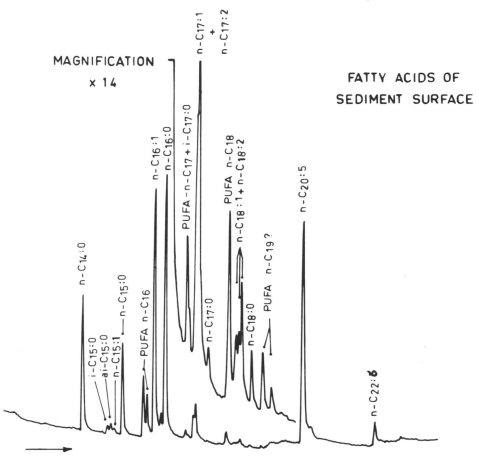

Figure 6. Total ion current trace from capillary GC/MS of the
fatty acids from the surface of the tidal flat sediment (see
Figure 5a).

and function as markers for this part of the organic matter of
the sulfate-reducing bacteria. The saturated iso and anteiso
fatty acids are present in extractable lipids; they are dominant in the residual fraction, probably bound to lipopoly-
saccharides and lipoproteins.

The Black Sea sediment and the Walvis Bay sediment
offered good possibilities for investigating the fate of
Desulfovibrio lipid material in view of the important role
of sulfate reduction in these environment and because reworking of the sediments by aerobic macrofauna is absent (Jannasch
et al., 1974; Deuser, 1974; Copenhage, 1953). The presence
of monoenoic branched fatty acids in the total fatty acid
mixture of Walvis Bay sediment with the "correct" double-
bond positions proved the contribution of *Desulfovibrio* bacteria
to the sedimentary organic matter. A large part of the other
monoenoic fatty acids present in this sediment have double-
bond positions indicative of an "anaerobic chain elongation"

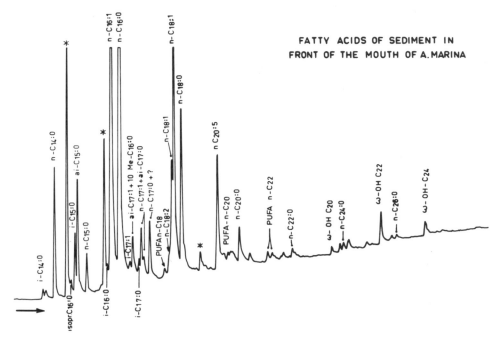

Figure 7. Total ion current trace from capillary GC/MS of
fatty acid in extractable lipids from the aerobic sediment
just in front of the head of *Arenicola marina* (see Figure
5b). The peaks marked with an asterisk are due to a silicon
oil contamination.

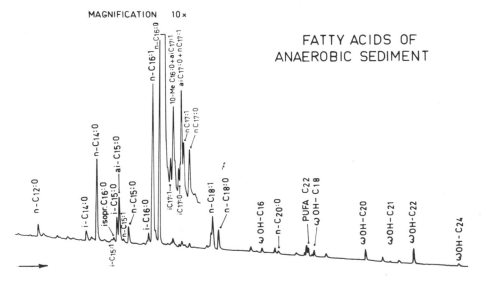

Figure 8. Total ion current trace from capillary GC/MS of the
fatty acids in extractable lipids from the anaerobic part of
the tidal flat sediment (see Figure 5d).

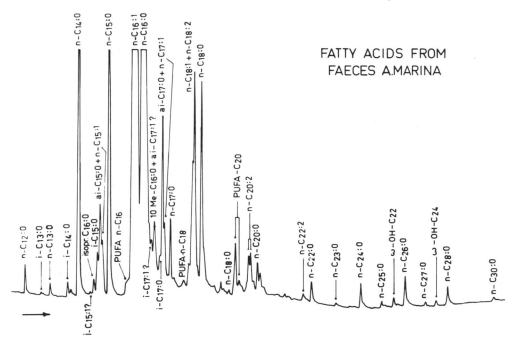

Figure 9. Total ion current trace from capillary GC/MS of the fatty acids in extractable lipids from faeces of *Arenicola marina* (see Figure 5e).

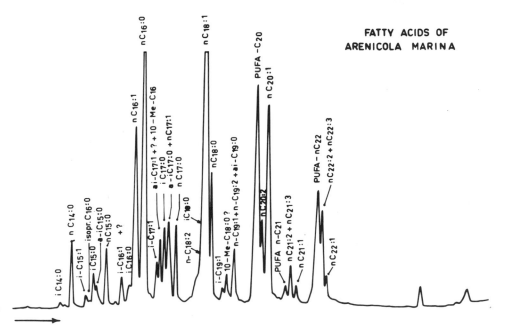

Figure 10. Total ion current trace from capillary GC/MS of fatty acids in extractable lipids from *Arenicola marina* (see Figure 5c).

biosynthetic history and are thought to be derived from
sulfate-reducing bacteria also. (Boon *et al.*, submitted to
J. Org. Geochem.) The relative abundance of the iso- and
anteiso-β-hydroxy fatty acids in this sediment confirms that
sedimentary β-hydroxy fatty acids originate from complex
lipid species dissolved in or bound to biomembrane structures,
as was postulated earlier (Boon *et al.*, 1977a).

The nonextractable residual fraction of the Walvis
Bay sediment contains a relatively large amount of saturated
iso and anteiso fatty acids (Boon, unpublished results). A
lipopolysaccharide origin of these acids--indicative of the
presence of bacterial cell wall material--is under investigation. The total fatty acid mixture of the Black Sea Unit 2
sediment is very complicated due to a greater diversity in
input of deritus. This mixture consists of monocarboxylic
acids, dicarboxylic acids, mono- and dihydroxy acids and
aromatic acids. Iso- and anteisomonoenoic fatty acids could
not be identified in this total fatty acid mixture. However,
isolation and analysis of the extractable complex lipid
fraction clearly demonstrated their presence as acyl moieties.
Apparently, the complexity of the total fatty acid mixture
had masked their presence. The nonextractable residual fraction of the sediment, compared to the Walvis Bay sediment,
contained relatively large amounts of saturated iso and
anteiso fatty acids. Moreover, traces of the monoenoic
branched chain fatty acids were present too, but in a different
distribution as compared to the extractable lipids.

The presence of the branched chain monoenoic fatty
acids in the extractable complex lipid fraction of the Black
Sea sediment points to an origin from phospholipids of *Desulf-
ovbrio* species. Hydrolysis of the phosphate-base group by
autolytic processes known to occur rapidly in these bacteria
(Boon, unpublished results) or by lipolytic action of other
microorganisms may have occurred. Contributions of nonextractable material of *Desulfovibrio* species is indicated by
the abundance of iso and anteiso fatty acids in the residual
fraction. The trace amounts of the branched chain monoenoic
fatty acids in the residual fraction of the Black Sea sediment
point in our view to a chemical incorporation of phospholipids
(or their derivatives) in the nonextractable matter. Such a
process could protect fatty acyl moieties from hydrolysis by
enzymatic processes due to exolipases).

Desulfovibrio and the Biocycle

The tidal flat environment (Wadden Sea, the Netherlands)
has a very complicated trophic structure (Beukema, 1976).
We will confine ourselves to those parts with sandy sediments,
commonly indicated as the *Arenicola* sand flats. The sediment

consists of medium-sized sand (250-500 μm), and it can be divided roughly into a number of strata. The sediment-water interface is aerobic, but below 1 cm oxygen is rapidly depleted and the activity of the sulfate-reducing bacteria manifests itself by the black color of FeS minerals formed. At a depth of 20-40 cm, there is a lag deposit of coarse particles consisting of shell fragments, dead gastropods, peat particles, coal and oil slick residues.

Above this layer, the sediment is continuously reshuffled and reworked, partly by deposit-feeding polychaetes, partly by endobiontic mollusks, especially in the upper layers. The lugworm *Arenicola marina* is estimated to turnover the sediment layer within one or two years, depending on the density of the organisms (Cadée, 1976). Since the maximum activity of sulfate-reducing bacteria is at about 5 cm below the sediment-water interface (Vosjan, 1975), the fate of the *Desulfovibrio* lipids seems to be predominantly determined by the action of deposit feeders (*Arenicola marina; Heteromastus filiformis*). Whether *Desulfovibrio* lipids pass into the geocycle depends, in this kind of sedimentary environment, mainly on the fate of these lipids moving through sedimentary biocycles.

The subenvironment of *Arenicola marina* (Figure 5) was choosen as a model system for investigation of the fate of *Desulfovibrio* lipids. The aerobic sediment just in front of the head of *A. marina* forms its daily diet. The constant feeding of the polychaete on this sediment is compensated for by a steady flow of sediment downwards, which is made up of a mixture of surface sediment and sediment flowing in from anaerobic layers. After digestion, the sediment is returned to the sediment surface as faeces (Krüger, 1971). The surface sediment is characterized by even straight chain polyunsaturated fatty acids, which points to diatoms (low C_{18} area) (Ackman *et al.*, 1968) and possibly to certain crustacea (odd straight chain polyunsaturated fatty acids) (Paradis and Ackman, 1976).

The fatty acids of the anaerobic sediment have bacterial characteristics, which is indicated by the iso and anteiso structures, the 10-methyl C_{16} fatty acid, the presence of odd chain fatty acids and a general absence of polyunsaturated fatty acids (Erwin, 1973; Shaw, 1974). Among these fatty acids iso- and anteisomonoenoic fatty acids are found as a reflection of a contribution of *Desulfovibrio* organic matter to this sediment. The sediment in front of the head of the worm contains fatty acids with both bacterial and algal characteristics, which is evidence of the mixing process mentioned above. Since this sediment is kept aerobic by the oxygen supply method of the polychaete, no growth of sulfate-reducing bacteria occurs here; thus, no extra amounts of iso- and anteisomonoenoic fatty acids are introduced. The fatty

acids of *A. marina* itself contain a significant amount of
algal-derived polyunsaturated fatty acids, but also present
a number of bacterial-derived fatty acids.

Iso- and anteisomonoenoic fatty acids are present as
acyl moieties in sterolesters, triglycerides, ether lipids
and phospholipids with the "correct" ω-7 double bonds. These
fatty acids are derived from ingested *Desulfovibrio* organic
matter present in the diet (sediment). Synthesis of these
acids by *A. marina* itself is unlikely, since that would imply
an enzymatic ability to biosynthesize iso and anteiso structures and to introduce double bonds into monoenoic fatty acids
by a chain elongation mechanism (Erwin, 1973).

The iso- and anteiso monoenoic fatty acids are picked
up from the diet, just as the polyunsaturated fatty acids,
10-methyl C_{16} fatty acids, and probably others, less easily
recognized because they lack peculiar characteristics in their
alkyl chain. The fatty acid composition of the sediment in
front of the head proves that these fatty acids are available.
The nondigestable part of the sediment, which is recycled to
the surface as faeces, contains small amounts of fatty acids
(mainly $nC_{16:0}$ and $nC_{16:1}$). The fatty acid composition of the
faeces depicted in Figure 9 may be different from completely
fresh faeces. The minor amounts of polyunsaturated fatty
acids and iso and anteiso fatty acids may be caused by rapid
growth of algae (benthonic diatoms) and bacteria on the faeces.

The phenomenon of deposit feeding in the tidal flat
environment is a way to remove digestable organic matter produced by algae and bacteria from the sediment. In the same
way the marker molecules in *Desulfovibrio* species are removed.
Therefore, a relevant contribution to the geocycle of lipids
biosynthesized by anaerobic bacteria in top layers of sediments
with a deposit feeding fauna is not expected. Further analysis
of deeper sediment may point out whether any *Desulfovibrio*-
type lipid material (or other characteristic molecules more
or less biosynthesized in the top layers) is part of the
"molecular lag deposit." Research on the quantitative role of
Desulfovibrio in the sedimentary biocycles and a possible
leak into the geocycle is in progress using specifically
[14]C-labelled *Desulfovibrio* bacteria.

ACKNOWLEDGMENTS

J.H. Vosjan and P.A.W.J. de Wilde (N.I.O.Z., Texel) are
gratefully mentioned for helpful discussions and for facilities
provided during sampling in the Wadden Sea. The Koninklijke/
Shell Exploratie en Produktie Laboratorium (Rijswijk, Z-H)
(Shell Research B.V.) is acknowledged for its donation of the
Black Sea sediment sample.

REFERENCES

Ackman, R.G., C.S. Tocher and J. McLachlan. "Marine Phyto-
plankter Fatty Acids," *J. Fish. Res. Bd. Can.* 25:1603-1619
(1968).

Beukema, J.J. "Biomass and Species Richness of the Macrobenthic Animals Living on the Tidal Flats of the Dutch
Wadden Sea," *Neth. J. Sea Res.* 10:236-261 (1976).

Bligh, E.G., and W.J. Dyer. "A Rapid Method for Lipid Extrac-
tion and Purification," *Can. J. Biochem. Physiol.* 37:911-
917 (1959).
Bloch, K. "Enzymatic Synthesis of Monounsaturated Fatty Acids,"
Bloch, K. "Enzymatic Synthesis of Monounsaturated Fatty Acids,"
Acc. Chem. Res. 2:193-202 (1969).

Boon, J.J., J.W. de Leeuw and P.A. Schenck. "Organic Geochemistry of Walvis Bay Diatomaceous Ooze. I. Occurrence
and Significance of the Fatty Acids," *Geochim. Cosmochim.
Acta* 39:1559-1565 (1975).

Boon, J.J., F. de Lange, P.J.W. Schuyl, J.W. de Leeuw and P.A.
Schenck. "Organic Geochemistry of Walvis Bay Diatomaceous
Ooze. II. Occurrence and Significance of the Hydroxy Fatty
Acids," in *Proceedings of the 7th Int. Meeting of Organic
Geochemistry,* Madrid, ENADISMA (1975).

Boon, J.J., J.W. de Leeuw, G. v.d. Hoek and J.H. Vosjan.
"The Significance and Taxonomical Value of Iso and Anteiso
Monoenoic Fatty Acids and Branched β-hydroxy Acids in
Desulfovibrio desulfuricans," *J. Bacteriol.* 129(3):1183-1191.
(1977b).

Cadée, G. "Sediment Reworking by *Arenicola marina* on Tidal
Flats in the Dutch Wadden Sea," *Neth. J. Sea Res.* 10:440-
460 (1976).

Calvert, S.E., and N.B. Price. "Upwelling and Nutrient Regeneration in the Benguela Current," *Deep-Sea Res.* 18:505-523
(October 1968).

Copenhagen, W.J. "The Periodic Mortality of Fish in the Walvis
Bay Region," *Invest. Dep. Fish. Mar. Biol. Div. Union S. Afr.*
14:1-34 (1953).

Degens, E.T., and D.A. Ross, Eds. *The Black Sea* A.A.P.G. Mem.
20 (1974).

Deuser, W.G. "Evolution of Anoxic Conditions in the Black Sea During Holocene," in *The Black Sea,* E.T. Degens and D.A. Ross, Eds. A.A.P.G. Mem. 20:133-137.

Erwin, J.A. *Lipids and Biomembranes of Eukaryotic Microorganisms* (New York: Academic Press, 1973).

Jannasch, H.W., H.G. Trüper and J.H. Tuttle. "Microbial Sulfur Cycle in the Black Sea," in *The Black Sea,* E.T. Degens and D.A. Ross, Eds. A.A.P.G. Mem. 20:419-426 (1974).

McCarty, R.D., and A.H. Duthie. "A Rapid Quantitative Method for the Separation of Free Fatty Acids from Other Lipids," *J. Lipid Res.* 3:117-120 (1962).

Krüger, F. "Bau und Leben des Wattwurmes *Arenicola marina,*" *Helgoländer wiss. Meeresunters.* 22:149-200 (1971).

Ourisson, G. "Samsara of Organic Carbon," *Pure Appl. Chem.* 33:73-80 (1973).

Paradis, M., and R.G. Ackman. "Amphipid Chain Fatty Acids," *Lipids* 11:863-870 (1976).

Ross, D.A., and E.T. Degens. "Recent Sediments of the Black Sea," in *The Black Sea,* E.T. Degens and D.A. Ross, Eds. A.A.P.G. Mem. 20:183-199 (1974).

Shaw, N. "Lipid Composition as a Guide to Classification of Bacteria," in *Advances in Applied Microbiology,* Vol. 17, D. Perlman, Ed. (New York: Academic Press, 1974), pp. 69-109.

Skipski, V.P., A.F. Smolowne, R.C. Sullivan and M. Barclay. "Separation of Lipid Classes by Thin-Layer Chromatography," *Biochim. Biophys. Acta* 106:386-396 (1965).

Vosjan, J.H. "Ecologische en fysiologische aspekten van na bakteriële sulfaatreduktie in het Waddengebied," Ph.D. Thesis, The University of Groningen, The Netherlands (1975).

CHAPTER 30

LOW-MOLECULAR-WEIGHT AROMATIC HYDROCARBONS IN COAL MACERAL PYROLYSATES AS INDICATORS OF DIAGENESIS AND ORGANIC MATTER TYPE

S. LARTER
A.G. DOUGLAS

Organic Chemistry Unit
Drummond Building
The University
Newcastle upon Tyne, England

INTRODUCTION

The pyrolysis of organic matter in tandem with a gas chromatograph (PGC) and/or a mass spectrometer (PMS) is currently being developed as an analytical technique. The method appears to be particularly apposite for the analysis of polymeric materials, and a number of reviews (Levy, 1966; McKinney, 1969), the results of correlation trials (Gough and Jones, 1975) and comparisons of different pyrolyzing systems (Walker, 1972) have appeared.

Characterization of sedimentary organic matter, particularly as regards its petroleum generating potential and/or type of polymeric kerogen, has been attempted by pyrolysis followed by little or no separation of the pyrolysates (Gransch and Eisma, 1970; Barker, 1974a, 1974b; Claypool and Reed, 1976; Larter et al., 1977). Scott et al.(1970) and Dungworth and Schwartz (1972) studied the pyrolysates of Precambrian kerogens, while Scrima et al. (1974) used PGC to formulate a model structure for Green River Shale kerogen. Giraud (1970) noted the presence of aromatic compounds in the pyrolysates of terrestrial kerogens and Leventhal (1976) used stepwise pyrolysis GC to study a variety of sedimentary kerogens. Also Maters et al.(1977) used Curiepoint PGC to analyze several kerogens including those from Green River Shale, Messel Oil Shale and Miocene lignite. In studies of coals, coal macerals, Holden and Robb (1958) heated coal samples directly in the ionization chamber of a mass spectrometer and noted the presence of aromatic compounds. Girling (1963) studied the pyrolysis products produced by programmed heating

of coals. Evans and Raphaely (1964) discussed variations in
the pyrograms of English and South African coals but showed
pyrograms of different macerals that were not dissimilar,
whereas Bricteux (1966,1967) noted differences in the pyrograms
of vitrinites and exinites. Romovacek and Kubat (1968) pyrolyzed coals and coal macerals of various ranks in molten tin
and noted the increased aromaticity of the vitrinite pyrolysates compared to the exinite pyrolysates; they also gave
crude rank parameters based on GC peak ratios and identified
many of the individual components in the pyrolysates. Suggate
(1972) gave more detailed rank criteria but did not identify
any of the compounds obtained on pyrolysis. Recently, McHugh
et al.(1976) used PGC of whole coals, with precolumn-hydrogena-
tion, to show variations in the distributions of some low
molecular weight aromatic hydrocarbons.

The present study aims to show how these low molecular
weight aromatic hydrocarbons may be used to indicate variations
in maceral microsctructure and also to show differences in the
"type" of organic matter of different macerals. For the
purpose of this study, the three maceral groups studied were
vitrinites, sporinites and alginites. The vitrinites and
sporinites were maceral concentrates, separated by sink/float
techniques (Allan, 1975), which were shown optically to be
mostly greater than 90% pure. The alginites are essentially
pure concentrates of algal material that occur torbanites.

EXPERIMENTAL

A nichrome-wound glass-sleeved ceramic tube (130 mm x
3.5 mm o.d. x 1.5 mm i.d.)heated over a 30-mm zone, acted as
a simple pyrolyser. The precolumn volume between the pyrolysis
zone and the GC column was 320 μl; it was kept at 300°C. The
probe was a stainless steel rod, (0.8 mm diam) fitted terminal-
ly with a platinum coil, which entered the pyrolyser via an
0 ring in a T coupling (for carrier gas inlet). Before pyrolysis the sample was extracted ultrasonically (dichloromethane,
2 x 15 min), dried, and powdered to pass 120 mesh. The flamed
probe was moistened (distilled water) and 0.5-3 mg of maceral
concentrate was struck to the coil; excess material was blown
off. (Vitrinites required larger quantities than the more
volatile exinites; *cf.* Larter *et al.*, 1977).

Pyrolysis temperatures (measured with a thermocouple)
were controlled to ±5°C. To pyrolyze a sample the probe
was rapidly inserted into the hot zone and left. Two GC
columns were used for this work. For pyrolysis at 500°C,
a 3-m column packed with Al_2O_3 containing 15% KCl was programmed from 60°C-360°C/10°C/min (nitrogen carrier, 30 psi). Pyrogram peaks were integrated and identified by copyrolysis of
standards with the macerals. For pyrolysis at 600°C,700°C
and 740°C a glass capillary column coated with OV-101 was
programmed from 25°C or 35"C-260°C/4°C/min (nitrogen carrier,

6 psi). Pyrograms peaks on capillary chromatographs were
identified by combined GC-MS using a V.G. Micromass 12B mass
spectrometer. (At all other times, peak detection was by FID.)
The ranks of the vitrinites were determined by reflectance
measurements that were related to fixed carbon values using
standard curves.

RESULTS

Pyrolyses at 500°C, 600°C, 700°C and 740°C of all the
vitrinites studied gave low molecular weight aromatic hydrocarbons in the C_6-C_8 range. Other higher molecular weight
aromatic hydrocarbons were found together with aliphatic and
alicyclic material of lower and higher molecular weight. Some
of the components identified by GC-MS are noted in Figure 1.
The vitrinites and other humic coals ranged in rank from 52%C
to 90%C, the sporinites from 77.3% to 86.8%C equivalent vitrinite rank and the laginites from about 50%C to 83%C equivalent vitrinite rank. This method of rank comparison facilitates
diagrammatic representation.

The ranks of the sporinites and alginites were measured
by reflectance readings on associated vitrinites, or vitrinite
clasts in the original samples, and it s this value that is
the "equivalent vitrinite" rank. It can be seen clearly in
Figure 1 that the vitrinite pyrogram has less straight chain
hydrocarbon material in relation to the aromatic components
than that of the sporinite, while the alginite pyrogram consists almost exclusively of straight chain material. Earlier
work in this laboratory (Larter, 1975) has shown the existence
of *n*-alkanes, *n*-α-olefins and *n*-α, w-dienes with chain lengths
ranging to 32 carbon atoms in the 700°C pyrograms of alginites.
While straight chain material is found in the pyrograms of
sporinites and vitrinites, the pyrograms contain many other
components; in sporinites saturated branched/cyclic and aromatic
material is present while in vitrinites aromatic and phenolic
species are dominant.

A considerable amount of work has been done in this
laboratory on the occurrence of linear aliphatic moeities in
kerogen pyrolysates, which shows that this material represents
kerogen degradation fragments and not residual extractable
hydrocarbons. The pyrolysis products of the exinitic macerals
would be expected to contain more aliphatic material than the
vitrinites on the basis of their respective hydrogen/carbon
ratios (Dormans *et al*, 1957; Van Krevelen, 1961). Also,
alginites are derived from algae, presumably with the retention
of much polymerized algal lipid (Cane and Albion, 1973) while
sporinites are thought by some (Brooks and Shaw, 1968; Achari
et al., 1973) to be largely oxidative polymers of carotenoids
esterified with fatty acids. The origin of the *n*-alkyl moeities
in vitrinites is less clear but probably results from inclusion

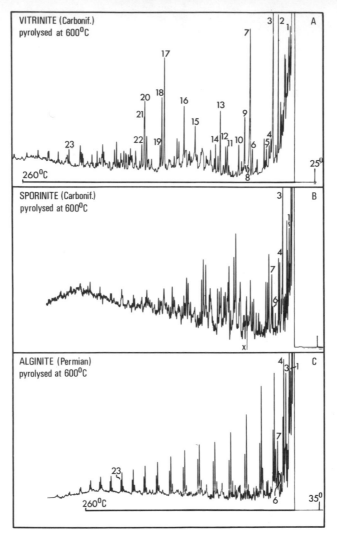

Figure 1. A. Pyrolysis of vitrinite (85.6% C, daf; Carboniferous (England) at 600°C. Chromatographic conditions: 40 m x
0.3 mm capillary column coated with OV-101, programmed 25°-
260°/4°/min nitrogen, 6 psi. B. Pyrolysis of sporinite (80.8%
C, equivalent vitrinite rank; Carboniferous (England) at 600%
C. Chromatographic conditions: as above but programmed from
35% C. Note that peaks emerging after the attenuation change
at X are double the signal strength of those emerging before.
Peak numbers are as in A above. C. Pyrolysis of alginite
(78.0% C, equivalent vitrinite rank, Permian, France) at 600% C.
C. Chromatographic conditions as in B.

Identity of GC peaks in Figure 1A. A. Benezene; 2. Methyl-
cyclohexane; 3. Toluene; 4. *n*-C olefin; 5. Dimethylcyclohexane;
6. Ethylbenzene; 7. *m*-Xylene; 8.[8]Styrene; 9. *o*-Xylene; 10. 2-
Methyloctane; 11. Methylethylbenzene; 12. Trimethylbenzene;
13. Trimethylbenzene; 14. Trimethylbenzene; 15. Naphthalene;
16. 2,6-Dimethylphenol; 17. 2-Methylnaphthalene; 18.1-Methyl-
naphthalene; 19. Trimethylphenol; 20. Dimethylnaphthalene;
21. Dimethylnaphthalene; 22. Dimethylnaphthalene; 23. Eicosane.

of fatty acid and fatty alcohol residues (possibly microbially derived) by esterification onto a humic acid type precursor. (Reactions of this type have been accomplished in this laboratory with "synthetic" humic materials and fatty alcohols.)

It was felt that some measure of the "aromaticity" of the parent kerogen should be evident from the pyrograms of the differing macerals (kerogens). Giraud (1970) had noted that continental (lignin-derived) kerogens, gave an "aromatic" pyrolysate, whereas marine kerogens gave predominantly "paraffinic" material. This, of course, is an oversimplification, since all the samples studied in the present work are of terrestrial, paludal or limnic facies, with some estuarine facies, but they give markedly contrasting pyrograms as regards paraffinic/aromatic affinities for alginitic and vitrinitic material (*cf*. Figure 1).

Measurement of some index of aromaticity can be made in a variety of ways; we decided that a simple concentration ratio of a small aromatic to aliphatic molecule would be suitable. Benzene, toluene and the three xylenes are found in the pyrograms of all three maceral types together with ethylbenzene and styrene. In the vitrinite pyrolysates these aromatic hydrocarbons are the dominant components, with toluene always being the major component, whereas in the alginites there are minor components, with ethylbenzene and styrene generally being present in trace amounts only. Leplat (1967) used the ratio benzene peak area/total pyrogram area as an aromatic index in pyrolysis studies of nonvolatile petroleum fractions. Other authors (Giraud, 1970; McHugh *et al*.,1976; Ramovacek and Kubat, 1968) have used the percentage of aromatics in the total pyrogram as an indicator of maceral/kerogen aromaticity.

One argument against including benzene in any index of aromaticity would be that it is difficult to produce benzene pyrolytically other than by cyclization of reactions. Svob and Deur-Siftar (1972) have shown that pyrolysis of alkylbenzenes proceeds by cleavage at the alkyl bond β to the benzene ring except when the α-carbon atom is highly substituted. Thus, pyrolysis of alkylated aromatic material would be expected to yield large amounts of benzyl radicals, which on protonation would yield toluene; this is indeed what we found.

We therefore consider that much of the benzene produced in these pyrograms does not constitute original aromatic materials but is predominantly a rearrangement product of pyrolytic fragments; this may also be true, to a limited degree, of the other low molecular weight aromatic hydrocarbons. Thus, toluene and the xylenes appear to be more realistic indicators of the aromaticity of the polymer. A plot of the ratio (R) of m-xylene/n-C_8 olefin in the pyrograms (600°C) of several maceral concentrates is shown in Figure 2. These figures are plotted against equivalent vitrinite rank (% C daf). (A plot of toluene/n-C_7 olefin gives a similar graph.) This ratio was

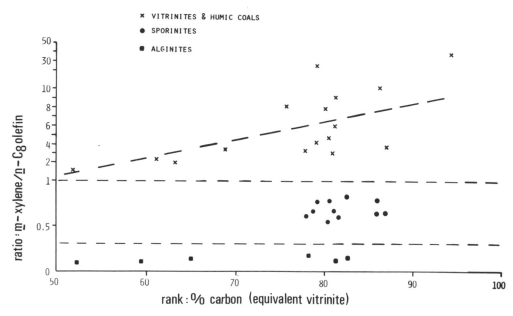

Figure 2.   Plot of the ratio *m*-xylene/*n*-C$_8$ olefin, against rank,
            for vitrinites, sporinites and alginites.

chosen since both the xylene and *n*-alkane, in view of its
generally greater peak height, to reduce measurement errors.
It can be seen clearly that all the alginites plot with ratios
below R = 0.3, sporinites between this and R = 1.0 and vitrinites
from R = 1.5 to R = >20.   On this basis, a clear distinction
of the type of organic matter can be made.

   Previous work using pyrolysis as a method of determining
the "type" of sedimentary organic matter has been published.
Gransch and Eisma (1970) and Larter *et al.* (1977) have all
used simple pyrolysis procedures to distinguish and classify
different types of sedimentary organic material.   Using H/C
and O/C diagrams, Dormans *et al.* (1957) and Van Krevelen (1961)
showed that as carbonization proceeds the sporinite, alginite
and vitrinite macerals become, as regards their ultimate
analyses, indistinguishable above a rank level of about 85% C.
Interestingly, Figure 2 shows that on the basis of this pyrolytic
"type" index, sporinites and vitrinites are distinguishable at
this rank level.   A number of authors (Girling, 1963; Romovacek
and Kubat, 1968; McHugh *et al.*,1976). have noted an increase
in the aromatic fraction of vitrinite pyrolysates with increasing
rank.

   It is interesting to note the corresponding rise in
the *m*-xylene/*n*-C$_8$ olefin ratio with increasing rank, indicating
that these two components do serve as a semiquantitative measure
of the proportions of aromatic versus aliphatic species in the
pyrolysates.   As mentioned previously, the dominant aromatic
hydrocarbon in the C$_6$-C$_8$ range, in all the pyrolyses experiments,

is toluene. Benzene is often the second largest component, followed by *m*-xylene, *o*-xylene and ethylbenzene. In pyrolyses of vitrinites conducted at 600°C, styrene is also present but in very small proportions (see Figure 1).

Although *p*-xylene was not confirmed by GC-MS in the vitrinite pyrolysates, its presence, albeit in minor quantities, may have been obscured by the ethylbenzene component since the GC retention time of these two components is very similar under the analytical conditions used (OV-101 stationary phase). McHugh *et al.*(1976) found *p*-xylene as the largest C_8 aromatic component on pyrolysis hydrogenation of an Australian coal, but this may reflect a purely thermodynamic difference under these conditions. Under conditions similar to ours, Bandurski and Nagy (1976) found, on progressive pyrolysis of a sample of the Orgeuil carbonaceous chondrite, a series of aromatic hydrocarbons of which *m*-xylene was the major C8 species.

The significance of the appearance of the alkyl benzenes in the pyrolysates, as relates to the structural environment they derive from, is not clear. That some toluene, for example, will be produced by dealkylation of a xylene is certain, but to what extent each aromatic species reflects a different environment is not known. We can illustrate that each aromatic species reflects a degradation product from a different environment by plotting the ratio toluene/*m*-xylene against a % C for vitrinites and humic coals of different ranks.

In the Figure 3, this ratio is plotted for pyrolyses conducted at 500°C, 600°C and 740°C. It can be seen that toluene decreases in relation to *m*-xylene with increasing rank and, at any particular rank level, higher temperature pyrolysis gives more toluene, indicating increasing secondary degradation of the xylene. While there is some point scatter, a clear trend of increasing proportions of more substituted products is seen with increasing rank. A reasonable explanation appears to be that toluene is being produced by β-scission of an alkyl chain, which links the phenyl group to the vitrinite matrix. Xylenes would also be produced by β-cleavage of a bonded tolyl group, as in structure A, but it is difficult to rationalize the occurrence of more tolyl groupings in higher rank coals than in lower rank ones, unless increasing carbonization results in the cleavage of one alkyl bridge of a doubly bonded aromatic ring that is the derivation of structure A from structure B.

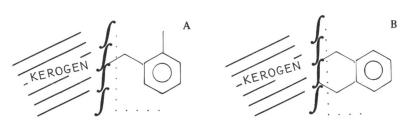

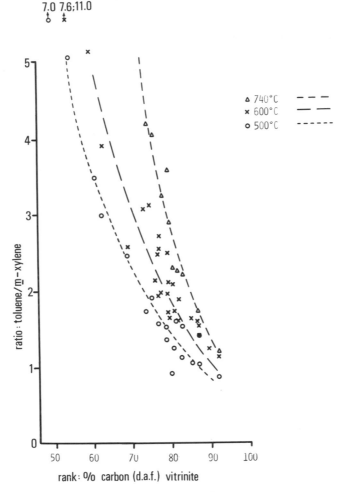

Figure 3. Plot of the ratio toluene/*m*-xylene, against rank, for vitrinites, using pyrolysis temperatures of 500°C, 600°C and 740°C.

This is thought to be unlikely since it is generally accepted that increasing aromatization is part of the carbonization process (Teichmüller and Teichmüller, 1968). The authors consider that double β-cleavage of structures such as B result in xylene formation from potential xylyl-producing structures such as B result in xylene formation from potential xylyl-producing sites that have been formed by ring-closing mechanisms; also this cyclization process facilitates aromatic lamellar growth and hence increasing aromatization. The pyrolytic cleavage of two β-phenyl bonds is not considered unreasonable as extensive radical stabilization in the vitrinite aromatic matrix would greatly assist reactions of this type. Thus, an increase in the proportion of alkyl-substituted benzenes attached to the kerogen macrostructure, via alicyclic linkages, would seem in evidence with increasing rank.

Many models of vitrinite structure have been proposed and readers are referred to Dryden (1963) for a review of the groundwork in this subject. Most of the models suggest a heterogeneous structure based on polycyclic aromatic hydrocarbon units linked via heteroatomic and aliphatic moeities. A typical structure is that of Given (1960) in which the vitrinite structure is based on a functionalized 9,10-dihydroanthracene with naphthalene as the main nuclear species. This proposal was later modified by Given (1961) to a dihydrophenanthrene structure, based on the work of Brown, Ladner and Sheppard (1960) and Brown and Ladner (1960).

Examination of Figure 1A shows the dominant peaks beyond the C_1-C_9 region are due to substituted naphthalenes. This program (vit. 85.8% C) is typical of a vitrinite of bituminous rank. Chakrabarty and Berkowitz (1974) have recently suggested, based on oxidation studies, that vitrinite (coal) has a largely nonaromatic "tricycloalkane or polyamantane" [sic] structure, but his has been questioned by Hyatsu *et al.*(1975), who detected many heteroaromatic residues in coal oxidation products. Degradative techniques applied to complex heterogeneous chemical entities often give data that are difficult to analyze quantitatively. It is possible that low molecular weight species in degradative experiments may represent either small primary degradation products or secondary degradation products produced by cleavage of larger groupings. In general, both mechanisms will produce small species in any nonspecific degradative technique.

Larter *et al.*(1977) showed that vitrinites gave a larger percentage of low molecular weight species on pyrolysis than other coal macerals, suggesting perhaps smaller substituents than in other coal maceral structures. Romovacek and Kubat (1968) noticed that the percentage of aromatic components in the C_1-C_{10} fraction of the 700°C pyrolysates of coals increased in relation to the nonaromatic component with increasing rank. Work in this laboratory has confirmed this. Pyrolysis at 500°C however gives different results.

Figure 4 shows the plot of the percentage aromatic hydrocarbons in the C_1-C_{10} range for the 500°C pyrolysis of vitrinites and humic coals. The percentages are simply derived by integration of the GC detector (FID) response and represent essentially the ratio benzene + toluene + xylene/aliphatic hydrocarbons. Carbon dioxide and water, which constitute a major portion of the low rank coal pyrolysates, are not detected. The general trend is a decrease in aromatic hydrocarbons with increasing rank from about 50% C to 83% C (daf).

No great significance is placed on the shape of the line, since it is based on restricted data; nevertheless, it serves to indicate trends. The overall trend showing a decrease in the percentage of aromatic hydrocarbons with increasing rank can be rationalized by saying that at 500°C pyrolytic cleavage

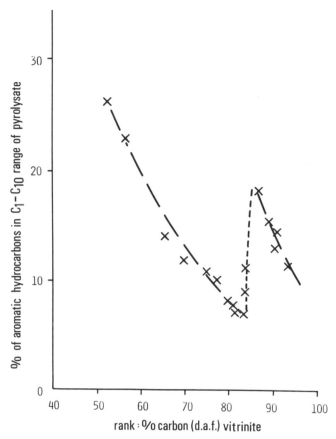

Figure 4. Plot of the percentage of aromatic hydrocarbons in
the C_1-C_{10} range of the pyrolysate, against rank, for vitrinites and humic coals pyrolyzed at 500°C.

is more selective and breaks the weaker aliphatic C-C bonds;
that is aromatic hydrocarbons are released in proportion to
the ease of their pyrolytic removal rather than, as at higher
pyrolysis temperatures, in proportion to the fraction of the
maceral structure which these groups comprise. Thus, as coal
rank increases and the structure becomes more inert, the
aromatic groupings become pyrolytically less labile and hence
decrease in relative proportion.
        The abrupt increase in the evolution of aromatic hydro-
carbons near the 85% carbon (daf) region can be explained in
terms of a structural hiatus in the evolving vitrinite structure
at this rank. Hirsch (1954) has proposed, on X-ray diffraction
evidence, that vitrinite undergoes a change in structure from
an essentially open layered-structured aromatic matrix at high
volatile bituminous rank (80% C, daf) to a highly condensed
aromatic lamellar structure at anthracitic rank (94% C, daf)
and between these ranks a "liquid," relatively mobile, lamellar
structure develops in the coking coal range. Therefore, it

seems possible that breakdown of an open structure to give more condensed but, strictly on a lamellar scale, more mobile units occurs with increasing rank. At the edges of these condensed units small aromatic groupings could find themselves in pyrolytically labile environments, and this may be reflected in the upsurge in evolution of these species around 85% C daf. As the lamellae undergo increased condensation, resistance to breakdown of the increasingly inert structure is indicated by a decrease in the percentage of aromatic hydrocarbons above about 88% C (daf).

SUMMARY

It is hoped that the value of PGC as a tool in determining both type differences between coal macerals and also as a method for investigating structural changes within macerals/kerogens with different metamorphic histories has been shown. Much more work is required on the structural relationships of pyrolysis products to their parent structures, particularly as regards the relationship of small to **large** fragments.

ACKNOWLEDGMENTS

The authors are grateful to Mr. K. Hall for invaluable technical assistance and to Dr. J. Allan for donating some of the samples used in this work. S.L. wishes to thank the Natural Environment Research Council for financial support.

REFERENCES

Achari, R.G., G. Shaw and R. Hollyhead. "Identification of Ionene and Other Carotenoid Degradation Products from the Pyrolysis of Sporopollenins Derived from Pollen Exines, a Spore Coal, and the Green River Shale," *Chem. Geol.* 12:229-234 (1973).

Allan, J. Ph.D. Thesis (unpublished), University of Newcastle upon Tyne, England.

Bandurski, E.L., and B. Nagy. "Polymerlike Organic Material in the Orgeuil Meteorite," *Geochim. Cosmochim. Acta* 40: 1397-1406 (1976).

Barker, C. "Pyrolysis Techniques for Source Rock Evaluation," *B.A.A.P.G.* 58:2349-2361 (1974a).

Barker, C. "Programmed Temperature Pyrolysis of Vitrinites of Various Ranks," *Fuel* 53:176-177 (1974b).

Bricteux, J. "Flash-pyrolysis and Gas Chromatography. Application to the Study of Coals and Their Derivatives," *Ann. Mines. Belg.* (1966), pp. 1543-1551.

Bricteux, J. "Combination of Pyrolysis and Gas Chromatography: A New Technique of Identification," *Ann. Mines Belg.* (1967) pp. 761-777.

Brown, J.K., W.R. Ladner and N. Sheppard. "Hydrogen Distribution in Coal-like Materials by High Resolution NMR Spectroscopy. I. The Measurement and Interpretation of the Spectra," *Fuel* 39:79-86 (1960).

Brown, J.K., and W.R. Ladner. "Hydrogen Distribution in Coal-like Materials by High Resolution NMR. II. A Comparison with IR Measurement and the Conversion to Carbon Structure," *Fuel* 39:87-96 (1960).

Brooks, J., and G. Shaw. "Chemical Structure of the Exine of Pollen Walls and a New Function for Carotenoids in Nature," *Nature* 219:532-533 (1968).

Dormans, H.N.M., F.J. Huntjens and D.W. Van Krevelen. "Chemical Structure and Properties of Coal: 20. Composition of the Individual Macerals," *Fuel* 36:321-339 (1957).

Dryden, I.G.C. "Chemical Constitution and Reactions of Coal," in *Chemistry of Coal Utilisation,* H.H. Lowry, Ed. (London: John Wiley and Sons, 1963), pp. 232-295.

Dungworth, G., and A. Schwartz. "Kerogen Isolates from the Precambrian of South Africa and Australia: Analysis for Carbonized Microorganisms and Pyrolysis Gas-Liquid Chromatography," in *Advances in Organic Geochemistry,* H.R. v. Gaertner and H. Wehner, Eds. (Oxford: Pergamon Press, 1971), pp. 699-706.

Evan, W.D., and P.B. Raphaely. "A Comparison Between the Petrology and Pyrochromatography of an English and South African Coal," in *Advances in Organic Geochemistry,* U. Colombo and G.D. Hobson, Eds. (Oxford: Pergamon Press, 1962), pp. 87-95.

Giraud, A. "Application of Pyrolysis and Gas Chromatography to the Geochemical Characterisation of Kerogen in Sedimentary Rocks," *B.A.A.P.G.* 54:439-455 (1970).

Given, P.H. "The Distribution of Hydrogen in Coal and Its Relation to Coal Structures," *Fuel* 39:147-153.

Given, P.H. "Dehydrogenation of Coals and Its Relation to Coal Structure," *Fuel* 40:427-431 (1960).

Girling, G.W. "Evolution of Volatile Hydrocarbons from Coal," *J. Appl. Chem.* 13:77-91 (1963).

Gough, T.A., and C.E.R. Jones. "Precision of the PGC of Polymers. IV. Assessment of the Results of the Fourth Core Correlation Trial Organized by the Pyrolysis Sub-Group of the Chromatography Discussion Group (London)," *Chromatographia* 8:696-698 (1975).

Granch, J.A., and E. Eisma. "Characterisation of the Insoluble Organic Matter of Sediments by Pyrolysis," in *Advances in Organic Geochemistry*, G.D. Hobson and G.C. Speers, Eds. (Oxford: Pergamon Press, 1966), pp. 407-426.

Hirsch, P.B. "X-Ray Scattering from Coals," *Proc. Roy. Soc. (London)* A226:143-169 (1954).

Holden, H.W., and J.C. Robb. "Mass Spectrometry of Substances of Low Volatility," *Nature* 182:340 (1958).

Huck, G., and J. Karweil. "Versuch einer Modellvorstellung vom Feinbau der Kohle," *Brennst. Chem.* 34:97-102,129-135 (1953).

Hyatsu, R., R.G. Scott, L.P. Moore and M.H. Studier. "Aromatic Units in Coal," *Nature* 257:378-382.

Larter, S.R., B. Horsfield and A.G. Douglas. "Pyrolysis as a Possible Means of Determining the Petroleum Generating Potential of Sedimentary Organic Matter," in *3rd International Symposium on Analytical Pyrolysis* (Amsterdam: Elsevier, 1977), pp. 189-202.

Larter, S.R. M.Sc. Dissertation (unpublished). University of Newcastle upon Tyne, England (1975).

Leplat, P. "Application of Pyrolysis Gas Chromatography to the Study of the Nonvolatile Petroleum Fractions," *J. Gas Chromatog.* 5:128-135 (1967).

Leventhal, J.S. "Stepwise Pyrolysis Gas Chromatography of Kerogen in Sedimentary Rock," *Chem. Geol.* 18:5-20 (1976).

Levy, R.L. "Pyrolysis Gas Chromatography. A Review of the Technique," *Chromatogr. Rev.* 8:48-89 (1966).

McKugh, D.T., J.P. Saxby and J.W. Tardy. "Pyrolysis--Hydrogeneration--Gas Chromatography of Carbonaceous Material from Australian Sediments. Part I. Some Australian Coals," *Chem. Geol.* 17:243-259 (1976).

McKinney, R.W. "Pyrolysis Gas Chromatography," in *Ancillary Techniques of Gas Chromatography*, L.S. Ettre and W.H. McFadden, Eds. (New York: Wiley Interscience, 1969), pp. 55-87.

Maters, W.L., D. van de Meent, P.J.W. Schuyl, J.W. de Leeuw, P. Schenck and H.L.C. Meuzelaar. "Curie-point Pyrolysis in Organic Geochemistry," *3rd International Symposium on Analytical Pyrolysis* (Amsterdam: Elsevier, 1977).

Romovacek, J., and J. Kubat. "Characterisation of Coal Substance by Pyrolysis-Gas Chromatography," *J. Appl. Chem.* 40:1118-1126 (1968).

Scott, W.M., V.E. Modzeleski and B. Nagy. "Pyrolysis of Early
  Precambrian Onverwacht Organic Matter (3 x 10^9 yrs old),"
  Nature 225:1129-1130 (1970).

Scrima, D.A., T.F. Yen and P.L. Warren. "Thermal Chromatography of Green River Oil Shale. I. Bitumen and Kerogen,"
  Energy Sources 1:321-336 (1974).

Suggate, R.P. "Coal Rank from Pyrochromatography," *New
  Zealand J. Sci.* 15:601-614 (1972).

Svob, V., D. Deur-Siftar and C.A. Cramers. "Pyrolysis Gas
  Chromatographic Analysis of Alkyl Benzenes," *Chromatographia*
  5:540-546 (1972).

Teichmüller, M., and R. Teichmüller. "Geological Aspects of
  Coal Metamorphism," in *Coal and Coal Bearing Strata,* D.G.
  Murchison and T.S. Westoll, Eds. (Edinburg: Oliver and
  Boyd, 1968), pp. 233-267.

Van Krevelen, D.W. *Coal* (Amsterdam: 1961), p. 120.

Walker, J.Q. "A Comparison of Pyrolysers for Polymer Characterisation," *Chromatographia* 5:547-557 (1972).

fossil   323
  micro-   25,170
  molecular   355
fossilzation   290
freshwater basins,
  sulfur in   125
fungi   289,323

gas vacuoles   102,103
geopolymers   301
geothermal reactions   296
global sulfur cycle   47-59
Gloetrichia   85
glutamic acid   146
glycine   144,146,147
grapestones   231-233
greigite   339
Guerrero Negro   214
Gulf of California   56,328
Gunflint Iron
  Formation   171,172

H$_2$S   245-252,325
  release to atmosphere
                        245-252
heteropolycondensates   27-29
heterotrophic
  microorganisms   189
high-magnesian calcite231-233
high pressure liquid
  chromatography   273
humic acids   293
hydrocarbons   301,375
  cyclic   260
  decomposition   21
  fractions   256
hydrogen sulfides
        47,49,110,121 *ff.*, 215
4-hydroxyproline   144,146
hypersaline conditions   229
Hyphomicrobium   193
hypolimnion   111,117,192

inorganic redux
  reactions   241
interstitial waters   3,4,
                     9,10,12,27

interstitial waters
  nitrogen concentration
    in   88
iron-humic complex   67
isotopic composition   121

kaolin particles   21
kaolinite precipitation   316
kerogen   272,289,
            293,302,314,375
Konojer Lake   123

labeled sulfate   49
lactate   129
lactate radioactivity   134
lagoons   57
Laguna Guerrero   255 *ff.*
Laguna Mormona
  (Baja California)   32,
        211,255 *ff.*,271 *ff.*
lake ecosystem   83
laminated mats   210
laminites
  carbonate   231
  fibrous   231
Lamprocystis   114
lead in fluvial sediments 151
light
  assimilation   115
  lethal effect   99
  quality   114
  sensitivity   98
lignine   288
lignite   287
limestone   172
Limfjorden   246,250
lipids   29-31,34,36,37
Lyngbya   212
Lyngbya aestuarii   256,272

mackinawite   339
magnesian calcite   351
magnesium concentration
  in algal mats   233
  in carbonates   233
magnesium-organic
  complex   233